Unidentified flying objects, or more popularly, flying saucers, have been in the news almost every day, with sightings all over the United States. One was even reproduced on television when a reporter was lucky enough to be on the scene!

No longer can the government issue blanket denials, for UFOs are an observed fact. The expert on the phenomenon is Renato Vesco, who has given us a well-researched, fully documented answer to the entire controversy. For over twenty-five years he has been studying the possibility of invasion from outer space and the coverup by the United States Air Force of sightings of unidentified flying objects.

In this tremendously readable, bound-to-be-controversial book, Mr. Vesco offers suggestions for future solutions and predictions of what may happen next. He discusses, too, why so many government officials want the general public to believe that these very real objects do not exist, while these same government officials have reliable information, based on their own studies, that our atmosphere has been invaded by space vehicles of another planet—a planet with a technology far superior than ours! The truth can no longer be denied. The layman's intelligence can no longer be underestimated. Our government must come forward with the facts.

INTERCEPT UFO

RENATO VESCO

ZEBRA BOOKS 🐅 NEW YORK CITY

INTERCEPT/ UFO

Originally published under the title *Intercettateli Senza Sparare*, copyright © 1968 by U. Mursia & C., Milan, Italy.

English translation copyright © 1971 by Grove Press, Inc.

Photos courtesy of Wide World Photos, Inc., and Compix, United Press International

ISBN: 0-8468-0010-1

Originally published as a Zebra Book in 1971 by Grove Press, Inc., under the title *Intercept—But Don't Shoot.*

This edition published by special arrangement with Grove Press, Inc.

First printing, February 1974

Printed in the United States of America

ZEBRA PUBLICATIONS, INC.
275 Madison Avenue
New York, N.Y. 10016

contents

PREFACE

"Intercept—but don't shoot!" Ever since the United States Air Force top brass issued this order in 1948, American pilots have been mockingly defied by the UFOs (Unidentified Flying Objects) that frequently invade the air space of the United States as though on peaceful missions of exploration. Why hasn't the Air Force authorized its pilots to shoot the mysterious invaders down? Fear of extraterrestrial reprisal? Diplomatic protests from the "unknown" power that possesses the biggest secret of our times? Technological awe dictated by ignorance? Or, finally, deliberate deceit dictated by circumstances?

These questions are conclusively answered in this book. We start from the affair involving the pilot Kenneth Arnold when

—at the western end of the U.S.-Canadian border—on June 24, 1947, he happened to see a squadron of circular-shaped airships in the distance. They appeared to come straight out of the pages of the headiest science fiction.

It was his flight report, in fact, that started the long series of sightings that is still going on. According to one's convictions, these sightings are the greatest mystery of the twentieth century, a gigantic hoax, or the prelude to the second redemption of humanity through the efforts of our "Brothers from Space"—which is how the pilots of the presumptive extraterrestrial space ships are referred to, especially in the United States. In effect, two decades of well-kept secret and an incredibly extensive pseudoscientific literature—unceasingly fed by over four hundred private investigatory groups working throughout the world—have ended by implanting in the public mind the idea that the UFOs either simply do not exist or are the artifacts of the people of another planet that are observing us—artifacts that are capable of flying through space at speeds approaching that of light—if, indeed, not faster—of neutralizing the effects of gravity and the forces of inertia, of disappearing at will, and so on.

The less these investigators know about aeronautics and the less experience they have had of the convulsive events of the last two years of World War II, the more strongly they hold their opinions.

It is high time that the UFOs—or Flying Saucers, a name that fairly accurately describes these machines' characteristic aerodynamic structure, which resembles that of an inverted plate—take their place somewhere between current events and history. And it is high time, too, that ufology, the absurd branch of "science" that nourishes the myth of extraterrestrial flying saucers manned by demiangelic pilots, be unmasked.

On the other hand, if we except those investigations carried out by military commissions (whose forced and deliberately windy public statements almost certainly say the opposite of what they have actually discovered), today, thanks to the mystical obfuscations of ufologists, the only statements worth taking seriously are cautious and ambivalent ones. One such is, for example, the declaration that Rear Admiral Delmar Fahrney, former commander of the Naval Guided Missile Section and honorary president of the National Investigations Committee on Aerial Phenomena, gave to the press. Fahrney declared in 1957 that according to "reliable information," it had now been proved that our atmosphere is periodically invaded by mechanical objects traveling at very high speeds, beyond anything that American or Soviet aircraft can at present attain. Reports of highly qualified observers state that the objects in question often travel in formation and execute maneuvers that seem to indicate that they are not under the complete control of some automatic system. Their actions, he said, force us to the conclusion that many of them are piloted. The objects appear to be unarguably the result of long research and exceptional technical know-how. Generally, working by exclusion, we cannot deny *a priori* that they have an extraterrestrial origin. This does not mean, however, that we must postulate one! Just as we cannot exclude *a priori* the possibility that some nation may have taken such a giant step with its own air technology as to move considerably ahead of technology of other countries. But this, he added, was highly improbable. That is a great deal to say—and also very little—after a good sixteen years of "reports," studies, investigations, and discussions.

Having said this, we are forced to one conclusion: just as the separate colored chips of some vast mosaic represent no more than shapeless fragments of various colored minerals, so the information brought together in the present volume—some of which appears in print for the first time—takes on meaning and value only if arranged according to a rigorously pre-established scheme that leads to one predetermined conclusion and only to that. Transposing or interpreting the material differently would mean distorting it or denying a whole complex of universal truths.

We will, then, eschew the inconclusive ravings of ufologists and come down to verifiable facts. For the moment we will confine ourselves to revealing *how* the idea of building airships of such unusual structure was born and to giving precise particulars about *who* is building them and to establishing the place *where* they take off on their flights, flights that concern the entire world.

—R.V.

INTERCEPT
UFO

CHAPTER 1

June 24, 1947:
"A Day to Remember"

In 1947 the state of Washington was one of the youngest "stars" in the American union.

Wedged between the Canadian border and the vast complex of the plateaus and mountains of Oregon—of which it is the natural geological continuation—it nevertheless boasted first-class economic development (in agriculture, mining, and aircraft construction) mainly because of its great port, Seattle.

The happy geographical position of what is considered one of the greatest Pacific ports and the self-sufficiency of its local industries had greatly contributed to isolating the state economically vis-à-vis neighboring Canada and had kept it from more active relations with British Columbia, equally mountainous but much less populated and gravitating in turn to the port of Vancouver. Its isolation was, then, purely the result of geographical circumstances, but it later made possible the sensational appearance of a "UFO incident" which was then shrouded in mystery (as, for that matter, the farsighted Anglo-Canadian promoters of the whole business intended).

Near the center of the Cascade Range—which cuts the state almost vertically into two unequal parts—rises the main bulk of Mount Rainier National Park, a complex of twenty-eight glaciers encircling the peak of Mount Rainier, well known to American visitors as the "great sacred mountain" of the Chinook Indians.

Cut by valleys that offer easy access and long since transformed into a great national park in order to preserve its characteristic local subalpine flora, this region receives crowds of visitors during the hot months and the winter season.

Toward the end of spring in 1947, the thaws having been slightly behind their usual seasonal schedule, there was no large group of excursionists to disturb the quiet awakening of the park.

In that picturesque natural scenery, despite the views of ufologists, it was not the appearance of alien beings or of secret forces but only chance and an airplane disaster that gave the initial impulse to the strangest phenomenon of our time.

During the night of the twenty-third and twenty-fourth of June, a Marine Corps C-46 transport crashed against the south shoulder of Mount Rainier. When the military bases on the coast received word that the plane was missing, they radioed pilots flying over the area, asking them to join in the rescue search.

On Tuesday, June 24, Kenneth Arnold—a businessman from Boise, in the neighboring state of Idaho—took off from the airport of Chehalis in a privately owned Piper Cub bound for Yakima and Seattle on one of his normal business trips for the Fire Control Equipment Company. He intended to look for the scene of the crash on his way.

At 3:00 P.M., twenty miles ahead he could see the highest snow-covered peaks of the Cascade Range thrust jaggedly into the clear skies. After searching long and hard without finding any evidence of a crash, he climbed back up to 9,200 feet and headed toward Yakima.[1]

He was skirting the spent crater of Mount Rainier when a sudden flash on his left attracted his attention: nine silvery objects appeared in, as he later said, the characteristic form of an inverted plate and they flew in a "diagonal chain-like line," similar to a formation of geese, toward the mountains at what was obviously supersonic speed.

Gleaming in the sun like sheets of burnished metal, the nine objects maneuvered easily for some time among the high peaks of the chain, occasionally rising and descending as they traced its profile. During a brief pause in the maneuvers the formation flew in a single line, stretching across the sky for almost five miles. Then, with the help of the instrument panel clock and his perfect knowledge of the area, Arnold was able to determine that the mysterious flying machines covered the distance between the south wall of Mount Rainier and the distant peak of Mount Adams in a maximum time of 102 seconds: consequently they were flying at a good deal better than 1300 miles an hour.

Since he knew that such high speeds were not envisaged even for planes then on the drawing boards, Arnold flew toward the rear of the formation to check whether these were real objects or merely a mirage. Approaching within a few miles' distance, he was able to note, but only imprecisely because of their renewed, continuous spinning through the sky, that they were indeed solid objects, perhaps metallic, that they were in fact perfectly circular and were about a hundred feet in diameter; moreover, they seemed to have no tail or any other visible kind of wing or rudder. At the center of each object, he noted finally, was a sort of shining cupola. Perhaps noticing the presence of an intruder, the nine discs abruptly interrupted their strange aerial acrobatics, formed an echelon, and took off toward the north, disappearing in the direction of the Canadian border.

Resuming his search for the military transport, Arnold extended his investigations to the north slope of the mountains; then, considerably disturbed by the inexplicable celestial ap-

paritions, he decided to inform the federal aviation authorities
of what had happened.

After he had landed at the Yakima airport, he drafted a
report of his flight in which he declared that he had caught
sight of nine large aircraft of a hitherto completely unknown
type flying above Rainier National Park.

For a number of years the Boeing Aircraft Company of
Seattle had been building giant airplanes (the last of the series
were the famous Super Fortresses, which were the pride of
the state), but none of them had anything like the absurd
circular shape described by the excited eyewitness. Consequently the (semiofficial) introduction of flying discs into the
history of aviation was greeted with skepticism and derision.

The Arnold Report was published only by a small magazine
dedicated to metaphysical, pseudoreligious, and extrasensory
studies—*Fate Magazine*—which because of its special editorial slant ("True Stories of Mystery and the Unknown")
presented it as putative proof of the arrival on earth of unidentifiable extraterrestrial objects.

UFOS SWARM ACROSS
THE WESTERN HEMISPHERE

In the days following the Arnold sighting local newspapers
were swamped with new and different reports of mysterious
overflights. Almost all of the reports came from areas close to
the point of the first sighting.

Now no longer afraid of being taken for a visionary, Fred
Johnson, a prospector from Portland, reported that he too
had seen the same aircraft—or at any rate another formation
of the same type—also on June 24.

On that day he had almost finished prospecting at Salmon
Dam, about 4500 feet above sea level in the Cascades, when
a strange humming and flashing of lights caused him to scan
the skies to find out what was causing the phenomenon. Six
shining aircraft "resembling enormous circular mirrors catching the sunlight" were flying over the area at a height of
3000 feet above the mountaintops. As observed through a tele-

scope during a sharp turn, one of them appeared to be of a flattened circular construction followed by a kind of short wavering tail (evidently a short trail of vapor or combustible gases). Worthy of note was the fact that for fifty seconds, during which two of the craft flew by at a low altitude, *"the compass needle went wild."*

But the report that caused the greatest sensation was without doubt the Dahl Report, which concerned certain strange events that had happened three days before on June 21.

At 2:00 P.M. on that day, Harold H. Dahl, while on harbor patrol in Puget Sound—an inlet of many bays and coves that runs from the Canadian border to Tacoma—was following the coast line of the wooded part of Maury Island. Suddenly he saw an irregular formation of circular shapes completely unlike weather balloons, with which he was familiar, descend from a thick white cloud. There were five large whitish aircraft, he later wrote in his report, whose diameters were in the neighborhood of 100 feet and which seemed to be involved in a complicated protective or rescue maneuver. In fact, they were slowly circling around a sixth craft that had stopped at some 1500 feet above the coast, probably because of mechanical failure.

Suddenly the UFO in the center rapidly descended to about 500 feet and stopped, apparently rotating on its own axis with a slight humming sound similar to that produced by electric motors. On the belly of the machine a kind of dark, central "hole" stood out distinctly; from time to time bright lights issued from it (perhaps the entrance hatch protected by a bubble of transparent material), and it seemed to have a series of smaller, evenly spaced apertures encircling it.

Five minutes later, one of the machines circling about at the higher altitude detached itself from the formation and descended until it rested on the motionless UFO. The two machines remained in contact for about four minutes, then slowly the one on top separated itself from the other and began to climb to a high altitude.

Afraid of being caught in the possible crash of the machine, Dahl steered his launch deep into a small bay, just in time to get out from under a rain of small, lightweight, whitish metallic fragments, expelled by the hundreds with a dull explosion from the motionless craft.

Moving away slowly at a low altitude, the UFO continued spewing out fragments, dark gray this time and different from the ones expelled shortly before; they resembled scraps of cast metal and they were obviously very hot, for when they struck the water they gave off little clouds of steam.

After a final, shorter but much more violent expulsion, the UFO, as though lightened, regained altitude and returned to the center of the formation, which disappeared at high speed toward the open sea.[2]

The Dahl Report, as was to be expected, also reached the editorial office of *Fate Magazine*. The editors thought it would be a good idea to institute a private investigation in Tacoma by the person they thought best qualified to investigate matters relating to "flying saucers": Kenneth Arnold, the first eyewitness to this whole strange affair.

At the end of the investigation some of the information seemed to confirm the validity of the sighting. Other information—for example, that about a mysterious "stranger" who knew all about the events in Puget Sound and who allegedly "advised" the eyewitness not to tell anyone any of the details of the sighting—threw instead a certain shadow of doubt over the report.[3] Arnold had, however, the distinct impression that some of the blank spots and contradictions that emerged from a comparison between the written report and the oral testimony given by Dahl himself and his direct superior, Fred L. Chrisman, were dictated by higher considerations—namely, fear of compromising their jobs or careers.

Called in because of a confidential telephone call, it is not clear from whom, the U.S. Army A-2 Intelligence Branch did not begin its investigation until July 31.

If we can unquestioningly accept the final report drafted some years later and preserved in the files of the A.T.I.C. (Air Technical Intelligence Center), the "tons of metal that fell from the skies and were visible on the beach of the island" consisted of no more than a couple of fragments of strangely porous lava rock that wouldn't even fill a cornflakes box. Arnold sent some of this matter to the chemical laboratory at the University of Chicago, which classified it as slag of volcanic origin. The rest of the matter—turned over to the A-2 agents—was lost in a serious but purely fortuitous airplane accident during the investigators' flight to Hamilton Air Force Base in California.

At this point the co-authors of the report, Dahl and Chrisman, under pressure from the investigating authorities, ended by admitting that the fragments were only mineral formations picked up at random on Maury Island—"oddities" that they decided to show the press as evidence of the wreckage of the flying saucer with the sole aim of heightening interest in their story.[4]

In any case, the stories of Arnold and Dahl, which were picked up and commented on even by big papers and mass magazines, spread with extreme rapidity; and with equal rapidity the sky of the entire United States became spangled (or at least so it seemed to most people) with swift silver or fiery saucers. From the Pacific to the Atlantic, a real psychosis gripped the American masses and millions of people began to scan the skies anxiously, hoping to make a fateful sighting.

At the end of the first week of July fully thirty-eight states already boasted at least one flight of mysterious flying objects, including both actual sightings and those merely presumed to be such.[5] Naturally, wherever these objects refused to appear —because of their special operative cycle—imagination was called upon and in the end all those who believed in the discs could boast of having seen them, describing them in the oddest ways.

While the whole United States seemed literally to have gone mad about flying saucers, Europe showed decided skepticism. The news of recurrent North American sightings was picked up by the British press. Finally even the authoritative London *Times* emerged from the austere reserve with which it had received the first news to come out and say that when it is very hot, the imagination tends to overwork. And the aviation editor of the *Daily Telegraph* thought he could give the quietus to the whole affair by declaring that the flying saucers seen by the Americans were nothing more nor less than the indirect result of the recent wave of export of Scotch whiskey.[6]

Nevertheless, running down a list of the most convincing sightings, one notes at once that *in June 1947 the mysterious overflights were apparently limited to the states in the northwest corner of the United States.*

Then, in the first week of July, strange luminous bodies appeared also in the skies over Oregon, Nevada, New England, and the Canadian province of Quebec. On July 8 it was the turn of California and New Mexico.

Finally, as the North American sightings multiplied, the discs made fugitive appearances elsewhere as well. In fact, on July 8 a flying saucer was reported from South Africa. This object, which appeared to the naked eye to be about the size of a phonograph record, circled for some fifteen minutes at a high altitude over Johannesburg. Then, after giving off a dense cloud of smoke, it disappeared rapidly upward. On the same day, in Sydney, Australia, a number of persons observed the passage of a swift, shining object—appearing oval in shape because of its angle to the horizon—whose structure tallied with descriptions given by American and Canadian observers.

After the first ten days of July, the skies of the entire Western hemisphere, virtually from pole to pole, were pierced silently and mysteriously by the phantom saucers.

U.S. AIR FORCE DENIALS

The existence of the strange celestial presences having been conclusively proved, public opinion in the United States was at first divided into two distinct currents.

One current leaned toward the thesis of secret, massive experimentation by the Army or the Air Defense Command with some new type of extremely powerful radio-controlled device for atomic bombing and believed that on occasion some defective models had got out of the control of their operators.

The other current maintained that these presences were globes of electrically charged air, were radioactive, hence shiny, and were the results of atomic explosions.

Asked for his opinion, David Lilienthal, chairman of the

Atomic Energy Commission, gave the press a sharp answer: "I can't prevent anybody from saying foolish things."

In the meantime strange rumors began to spread among the public, giving rise to ill-concealed uneasiness. Were the discs interplanetary messages sent from the dying planet Mars? Or were they, perhaps, Russian missiles propelled by special engines that even harnessed the still very young but already terrible energy of nuclear fission? As a result, a reluctant Air Force staff felt compelled to conduct an investigation in order to quiet the press and reassure the public.

Exactly ten days after the Rainier Park incident, the U.S. Air Force in its first, very brief statement declared that the whole story was merely the fruit of mass hallucination.

This peremptory brush-off served only to confirm many Americans in the view that some kind of automatic exploratory expedition to the earth was being carried out by the inhabitants of another planet (some said Mars, others Venus, and still others named even Saturn) by means of machines that were different from our missiles but whose scientific purposes were more or less analogous to those of our present-day interplanetary probes: Lunik, Venusik, Explorer, and Mariner.

After all, hadn't a widespread rumor originated in England, which turned news about some mysterious celestial phenomena (the so-called Soviet "phantom rockets") that had excited the Scandinavian countries during the spring of 1946 into science fiction? This rumor unequivocally had it that certain Soviet astronomers had "confirmed" that beginning with the end of the last war, interplanetary projectiles had occasionally been fired at the earth, and, moreover, that "something" more alive than the incandescent material of a projectile had descended some time before from the depths of interstellar space at some unidentified point on the Siberian tundra.

At the time Kenneth Arnold was described as "the first man to see the Martians." In any case, although he was not convinced that the affair concerned Martians at all, Arnold vehemently disagreed both with those who denied the existence of the saucers and with those who declared that they could at most be aircraft constructed by the Soviets or the American Air Force. It was no mirage, he protested. He had been flying for years and knew those mountains as well as he knew the insides of his own pockets. He had never seen anything like them or anything so fast! The Air Force and the press could say he was an Einstein, a Flash Gordon, or just another screwball, but he knew damn well what he saw!

Finding himself purely by chance on the crest of a wave of unexpected if ephemeral notoriety from the day that Ray Palmer, the editor of *Fate*, had entrusted him with the investigation of the Dahl Report, Arnold began to fly back and forth across the United States investigating various sightings and collecting material for a book—*The Coming of the Saucers*—which he afterwards wrote with Palmer.[7]

He sought conscientiously to collect and evaluate the best reports in order to try to solve the mystery. Nevertheless, for the great majority of Americans he remained "the first man to see the Martians" . . . and the UFO question, born in this original sin, became a subject for jokes and denials from experts.

In the second week of July the Pentagon thought it advisable, in view of the discordant reactions of the public, to offer through its own spokesman something more specific than the too vague conclusions of the U.S. Air Force: "The mysterious devices that some people claim to have seen for some time in the skies are probably the sunlight reflected on cloud formations moving at a high altitude, or exploded meteors whose microscopic residue reflects the sunlight, or very large and considerably flattened hailstones which, falling through the atmosphere, begin to glide and, rising and falling, give the illusion of horizontal flight."

Thanks to this ingenious "clarification," the press accused the military authorities of desperately trying to cover up some dangerous fact. One indefatigable reporter discovered, for example, that at the time of the first sightings Air Force General Carl Spaatz had been spending a long time in these northwestern areas. Spaatz dryly retorted that he vacationed there every year to pursue his favorite sport of salmon fishing. Thus the secret hope that there would be an official and sensational statement on the matter collapsed, but as a kind of compensation, a flying saucer did in fact fall on United States territory.

THE YELLOWSTONE "YO-YO"

On July 7, 1947, a twin-engined P-38 fighter that had been converted into a photoreconnaissance plane for the photographic service of U.S. Army Ordnance was flying at about 30,000 feet in the direction of the Air Force base in Bozeman, Montana.

The sky along the extreme northern edge of Yellowstone National Park was completely free of clouds. Except for a little trouble with the oil system of the engines—a not particularly serious matter, in any case—the flight was proceeding routinely.

Suddenly the photographer shouted: "Look! They're coming! They've almost caught up with us!"

"What? Who's coming?" asked the astonished pilot. What could possibly threaten this lonely flight? The war had been over, definitely over, for some time.

"Those things the papers are always talking about."

For a few moments the sinister shadow of a new Pearl Harbor hovered in the minds of the American airmen. The "cold war" was by then an unpleasant but obvious political state of affairs, and hadn't the immense Asian north shown itself to be an impenetrable fortress hostile to the Western peoples?

The European news release of an American wire service that had somehow learned about this militarily "classified" episode quoted Lieutenant Vernon Blair:

". . . And then turning around to speak to the photographer I saw the yo-yo behind me. I call it a yo-yo because I surprisingly thought of that toy that I used to play with as a child. We had orders to shoot them down at any cost, but I didn't remember that until afterwards, and although I was flying at 360 miles per hour, the strange aircraft quickly overtook me. I was, however, able to observe it for a few seconds: it had the shape of a very flat oyster and was, as it seemed to me, about fifteen feet or so broad, and about three feet thick. It was flying without making any sound, I mean any sound louder than that produced by my own plane, and emitting a light, luminous trail. Then, as soon as it had overtaken me and I was about to try to follow it, I saw it open in two, just like an oyster, and flutter down. I noticed that it was catching up with at least a dozen yo-yos proceeding in an irregular formation, almost like fighters peeling off for an attack."

"Are you sure that they were metallic objects and not, for example, simply shiny spots moving of their own accord or the effect of some such mirage?"

"The mysterious aircraft seemed to be made of aluminum. They were pearl-gray in color and on the upper side they all had a shining bubble of some transparent material."

"Did you see who was flying them? And why didn't you take any pictures?"

"We wasted some time watching them fly by and trying to determine whether there was anyone on board. They moved quicker than we could act!"

"Did the leader by any chance graze your plane?"

"No, absolutely not. I have no idea why he fell. Perhaps he was already having mechanical trouble or perhaps he accidentally got into my slipstream and was torn apart. As I said, we were going pretty fast."[8]

The photographer confirmed that he did not have time to aim his large vertical camera at the formation because the objects flew by too rapidly, and his report on the event coincided in its main particulars with that of the pilot (who was described by his direct superiors as a "serious and honest officer, who takes his job seriously"). He added that since he had concentrated his attention on one of the craft that had briefly approached the P-38 more closely than the others, it seemed to him that he had glimpsed a man, the pilot, inside, lying flat in the cabin and looking out the glass porthole in the front of the bubble.

The terrain in which the contraption fell is quite rough and thickly wooded. The staff at the base in Bozeman, authorized by the Pentagon, immediately began a series of careful inspections in the area with search parties and army helicopters, but without any positive results.[9] Perhaps the Martians had collected those precious fragments?

A few Americans wept over the sad fate of the unknown

hero who had perished in order to further the secret progress of American aviation. More, however, were afraid that the Martians would be angry. But nothing happened. In fact, flying saucers continued to swarm for a while, harmless and elusive, in the skies of the Western hemisphere, following certain broad but well-defined routes (though no one at the time noted the fact), as though they were guided by a careful plan to carry out an ambitious and difficult end that was perhaps rendered possible solely by their strange form.

In any case, the frivolous appellation of "yo-yo" that Lieutenant Blair had conferred on the strange craft, and its similarity to the well-known toy that gave us many pleasant hours in our youth, anticipated later observations on its peculiar "biplanar" form (that is, of two circular bodies, one atop and slightly apart from the other). These observations were reinforced by at least a dozen reputable eyewitness depositions in succeeding years, suggesting that the contraption seemed to revolve around its own axis.

The luminous trail was a dead giveaway of the presence of a jet engine, although of a special and still completely unknown type: using hot, burned air that formed a propelling jet. Even though in those years propeller-driven planes were still the dominant type, jets being an exclusively military rarity, there was really no call, even then, to seek to explain these things by attributing them to the inhabitants and technology of the remote planet of Mars.

The press, however, did not give up but asked, among other things, why this little saucer—which after all had supposedly traveled tens of millions of miles through cosmic space without any trouble—had then so ignominiously broken up in flight a short distance in front of the P-38 that it had overtaken. Could it have been that the warm, dense atmosphere in the altitudes that our planes fly at was harmful to the Martian flyers? Neither then nor later was anyone able to give a plausible explanation of the event.

Nevertheless, the considerations that are forced upon us today are of quite a different nature: *while the U.S. Air Force was publicly denying the existence of the discs, it secretly issued orders to its pilots to shoot them down, no matter what*

*the cost—in complete agreement with the secret orders that
the other two military branches issued to their flight crews.*
Contradiction and confusion? Not in the least. Deception,
rather.

A deception that has been going on for nearly two decades.

APPENDIX TO THE "MANTELL CASE"

As we have seen, toward the end of July 1947 American sightings of unknown flying objects became fewer and further between; during August a few isolated UFOs appeared only over
Europe. Then sightings ceased completely. The press looked
for its own explanation of the matter, questioning any experts
who were not muzzled by Air Force directives.

A compact front of astronomers rejected *in toto* the idea
that a new and unknown form of flight could exist. They
explained all the objects sighted as meteors, which at that time
were indeed on the increase because of the regular annual
appearance of the meteoric wake of Aquarids II.

The prudent silence or tentative observations of some civilians who were authorities on aeronautical matters were
prompted by the fact that the form and speed of the objects
as reported by the most reliable witnesses might also come
within the scope of technical secrets known for the moment
only to the military.[10]

Other authorities, versed in the most disparate disciplines,
wanted, or were induced, to have their say. Some accepted the
official "explanations" without discussion. Others leaned toward
explanations based on the appearance of mirages similar to the
Fata Morgana. There were those who referred to the increased
launchings of new types of weather balloons and those who
considered instead the possibility that some new atmospheric
phenomenon connected in some way with the growth of radar
installations had developed. There were even those who said
that the whole thing was a gigantic mass hallucination that
could be traced back to spots before the eyes, the so-called
muscae volitantes which for a brief time afflicts those who stare
at the clear sky or some light source for a protracted period.

In America these declarations naturally satisfied neither the superpatriots—who wanted the discs to have the Air Force star on them—nor those who were expecting the Martians.

Moreover, the first group observed, not without a tone of vexation, that with these perhaps still experimental machines sent all over the world, an accident might jeopardize this extremely well-kept national secret. Or—as the second group of malcontents insinuated—these saucers were really photographic reconnaissance machines of great range—furnished with an automatic avoidance device that kept them from crashing into any sort of obstacle (earth, airplanes, antiaircraft missiles)—which had been constructed on the basis of the plans of certain German projects dating from 1944. But in that case what would be the point of America spying on itself? Only Russia, which also had a corner on "secret weapons," would have been able to use the invention profitably in order to learn about America's industrial and military potential.

The U.S. Air Force again issued vehement denials. Flying saucers, whether Russian, Yankee, Martian, or from anywhere else, were nothing but tall tales. And the witnesses of the by now innumerable overflights were rewarded *en masse* with the very unflattering description of hallucinated visionaries.

Authoritative denials and journalistic pressures mingled for another few months without throwing any substantial light on the exciting mystery. In order to reassure the public and to cut short the press's inconvenient probing that kept the question alive (although the discs had by now not been seen for some time), on December 30, 1947, the Secretary of Defense, James Forrestal, signed an order that set up a permanent committee of inquiry on flying saucers.

Placed under the Air Matériel Command (A.M.C.) at Wright-Patterson Field and headed by Professor J. Allen Hynek, then the director of the McMillin astrophysical observatory of Ohio State University, the commission set to work immediately, sending special questionnaires to witnesses who had happened to see unusual celestial phenomena—questionnaires that would be subjected to analytical and statistical evaluation by a group of civilian and military experts.

Although not openly stated, the basic aim of the commission

was to attribute the sightings either to nonexistent things or to mistakenly identified things that already existed: psychopathic hallucinations, hoaxes, optical illusions, weather balloons, parhelia, lenticular clouds, meteorites, ordinary planes flying at high altitudes, flocks of migratory birds, and the like.[11]

To the 117 sightings of 1947 that they culled from the most responsible press reports, the commission added some 436 individual questionnaires covering the entire two-year period that followed.

The hard nut of the inquiry was a sensational bit of evidence from Kentucky known as the "Mantell Case." The episode is so well known that we need not report it here in detail, but there is one aspect, still almost totally unknown, that is worth noting because it throws real light on the complicated UFO question.

Briefly, then, the tragic affair began in the neighboring state of Indiana. At 2:30 P.M. on January 7, 1948, a high-flying, shiny, flat, circular object passed over the town of Madison at a speed of at least 500 miles per hour.

A series of telephone calls from Elizabethtown, Lexington, and Fort Knox—the famous national safe-deposit box—shortly after alerted Godman Field, a military air base. A gigantic shining object was, in fact, moving swiftly through the skies of the area, giving the impression that it was carrying out a methodical exploratory mission. At 3:00 P.M. this object, or perhaps another of the same type, appeared directly above the base.

Observing it through binoculars, Colonel F. G. Hix concluded that it was a flaming disc of gigantic size—in all probability its diameter was about 150 feet.

Three F-51 Mustang fighters were returning to the base under the command of Captain Thomas Mantell. The squadron received radio orders to identify this object, which in the meantime had begun to move away. Shortly thereafter two of the fighters had to return to the field, having run out of fuel. Captain Mantell continued in pursuit and at 3:15 P.M. he reported: "I've sighted the thing. It looks metallic and of tremendous size. It's rotating rapidly and surrounded by reddish streamers. It looks like an ice-cream cone topped with red, intermittently flashing at the top."

According to official sources his last radio message said: "It's still above me, making my speed or better. I'm going up to 20,000 feet and if I'm no closer, I'll abandon chase."[12]

However, one of the personnel at the Godman control tower later revealed to a member of the British Flying Saucers Bureau, a private association dedicated to the investigation of UFOs, that there was a sequel to the story. Shortly afterward, Captain Mantell did manage to get within closer distance of the UFO when it made a brief stop in the air.

"My God!" he then exclaimed on the radio. "There are men in it!" The rest of his words, if there were any, were drowned out by an indescribable crescendo of noise. Then came a terrible crash and radio contact was broken.

While Captain Mantell remained disturbingly silent, another white-gold circular object enveloped in a red halo and with a long amber-colored contrail crossed the skies of Ohio, passing very rapidly over the Lockbourne air base at what was surely a stratospheric altitude. At almost the same time, within a few miles of the airport of Wilmington, Delaware, a sort of ball of fire surrounded by a cloud of greenish gas appeared in the sky from the southwest and for a good thirty-five minutes executed strange maneuvers in space—continuous alternation of turns and vertical climbs and dives. Finally it flew off at a "terrifying" speed. And that was the last sighting on that memorable day.

At dawn the next morning, after a telephone call from the local police near Fort Knox, several platoons sent by the command at Godman Field found the wreckage of the Mustang spread over a vast area.[13]

The press was forbidden access to the site of the accident. There was no authorized photograph and no statement to the press, as is usual under the circumstances. This was not, in fact, one of those simple aviation disasters that spatter the records of mechanical flight. The "Mantell Case" was a mysterious episode that was rendered even more puzzling by the report that some of the wreckage appeared to have "tiny perforations and to be almost porous or rough," as though it had been struck by a combination of a blast of intense heat and a violent abrasive jet.

REPORT NO. 102

On December 27, 1949, Professor Hynek sent a—naturally "final"—report to Washington on the investigation (for the record, its official title reads: Report No. 102-AC/49-15-100/ Project SIGN), and Order No. 629/49 of the Command of the U.S.A.F. marked the official dissolution of the commission.

In two years of work 375 of the most reliable reports had been analyzed, $34,000 had been spent, and the conclusions were, as might have been foreseen, that "basically nothing proved the existence of the flying saucers."

Nevertheless, of the 228 sightings that were made public only 194 were explained exhaustively or in accord with the stated premises of the backers of the commission. Thirty-four cases were in fact considered inexplicable. For example, the accident in which Captain Mantell lost his life was at first explained away as an attempt on his part to intercept the planet Venus, which was especially bright that night, then as an equally futile attempt to pursue a very high cirrus cloud that had caught the reflections of the sun, and finally it was simply brushed aside as "contact with an unknown object."

Given the small number of "unexplained" sightings, the commission considered that it was within its rights to reach a completely negative conclusion, at the same time, however, prudently advancing the hypothesis that the thirty-four cases in question could be ascribed to special atmospheric phenomena that had been incorrectly described or were still little known scientifically.[14]

For some time the disappearance of the unknown machines from the skies seemed fully to support the explanation that no mystery did in fact exist, and on American airfields those who reported sightings were made the butt of all sorts of jokes. They had seen pie pans flying upside down, had they? Fine! Anyone who still saw some rare, isolated UFO was of course careful not to talk about it.

The unexpected conclusion to the official investigations had an equally unforeseen consequence. Those who disseminated false reports about Martians and such things—people who had "worked" secretly before—vigorously fanned the flames of disappointment and, with the help of those newspapers interested in sensationalism, spread a series of increasingly amazing and unlikely news stories among millions of unsuspecting readers.

On the other hand, outraged by the negative views of the U.S.A.F., numerous people who had seen UFOs began to listen, though with some misgivings, to certain rumors that had been making the rounds for some time but that now began to grow. As often happens, the minority led the majority along, and soon much of the American public believed in the Martians (or the Ethereans, or the Wolfians, or what have you).

The authorities, however, maintained their curiously "incoherent" attitude. From the spring of 1948 American military pilots had orders to intercept and shoot down the unknown invaders. Then the orders changed, doubtless because of the Mantell case: *Intercept but don't shoot except in the case of an obvious maneuver on the part of the UFO.*

The instructions of Major General Ramey of the Air Defense Command aimed simply at acquiring clear ocular or photographic evidence and precise details that might in some manner interest the Air Force Technical Intelligence Center. (Science "worked" for the public, but it demanded "details" for the military.)

The order was never revoked. Meanwhile, in the secret corridors of the Pentagon a new policy began to form, a policy of silence and denials that years later led ufologists to talk about a "Flying Saucer Conspiracy" that had been arranged in high places against the flying discs or, more precisely, against our Brothers from Space and their antiatomic and pacific mission.

In reality, what was taking shape, and in really high places, was a sort of "conspiracy of silence" that was adopted in order not to shake the prestige of the Republic, which, although at the zenith of its political and technical hegemony, possessed no aircraft able to emulate the then almost legendary speeds of the UFOs.

NOTES

1. In fact, the transport was found the following day on the slopes of the South Tacoma Glacier, considerably south of Arnold's route.

2. To better evaluate the Dahl Case, compare it with the following episode: February 18, 1950, Sjaelland (Denmark)—Christian Sandersen, owner of a small plot of land on the east coast of Sjaelland, reporting to the press the nighttime flight several miles out to sea of two "flying saucers," said: ". . . When I saw them, the first was proceeding at a very high altitude. The other, however, was flying at about 1500 feet and seemed hesitant about what course to take. It was going back and forth and spinning furiously as it climbed, then it slowed down its motor, descending to about 500 feet. The disc at the higher altitude had meanwhile stopped and seemed to be waiting. After a few moments during which it was motionless, it descended rapidly and brought itself almost in contact with the other; it remained in that position for several minutes, then it rose again and disappeared. A few seconds later, the 'hesitant' disc exploded in a blinding ball of flame that seemed to consume the whole thing." It is true that the "ball of flame" could quite reasonably be explained by the instantaneous combustion of its remaining fuel by means of some timing device and that the momentary contact between the two craft can be logically explained as an attempt to rescue the endangered crew, effected perhaps by the pilots' transferring from the bubble on the back of the nonfunctioning disc to the bubble on the belly of the rescue ship (these structural elements are quite clear in the later Brazilian photographs of 1952). The local press, however—still under the influence of the then very recent American "Report No. 102," which unequivocally denied that any unidentified flying objects existed—gave no credence to Sandersen's story. Yet only three days before, the same Danish press had given considerable play to certain military statements designed to calm public opinion concerning repeated signals that radar stations and the Coast Guard

had picked up of very high and fast overflights of *unidentified* air formations, cautiously suggesting that the Soviets were carrying out cartographic research in the Baltic!

3. *Cf.* Gray Barker, *They Knew Too Much About Flying Saucers* (New York, University Books, 1956), pp. 136–150; Harold T. Wilkins, *Flying Saucers on the Attack* (New York, Ace Books, 1967), pp. 46–64.

4. *Cf.* Prof. Donald H. Menzel, *Flying Saucers* (Cambridge, Mass., Harvard University Press, 1953), pp. 38–48; and Capt. Edward J. Ruppelt, *The Report on Unidentified Flying Objects* (New York, Ace Books, 1956), pp. 37–41.

5. Among the many "saucer psychosis" cases, one is worthy of note: the claimed sighting of a UFO on September 28, 1947. Air currents had caused one of the many weather balloons that are periodically launched in the area around New York to drift over the city. Perversely, the state of New York had not had any sightings of unidentified flying objects. Could not, then, the round and shining body that swiftly and nimbly disappeared and reappeared here and there among the gray clouds have been one of the rare and eagerly awaited contraptions? The sensation caused by its appearance was such that the local radio stations hastily broadcast a statement on the true nature of the object, but since this did not have the desired effect, it was proposed to send up a fighter plane to shoot down the intruder. Fortunately an offshore wind carried the sphere away from the city, disappointing those—and there were many—who were eagerly awaiting a local landing of astronauts on a visit to the biggest city on earth.

6. This assertion immediately had an unexpected as well as an unmerited notoriety. When the hypothesis that the mysterious machines seen by the Americans were a new kind of Soviet long-range weapon launched from some secret Siberian base was advanced in the United Nations, Molotov rose up angrily and declared: "The flying discs are of English origin, because

the only thing responsible for such visions is the too-abundant consumption of whiskey, which overstimulates your imaginations!"

7. Kenneth Arnold and Ray Palmer, *The Coming of the Saucers* (Amherst, Wisconsin, The Amherst Press, 1952).

8. In the autumn of 1948 the operational staff of the U.S. Air Force circulated a directive to all fighter units equipped with jets to be on guard against the serious danger presented by the turbulent propeller wash from piston-engined bombers—a danger that had been pointed up by a series of fatal accidents. During mock combat exercises against a formation of four-engined B-29s, an F-84 jet fighter that had entered the slipstream close behind the propellers of one of the bombers had literally disintegrated in flight, and the same fate had befallen an F-80 fighter during a similar maneuver. Finally, another fighter that had come into contact with a bomber's propeller wash had been hit violently in a vertical line along its left side, losing an auxiliary fuel tank along with a part of the wing tip because of the violent vibrations that resulted.

9. At least this was the official version distributed to the various staffs of the Air Force and Army concerned with the searches, and sanctioning the results of the investigation.

10. The Italian press reported the comment of Charles Gardner, then considered Britain's best aviation editor: "Whatever the truth may be about the American 'flying saucers,' there is one aspect of the matter that has considerable importance for high-speed aircraft designers. All of the witnesses that have 'seen' the mysterious objects agree on their circular form, which would represent an evolution in the projects worked out by a number of scientists in the last ten years. One witness has described the strange craft as resembling a giant lens, another has said that it has a low cupola, but most have gone no farther than a simple comparison with an inverted plate. . . . There is no doubt that the problem of passing through the 'sound barrier' will force us to make considerable modifications in the

shapes of our flying machines. . . . In order to overcome such difficulties many scientists have suggested a 'delta'-shaped wing, or a right-angled triangle . . . without tail or fuselage. . . . From the 'delta' to the semicircle and from this to the full circle are two clearly connected steps. . . . We know that the 'flying triangles' will actually be built and therefore the semi-circles and even the 'flying discs' are not after all so farfetched as might seem at first sight. I would, however, be surprised if all the enormous problems of such a heterodox and supersonic machine had already been resolved and if a 'flying saucer' with men on board had already flown. . . . The Americans are building jet planes that approximate the speed of sound (746 miles per hour at sea level) and we hope that England will soon achieve the same results. It seems incredible to me that someone is not only four or five stages in advance on the road of aeronautical progress but that he has also built so many of them that he can launch them by the scores across a continent." To understand Gardner's technical assessment and his doubts better, it should be pointed out that it was precisely at that time (on June 19, 1947, to be exact) that the Americans had taken the world speed record from the British, and were the first "officially" to fly faster than 1000 kph in a modified P-80C jet fighter. The timed speed was 1003.811 kph. Because of the lack of more precise data Gardner had, however, made a technical mistake in supposing that the flying saucers were derived by simple evolution, in the aerodynamic sense, from the 'flying wing,' or that they were a development in construction in the area of so-called low aspect-ratio wings.

11. Professor Hynek's serious preconceptions concerning the UFOs can be deduced, for example, from the introduction to *Project Blue Book, Special Report No. 14* (Analysis of Reports of UFO), Project No. 10073, May 5, 1955, issued by the Air Technical Intelligence Center at Wright-Patterson Field, in which is written: "The unfortunate term 'flying saucer' or 'flying disc,' because of its widespread and indiscriminate use, requires definition. Many definitions have been offered, one of the best being that originated by Dr. J. Allen Hynek. . . . Dr. Hynek's definition of the term is 'aerial phenomenon or sighting

that remains unexplained to the viewer at least long enough for him to write a report about it.' " Is this an ironic evaluation of things that had to be kept secret, or pure scientific near-sightedness?

12. The speed of the pursuit is closely related to the operating characteristics of the F-51D Mustang fighter (Packard Merlin V-1650-7 supercharged piston engine developing 1630 HP and driving a four-bladed propeller), which could climb in 18.5 minutes to an altitude of 25,000 feet, there developing its maximum horizontal speed (450 mph), and had a service ceiling of 43,500 feet.

13. According to *Le Courrier Interplanétaire* of Lausanne, an almost exact repetition of the Mantell Case—this one known in ufological circles as the Merkel Case—allegedly took place on January 9, 1956. Toward dusk a number of UFOs appeared in the sky over southern Indiana. Several jets and one propeller-driven plane belonging to the National Guard and stationed at the airport in Louisville, Kentucky, immediately scrambled to intercept. The maneuver failed owing to the growing darkness and the fear that their fuel supply would give out. Nevertheless, Colonel Merkel—thanks to the greater range of his propeller-driven fighter (a P-51 Mustang)—continued the pursuit, radioing the control tower that he had observed without any possibility of doubt a mysterious shining object that performed evolutions along a bank of clouds directly above him. Still having sufficient reserves of oxygen and gas, Merkel climbed to 30,000 feet, trying to approach the UFO and reporting that it was flying at a considerably higher altitude. Merkel then climbed steeply at full throttle, but almost immediately radio contact was lost and after a dizzying dive, the fighter seemed to explode a few hundred feet above a farm near Blooming-ton, destroying the building and scattering fragments of metal over a radius of about 1300 feet. Since we do not have an official version of the fact, it would be hazardous to draw any conclusions; nevertheless, the ufologists' conclusion that intelligent beings were on board the unknown craft and became

hostile only when approached without invitation scarcely appears credible.

14. *Cf.* Prof. J. Allen Hynek, "Unusual Aerial Phenomena," *Journal of the Optical Society of America*, XLIII, 4 (New York: April 1953), 311–314.

CHAPTER 2

A Bit of Science Fiction

In the spring of 1949 a dozen reports filled with unimportant information that could easily be traced to ordinary phenomena having nothing to do with UFOs led the investigators of the Hynek Commission to hope that the wave of "sightings" would peter out naturally, since the affair had already lasted so long and crowds are notoriously fickle.

But their reasoning was faulty, for reports continued to trickle in; and in June something like a second Mantell Case almost occurred.

It happened in the space of a few minutes over the Tierras Calientes hills in Mexico. Its engines droning regularly in unison, a four-engined American military plane was crossing the Yucatan peninsula toward its base in Texas. Not a cloud was in the sky. Only a distant point of light stood out in the heavy tropical calm—obviously a motionless weather balloon at about the same altitude as the plane. As the distance between the two gradually shortened, the point of light began to take on a more definite shape, revealing the unmistakable characteristics of a saucer.

"Attention all crew members," the captain said distinctly over the intercom. "Unknown flying object at eleven o'clock."

The disc remained motionless in space at an altitude of about 8000 feet, with a light layer of vapor or whitish smoke hovering around it. When they had got within a mile of the object the flyers began to observe it attentively, hoping to make out some details of its construction that they could report to their superiors. But they hoped in vain.

After oscillating a number of times around its vertical axis like a top coming to rest, the mysterious machine suddenly started up, moving almost slantwise and quickly approaching the plane.

"What's he doing?" the co-pilot exclaimed apprehensively. "He's coming right at us!"

The disc almost brushed the left wing tip and then began to circle rapidly around the plane, bewildering the flyers. In order to escape this senseless, annoying maneuver, the pilot dived abruptly and took the plane down to about 3000 feet.

After stopping briefly at the original altitude, the disc also dropped down to 3000 feet and began to repeat its passes around the plane, gleaming like a mirror in the sunlight.

"He won't go away!" the captain said in alarm. "That damn son of a bitch is going to end up by crashing into our wing unless . . ." but he didn't get a chance to finish. His engines began to show a disturbing irregularity, either because of the violent eddies caused by the speed of the unknown object or because of some sort of interference with the plane's ignition system. As a result of the violent buffeting, the ailerons and the tail began to show signs of weakening.[1]

Having completely lost control of the plane, the captain regretfully had to order the crew to bail out. Under the umbrellas of their chutes, the flyers angrily watched the disc rise vertically to its original altitude and wait while the plane crashed into the swamp below.

When, after considerable difficulty, the flyers got back to

their base and were being questioned, they declared among other things that, "properly speaking," the object had committed no act of aggression nor had it even indirectly employed a weapon. "We do not know if there were any men on board the disc, but it seems logical to assume that it was under human direction, because at first the machine hesitated slightly before dropping down to our lower altitude. An electronic device would have caused it to follow our plane from the moment we began to dive. . . . That flying in circles around our plane by that huge shining machine was truly frightening, blinding and bewildering us. . . . It was utterly impossible to maintain course."

The press did not learn about the results of the inquiry, for the exact place where the events occurred was kept secret and even the names of the flyers were never revealed.

What little trickled out about the episode—all, in fact, that has been reported—led *Fantastic Stories* buffs to proclaim: "The Martians are interested in our means of flight! When they're certain that our techniques are inferior to theirs and that we're no threat to them, they will undoubtedly land and establish friendly relations." And, encouraged by the circulation of stories about flying saucers piloted by tiny creatures, the wild speculation began on the best way to welcome them, what they would probably look like, the likelihood of their speaking English, the best ways of communicating with them in case they had no vocal organs, and other such subjects.

THE "JEKAMS CASE"

The permanent inquiry commission was getting ready to present the results of its fruitless two-year investigation when, on August 19, 1949, the Air Force itself was imprudent enough to nearly wreck the laborious edifice of arguments that was supposed to prove that the UFOs did not exist.

The Air Force command of Baltimore suddenly called a press conference and an authorized spokesman stated, to the understandable confusion of everyone present, that two different "prototypes" of airplanes which might solve the mystery of the famous saucers had been found on an abandoned farm near Glen Burnie.

The two machines had been built just before the war by one Jonathan E. Caldwell with the aid of a local mechanic, and one of the machines had even flown.

The Air Force statement said it was possible that Caldwell had conducted subsequent experiments with improved models based on the two inoperative prototypes that were discovered in the barn on his farm. The technical officer in charge of the Air Force's investigation said that in flight both models could resemble a flying saucer and could be prototypes of other perfected machines that might actually have been seen in American skies. Now the Air Force would have to locate Caldwell and find out if he had done any work on them since then, and for whom.

The two machines had been abandoned for years on that ramshackle farm and were falling to pieces along with it. Restoration was out of the question. Besides, Caldwell had conceded that it would be financially impossible to realize his ideas.

The builder had tried to combine the advantages and dynamic principles of the airplane and the helicopter and as a result the models had round wings and contrarotating propellers. But that was more than enough to stimulate even the most sluggish imagination. Hadn't the saucers remained motionless in the air just like helicopters? Weren't they perfectly circular like Caldwell's full-size models? And finally, didn't they seem to prefer the skies over the United States, the native country of the builder—who, incidentally, could not be found?[2]

The short official report started a sort of pilgrimage to the supposed "hatchery" of the first Yankee saucers, which was featured as the lead story in the picture weeklies.

It seemed that the mystery of the saucers was about to be solved in a way that would uphold the prestige of the United States. But then on August 20, less than twenty-four hours after the press conference, the same source that had announced the discovery demolished the myth that the saucers were made in the U.S.A.

The same command stated through another equally authoritative spokesman that the two experimental craft discovered in Maryland "have absolutely no connection with the reported phenomena of flying saucers," that were supposedly observed in the two years 1947–1948. The Air Force now charged that when the two unusual craft that had been constructed before the war by an engineer who cannot now be located were discovered, the press had indulged in the most fantastic speculations, but unfortunately, said the Air Force, the mystery of the flying saucers nevertheless remained unsolved. Had some superior called the rash Baltimore command to order? . . .

In their fervor to investigate Caldwell's creations—according to the press, other frustrated inventors claimed priority for similar ideas—the newspapers got sidetracked. Then they soon turned to more pressing subjects.

Russia was secretly overcoming its disadvantage in the field of atomic power. But in order to maintain its own undisputed mastery of this terrible power, America was multiplying its nuclear establishments and preparing new types of bombs. The growing industrial hunger for radioactive minerals had led American authorities to encourage prospecting for them on United States soil, and thousands of volunteers attracted by the prospects of wealth envisioned in their "uranium fever" began to crisscross the most inaccessible reaches of the country, armed with Geiger counters, patience, and, most of all, with hope. The principal scientific institutes also contributed to the prospectors' efforts by forming expeditions specifically equipped for prospecting for minerals.

In 1949 one of these expeditions, headed by Professor Jekams and made up of five geologists and two Indian guides, had been hiking for several hours in a sharp September wind toward Mount Rainier, in the very area of the famous first sighting. The group crossed over the moraine of the Carbon River glacier, left the edge of the thick pine forest, and climbed along the bare, rocky ledges. As yet they had not found any trace of the precious mineral.

The sky was perfectly free of clouds and the sun beat implacably against the flanks of the mountain, probing into the lava beds. Exhausted by the long hike and the hot sun, Professor Jekams leaned back against the rock face. He was estimating how much farther they still had to go when a shadow appeared on the ground.

What kind of cloud can form in a few seconds in such a cloudless sky? the geologist wondered as he raised his head to investigate the curious phenomenon.

"Three flying saucers of exceedingly large dimensions," he recounted later, "were banking in the clear sky. Two of them remained at an altitude of about 5000 feet. The third, which was casting its shadow on the ground below, was at only 1500 feet and almost directly above us. We estimated that it could not have been less than 250 feet in diameter."

Frightened by that gigantic mass of metal which hung in the air as though suspended by an invisible thread, the group took refuge under some boulders and awaited developments.

"With a strange wavering motion, the nearest disc suddenly moved and slowly began to descend toward nearby Dome Peak, not stopping until it was about fifty feet from the summit. From the underside, which seemed to revolve around a central fixed part of the machine, came occasional flashes and sparks accompanied by a humming like that of a fan, almost as though the engine of the craft was idling. The enormous circular mass remained motionless for a few moments and then began to rise and fall laterally."

"Did it rise and fall the way weather balloons sometimes do?"

"Not exactly. To be perfectly accurate, it wobbled like a top coming to rest, but much more slowly. The maneuver was also accompanied by slight gains and losses of altitude. It almost seemed to be dancing in the air and, through an association of ideas, the evolutions reminded me of the well-known dance of the bees. This curious maneuver lasted almost a quarter of an hour, then the craft rose vertically at fantastic speed."

"What about the other craft?"

"After waiting at a high altitude for the first disc to return, the other discs also descended and repeated the same movements one after the other. All three regrouped at about 5000 feet in a triangular formation, and a little later they disappeared beyond the horizon," that is, toward the Canadian border—as usual.[8]

THE SUPPOSED
"NEGATIVE POLE" OF GRAVITY

When the public information office of the Department of Defense allowed the facts in the Jekams Case to become public, those who believed the flying saucers came from an extraterrestrial source found a simple explanation for the inexplicable maneuvers of the UFOs on the summit of Dome Peak in the operation of antigravity.

The hypothesis that the UFOs were using antigravitational energy was originally advanced by the versatile British writer Gerald Heard. He took it up from rumors making the rounds during the period of the first sightings in 1947. One of these rumors, for example, seriously reported that an American private plane had been mysteriously stopped in mid-flight and held suspended in the air by a flying saucer that then flew around it for a considerable time, apparently in order to study it! The antigravitational energy hypothesis found its most ardent champion in former Marine Major Donald H. Keyhoe, who, unable to perfect his theory by reason of the obvious lack of hard scientific data, broadcast it to the public at large through his best-selling books on flying saucers, which at first he claimed were of Martian origin and, after this claim was shaken by the attacks of astronomers, of unspecified interstellar origin.

According to Heard, magnetism was only the opposite pole of the gravitational force that keeps us attached to the planet, and the flying saucers could resist this force with a "counterforce, a negative reaction to the pull of the earth, as on the negative pole of the magnet objects are not drawn in but driven out." Thus the discs could hover and move through the air as though held up by some mysterious gigantic magnet, and "maybe they go to the South Pole because, down there, at the end of the world-magnet, they can recharge themselves best?"[4]

Starting off from the convenient hypothesis that it is technically possible "somehow" to have an influence on the earth's magnetic field, producing a "precipitation" or a variation similar in concept to a current drop in electricity, Major Keyhoe hypothesized that the UFOs would cause continual magnetic precipitations in the zones they were flying over and would draw from them the power needed to stay aloft and move. In short, they could move on a sort of magic and invisible antigravitational carpet which unrolled in front of them and rolled up behind them as they flew along.[5]

Of course the inexhaustible energies of the cosmos, and specifically the direct transformation of the electromagnetic energy of cosmic rays into mechanical energy, was not forgotten among the rash of hypotheses put forward.

In 1953, Lieutenant Plantier was garrisoned at Blida, in Algeria, when his commanding officer, Captain Rougier, saw a flying disc and described it to him, making such an impression that the idea struck Plantier that it might be possible to realize something similar right here on earth. The technical-minded Plantier then sought to work out theoretically a machine capable of executing all the evolutions that had been attributed to flying saucers over a long series of observations. Finding the power sources then available to man to be inadequate, he decided to rely on cosmic rays, which develop far more energy than the complete disintegration of the atomic nucleus—a state impossible to achieve.

In September 1953 he published the results of his theorizing in the magazine *Forces Aériennes Françaises* under the title "La Propulsion des Soucoupes Volantes par Action Directe sur l'Atome." Naturally, Plantier avoided sketching out the mechanical arrangements that could put the idea to actual use, considering them to be an undertaking beyond his capabilities. He merely imagined that cosmic radiation passing through the disc—simplistically conceived of in the form of a huge symmetrical biconvex lens surmounted by an elegant hemispherical glass dome—would activate a special internal "field force." Reacting against the natural magnetic fields, whether terrestrial or sidereal, this field force would annul the force of gravity and inertia, enveloping the aircraft with something definable only as a kind of enormous boundary layer, and would develop those bright lights that keep changing color and so impress and perplex ufologists. The maneuvering of the machine in space would be effectuated by partial or complete masking of the propulsive "force field."[6]

A SERIES OF HOAXES

Thanks to the inexhaustible vein of ideas and speculations opened up by the notion of antigravity, as expounded by ufologists, the inflammable question of the "nationality" of the discs also found easy explanations in the lively imaginations of sensationmongers.

In September 1949 American papers published under large headlines the details of an unprecedented event. An enormous unknown airship had fallen in flames near the Mexican frontier. Buried in the wreckage, a tiny "magnetic radio" emitted incomprehensible signals at regular intervals. Probably —according to one reporter—the Martian base from which the ship had taken off was trying to reestablish contact with the members of the ill-starred expedition. The story went on to say that the body of one of the pilots had been recovered almost intact. He was only about three feet tall. He was humanoid in form, but he had huge eyes without eyelids, tiny pointed ears, and a mouth that protruded but otherwise resembled ours; his head was enormous in comparison to the rest of his body. According to the reporter, the tiny corpse had been promptly sent to the Rosenwald Foundation in Chicago for careful autopsy. The foundation naturally denied the story vehemently. And finally it turned out that the "eyewitness" of the event—and also the onlie begetter of the sensational news —was a certain Roy L. Dimmick—a salesman for the Apache Powder Company, a gunpowder firm—"a very respectable man from every point of view."[7]

A wild yarn about a disc flown by pilots from Jupiter who were dressed in the style of our great-grandparents got short shrift. Then there was the story that at the beginning of March 1950, in the Chilean Andes, a geographical expedition had found some fragments of a disc-shaped astro-ship that had exploded when it tried to force an entry into our atmosphere. A minor newspaper variant on this story had it that the fragments were found "in a wild region of the Rocky Mountains" and that there was no doubt they came from interstellar space, for "the pieces are made of a still-unidentified metal; moreover, the fact that they were immediately sequestered by a military scientific commission that has since refused to give any sort of report on them proves the importance of the find."

A newspaperman named Perry Heard declared that he encountered four policemen one evening along a deserted road in Missouri. They were taking in a strange dwarf who was babbling in an unknown language into a sort of small oval box. "Perhaps," wrote Heard, "he was a Martian transmitting news of his capture by the Earth people. I wanted to snap a few pictures, but the policemen brusquely ordered me away." Frankly, it must be agreed that this story of a Martian transmitting interplanetary news is a brain wave that tops them all. It was a natural for a freewheeling American reporter.

For a few more months an incredible number of hoaxes of the same sort kept the thick ranks of American UFO buffs in a state of continual agitation, for they were sure that they were in on the most wonderful event of the century. The time was now ripe for writing any sort of "scientific" nonsense. In fact, the so-called Scully Report was born in this atmosphere of hoaxes. It was a collection of improbable revelations put into book form by the humorist Frank Scully, who, however, masked his real professional identity. According to the publisher's preface, the book was actually written by "an American specialist in scientific research." Its first printing of 40,000 copies, which was quickly sold out, brought to every corner of the United States the marvelous story of the little men who came from the planet Venus on a disc-shaped astro-ship propelled by magnetic energy at speeds faster than light.

After the fantastic success of the report, Scully even claimed that the bodies of these little men could be seen in a secret room of the Pentagon preserved in hermetically sealed bottles of alcohol, and that President Truman had taken a personal interest in the matter and had shown privately a number of times a movie film that illustrated the mechanical details of several Venusian interplanetary ships recovered in the middle of the Arizona desert.[8]

NEW ADVANCE UNITS FROM MARS?

Only a few months after the Air Force's easygoing Report No. 102 was written—that is, in the spring of 1950—a third wave of UFO sightings heightened the atmosphere of comedy.

During the first two weeks of February, strange incandescent objects had appeared over Arizona and Florida, over Algeria and Denmark, off the Chilean coast, in the skies of Patagonia, and even over the frozen reaches of the Antarctic, where Captain Augusto Orrego made a number of photographs of three huge flying saucers that spun in echelon in the polar sky above the Arthur Pratt naval base.[9]

In March UFO activity intensified and extended over the entire Western hemisphere, showing special preference for Central America, where their flights over Chihuahua, Durango, and Mexico City were of spectacular proportions.

On March 18 a number of silvery saucers—perhaps twenty —invaded the sky over Farmington, New Mexico, continuously changing speed and direction. H. F. Thatcher, director of the local surveying institute, was able to determine the approximate altitude (fifteen to eighteen miles) and their average speed (between 950 and 1000 mph) by triangulation. For nearly an hour these mysterious flyers crisscrossed the sky in a complex geometric pattern, intent on some unknown mission.

But where on earth or in space had those machines come from? The answer was simple, according to ufologists. From the twenty-third to the twenty-eighth of March, Mars was at its closest distance to earth. These ships were only the advance units of the enormous flotilla of astro-ships that penetrates our atmosphere when Mars is in that position. And in fact, almost as confirmation of this strange idea, sightings of UFOs in the following days grew to an astonishing crescendo.

On March 27, one of those ships, which many people were now inclined to believe really were reconnaissance craft from the "red planet," was seen by a very well-qualified observer. Former civil aviation inspector Bertram Toten came upon the disc at an altitude of about 5000 feet some forty miles from Washington, D.C. At the moment of sighting it was spinning like a top in a slow but steep descent. Afterward he dove in order to follow it, but the unknown object suddenly stopped, wavered slightly and then sharply shot off, climbing, and disappeared into the clouds.

In the routine report he wrote for the authorities, Toten conservatively estimated the disc's speed as it flew off to be in the neighborhood of several hundred miles per hour; he gave its diameter as about thirty-five feet and its thickness in the center as about fifteen feet or perhaps a bit more and reported that it was followed "by a short, luminous misty contrail doubtless produced by some kind of jet engine."

At the end of the bloodless adventure, Toten also noted that he had seen no evidence of aggressive intentions in the behavior of the presumed pilots of the disc, and that "because of its fantastic agility it was impossible to learn anything about what kind of engine it had, whether rocket or turbine, or how it was able to maneuver, since it had no steering surfaces."

At this point, for the nth time, certain American papers wondered whether or not the military authorities were not hiding something—for example, some extraordinary national secret that might indeed be called a "flying saucer."

Taking the ball on the bounce, the well-known radio reporter Henry J. Taylor launched his sensational "trial balloon." On the evening of April 3, 1950, during a broadcast from Los Angeles, what later were sarcastically termed the "Taylor revelations" by ufologists threw the United States into a state of temporary euphoria.

The flying saucers, the well-informed reporter declared, were two types of highly secret American military inventions. The first was a genuine saucer that whistled through the air, could climb to 30,000 feet or more and dive to 1500 feet and disintegrate in the air. These machines were pilotless and varied in size from 18 inches in diameter (like the one found in Galveston Bay, in Texas) to a huge 250 feet, and they had been flying for three years.

The other objects that many people took for flying discs were really "Flying Phantoms," he said; that is, jet planes like the XF-5U that the U.S. Navy had admitted was now in development. They were wingless circular objects that could fly at fantastic speeds. Those who had seen them said they resembled flying cigars, but in fact any circular body that moved at a very high speed would appear to be elongated both because of the trail of air that followed it and because of other complicated optical phenomena.

There were alleged to be several types of flying saucer, just as there were several types of conventional planes, he went on. Experiments on them began on June 25, 1947, and since then the experiments had been conducted on an ever increasing scale. Some were really flat, with the outer edge raised like a saucer or basin turned upside down. Others were thicker at the center, like pies. One of the latter type had been photographed in Wildwood, New Jersey, and had been seen elsewhere. Some were piloted, others were not. They left no contrail or exhaust, gave no exterior indication of their method of propulsion, and were absolutely silent. They could stop momentarily in the air and move off again toward the right or left, fluttering and picking up speed, lazily at first, you might say—as airline pilots had unanimously reported—until they shot off like lightning.

The construction of the flying saucers had gone through several phases of development, reaching its most intense experimental stages coincidentally with the public sightings of July 1947, January 1948, and the present period. At each of these three phases the saucers had become bigger and better.

I know, said Taylor, what these so-called flying saucers are for, but am not at liberty to say what it is, for it is an important and wonderful military secret. When the competent authorities are ready to make the matter known to the public, I will be delighted to tell you the whole story, for it is a fantastic bit of news, something truly wonderful for our country.

The second mystery in our skies had not only been seen, it had been heard, he said. Generally this object hums through the night, with flames coming out of square openings around the edge of the body; at first sight these openings look like windows. This "Flying Phantom" is in reality a huge jet plane that looks like a cake. Its shape is more or less circular and around the edge of the disc is a row of jet exhausts. The engines are inside. In flight, it looks like a flat disc flaming through the air, and its speed is so great that I am not permitted to mention it. This disc is not from Mars or Russia but from Maryland. The U.S. Navy has confirmed it, and I have been authorized to release the news. But any further information must come from the military authorities.

If you find a flying saucer on the ground, he told his audience—which is not very likely, since most of them are made of a material that disintegrates in the air and disappears after a certain period of time—you would find stamped on it in black letters the following words, which were found on the small plate that fell in Texas: "Military secret United States of America Army Air Forces," then a number and this: "Anyone damaging or revealing description or whereabouts of this missile is subject to prosecution by the United States Government. For recovery, call immediately" (here follows a telephone number and the address of a military air base). "Non-explosive." The flying saucers did exist, he added, and that was really good news!

MORE "GOOD NEWS"

After the sensation caused by this story, a U.S. Navy spokesman—one who really was authorized to speak for the Navy—energetically denied that any research or experimentation on types of planes or missiles that could even remotely be mistaken for flying saucers was taking place under Navy auspices.[10]

By a strange coincidence (but is that all it was?), in 1945 McDonnell Aircraft had test-flown the first 500-mile-per-hour jet fighter, known as the Phantom, which was built specifically for the U.S. Navy: the XF-1H, which later received the designation FH-1 and became very well known in aviation circles abroad as the first American carrier-based jet fighter.

In addition, Taylor's XF-50 was identified as the V-173, the Flying Pancake, designed by Charles Zimmerman, which was flown in November 1942 as a test for the production of planes with circular wings for use on aircraft carriers. The perfected experimental version, the XF5U-1, known as The Skimmer, was built in 1944 but was, however, destroyed four years later, unbeknownst to Taylor, during a secret test flight. According to one writer, the intrinsic and incurable aerodynamic instability of low-aspect-ratio wings led the Navy technicians at the time to drop the development of a formula that had been super-seded by new developments in wing flaps, and the surviving V-173 ended up in the Naval Air Station in Norfolk, Virginia, where it still lies in storage.[11]

On the heels of the Taylor "revelations," the technical press carried stories on the "total combustion" take-off rockets for heavily loaded planes that had been designed in Germany in 1944 by Professor Hermann Oberth; the sheaths of these rock-ets were made of nitrate of ammonia and disintegrated in the air after their fuel was spent. Nevertheless, it was immediately apparent that the radio-controlled antiaircraft devices that completely destroyed themselves and that Taylor mentioned in his report were launched from nowhere but his brain.

On April 4, while visiting the military base at Key West, President Truman himself unequivocally denied the Taylor story, declaring that he was completely in the dark as to the alleged facts. From Washington the Secretary of Defense, Louis Johnson, doubled the dose, asserting jokingly that he would be delighted to have the department purchase a couple of squad-rons of flying saucers if that would help national security in any way. Nevertheless, a few days later Taylor calmly reversed his field, falling back on a much more modest thesis. In a broadcast over the A.B.C. network he declared in effect: Offi-cial American denials of the existence of our flying saucers are worth a billion dollars to Russia and its "cold war." It will be a stroke of real luck if the Kremlin does not seize the oppor-tunity to announce that Soviet scientists are launching flying saucers all over the world. With things as they are, the Ameri-can people will have no other choice than to conclude that the saucers that are regularly sighted are produced by Russia—which is not the case—and that they are concealing in their mysterious womb the danger of a new Pearl Harbor instead of the proof of simple American activities.

The United States, he said, could raise the morale of the peoples of Western Europe, influencing them in its favor, when-ever it simply declared that it had no other comment to make aside from the fact that America was creating a number of use-ful, if incredible, instruments. These were not dangerous in-struments but good news for peace-loving peoples.

Near Minneapolis and elsewhere in the country, he said, we had for some time been launching balloons for the study of cosmic rays, enormous translucent things made of plastic that on the ground were only a hundredth of their size. At high altitudes expansion causes a balloon to blow itself up into a gigantic monster a hundred feet tall and seventy feet in diameter, as tall as an eight-story building, all in pulsating plastic. At an altitude of 100,000 feet some of these come under the influence of the high winds of the stratosphere and reach speeds of two hundred miles per hour. At sunset, because of their great height, they remain illuminated, assuming a reddish tint. The rays of the sun, angling upward and illuminating their undersides, give the balloons the appearance of flat, circular objects that are burning and flying in the sky.

Their instruments, Taylor reported, are then returned to earth by means of parachutes while the sphere, its job done, explodes and the large pieces of plastic material that fall to the ground cause great astonishment when they are found. The instrument basket has flashing lights that can be seen at incredible distances. These were apparatuses in normal use, he said, and he could not understand why the Air Force could not openly discuss them!

This statement—also appearing under the label of "good news"—brought to public knowledge the thesis of Professor Urner Liddel of the U.S. Navy's Research and Study Office, who claimed that the mysterious flying saucers were nothing other than the Navy's Skyhook balloons. The idea was not new, but the type of balloon was.

Yes, confirmed Professor Liddel, who at the time was in charge of the nuclear physics branch of the Office of Naval Research, the flying saucers were really blown-up balloons in the true sense of the word. They were simply the so-called Skyhook balloons used for research into cosmic rays. Nothing was more likely than that Captain Mantell had lost his life following one of these balloons.[12]

All these highly placed authorities entering the picture had the effect of leading many Americans to the inner conviction that "in spite of everything" the denials really threw a smokescreen over the existence of some American secret weapon.

On May 23 a Gallup Poll established the following: 92 percent of Americans still believed in Taylor's version of the flying saucers; 5 percent thought they were extraterrestrial; and three percent believed they were Russian.

The view that military circles supported—namely, that the UFOs did not exist—could not have been more thoroughly rejected.

Following the disappearance of the mysterious airships toward the end of 1950, the stocks of the most obstinate proponents of the Martian theory collapsed because all during the spring they had imprudently maintained that the space explorers would surely soon land. June came and the explorers remained completely indifferent and idle even in the face of the outbreak of the Korean War.

The failure of the American flying saucers to appear on the battlefields of Korea, when their intervention might have averted the hasty retreat of the American expeditionary force toward the port of Fusan, caused the percentage of Americans who believed that the U. S. Air Force had secret arsenals to fall practically to zero.

In the general confusion, the theory of an extraterrestrial source for the UFOs gained a few points. By consulting old almanacs and medieval chronicles, interpreting ancient myths in the most personal way, and rummaging among the dusty files of old newspapers, a number of "scholars" then discovered that more than once in the chronicles of the distant past there were references to the transient appearance of mysterious shining flying bodies. During 1951 this discovery allowed the ufologists to pass over their recent cropper in silence and to proclaim to the four winds that "flying saucers have visited the earth before and they are almost as old as mankind itself—perhaps even older!"

ALLEGED UFOS IN THE PAST

One of the first people to occupy himself in studies of celestial phenomena was Charles H. Fort, who died in 1932, fifteen years after the term "flying saucer" came into use. Having spent his life compiling books of strange air stories, he was convinced that supernatural beings from other worlds had visited earth through the centuries.

Today ufologists consider Charles Hoy Fort as a sort of illustrious precursor, so much so that in order to honor his memory (and to reap financial returns) his literary labors have been reprinted in a huge volume under the title *The Books of Charles Fort*.

It would be pointless to give here an example of the prose of this honorary ufologist, for the evidence he gives is of more interest to the investigators of ordinary celestial phenomena. But his methods of interpretation and research, transferred to the present day, have influenced many, among them, for example, the British writer Harold T. Wilkins, an avant-garde ufologist-archeologist-mythologist. In his heavily documented collection Wilkins has managed to list several hundred alleged UFO sightings in the past, the oldest of which goes back to 222 B.C.[13] On the basis of the same criteria, the American ufologist Desmond Leslie was the first to extend the "genealogy" of the UFOs to the remotest and most legendary times of prehistory.[14]

It is not very difficult to tear down the enormous edifice of ancient evidence that the ufologists have constructed. Examples prior to the eighteenth century are too vague to have any significance or determining importance and—if seriously examined—can be quite easily explained by ascribing them, case by case, to the appearance of ball or pearlitic lightning, multiple meteorites or the fall of large aerolites, to the sudden formation of lenticular clouds, or to some rare phenomenon of atmospheric mirage inexplicable to the ancients.

Almost all the more recent evidence falls perfectly in the area of the historical development of aerostatics.

If we add to this the fact that ufologists have often knowingly altered the texts of old accounts in order to better adapt them to their own ends,[15] we must agree that, despite the newness and complexity of the UFO problem, it was not necessary to expend so much imagination. *Human technology, especially when directed by the military—who, within broad limits, don't have to worry about money—has advanced much more than seems apparent or than is publicly known.* And we must also admit that there was no reason to think up forms of propulsion capable of shifting at will and to their own advantage the so-called "neutral point" that exists between the various planets.[16]

Some ufologists, seduced by the idea that this "neutral point" actually exists, have indeed proposed starting practical research into the field of antigravity propulsion; and some ingenuous experiments have been carried out with "promising" results—promising only because of the enthusiastic researchers' happy ignorance of certain physical laws.

It was maintained that levitation as practiced by mediums is without doubt a verified physical phenomenon and that it acts against the force of gravity. We know very well—the enthusiasts proclaimed—that long ascetic practice and possibly some still-unknown drug can induce it in normal subjects as well, and who knows but what this may not be precisely the right way to arrive at the formulation of the mysterious basic laws of antigravitational flight, just as the study of the flight of birds revealed to man the first rudiments of mechanical flight![17]

In any case, even though a number of world powers were already beginning to conduct special research into subatomic particles in order to isolate hypothetical "gravitone"—research that was undoubtedly serious but that still has not yielded any practical results—in the field of this new science (called electrogravitics in the United States), the evidence for antigravity as the means of propulsion for the discs was completely negative at the beginning of 1952.

PRELIMINARY RECAPITULATION

In the spring, when the UFOs reappeared over a number of states and over neighboring Canada and Mexico, the press as usual gave a good deal of publicity to the most clear-cut episodes.

The argument over whether they were Martian discs or Soviet discs—the United States having now been ruled out—started up again, and the investigation that had gone under the successive names of projects Sign, Grudge, and Twinkle was hurriedly exhumed and given the conventional unromantic name of Project Blue Book.

The direction of the new inquiry was taken over by the Air Technical Intelligence Center (A.T.I.C.) of Wright-Patterson Field, which proclaimed that it wanted to get "to the bottom of the question."

For a start, more than 1300 sightings reported between the fateful June 24, 1947, and March 25, 1952, were carefully re-examined, with the result that: "23.54 percent of the reports speak of disc or spherical shapes; 8.25 percent of spindle shapes resembling cigars or rockets; 2.55 percent of flying wings; 0.6 percent of groups of lights." Whence it was deduced that "38 percent (of the sightings) can be attributed to astronomical or atmospheric phenomena; 13 percent to research balloons; 22 percent to flocks of migratory birds or airplanes flying in the stratosphere; 10 percent to other phenomena that cannot be explained because not enough details were reported; and 15 percent to unexplainable phenomena."

While the preparatory work for the new inquiry was getting under way fast and furiously in the offices of the A.T.I.C., for the fourth time unknown flying bodies began to reappear, the sightings growing in intensity with a frightening rhythm.

It is at this point that the first "contactees" appear, that is, those fortunate mortals who boasted of being in friendly communication with the superhuman visitors from space by means of direct contact, telepathy, light signals, or small personal radio transmitters. And the story of the supposed extraterrestrial origin of the UFOs became terribly complicated.

NOTES

1. See article in the magazine *Ali* (Milan), May 12, 1952. And *cf.* American press reports, March 29, 1950: Pilots John Power and Miguel Angel Delgado of the Venezuelan Air Lines encountered over Caracas a mysterious flying body resembling an enormous tortoise surrounded by whirling gases. Quickly approaching their DC-3, it passed by, nearly touching the

plane. The air turbulence was so violent that Power, who for a moment was afraid that they were going to be hit by the "tortoise," was able to keep the plane on its course only with great difficulty and with a quick acrobatic maneuver. (Clearly a supersonic shock wave was formed on the wing involved as the object flew past and was caused by the differences in speed between the aircraft and the propulsive jets of the "tortoise.")

2. In 1932 Caldwell had built a full-size flying model of a plane with circular wing of the "parasol" type, so called because it was raised above the fuselage. The first product of the Glen Burnie "factory" was an agile and interesting machine for the time, but it had the advantages and, above all, the serious defects of all low-aspect-ratio wings—lateral instability. Its characteristics were tested the following year by Professor J. Owen Evans in the large wind tunnel in Los Angeles. Then the noted American flyer Jimmy Doolittle flew it and established its modest speeds (top speed of 97 mph, landing speed of 23 mph). Thereupon the builder optimistically announced to the press the future preparation of a plane with a circular wing thirty-five feet in diameter, fifty tons in weight and with a speed of 225 mph, which would be followed by a "flying circle," with a wing diameter of seventy-five feet and thirty tons in weight, for transatlantic flights. In the meantime he had constructed a slightly modified second prototype that ruined him. In 1936 it crashed, killing the test pilot. After this incident Caldwell could no longer find any pilot willing to fly his strange machines. He unsuccessfully tried to interest the armed forces and a number of aircraft companies in his projects. In 1940, before leaving Glen Burnie, he gloomily told Evans that only the lack of $5,000 stood between him and "an astonishing result." (Could it have been a kind of helicopter with a central cabin and contrarotating rotors?)

3. Later on, one member of the Jekams expedition who was interviewed by the press let slip a detail that the investigatory authorities had classified as "top secret": during the entire period of the strange "dances" the Geiger counters "kept on clicking, picking up repeated signs of intensified radioactivity in

the area." The hypothesis that the three UFOs had refueled with some invisible energy—obviously still unknown to science —gushing from the top of the mountain, as ufologists later declared, or that the craft had carried out "a complex operation of electrostatic diselectrification, assisted in this perhaps by the weakness of natural radioactivity of the local lava," as suggested by another member of the expedition, must be excluded. On the other hand, it is possible that the aircraft one by one dumped atomic slag or "ashes" that were somehow related to the propulsion system of the devices, or to the operating cycle of UFOs in general, into the crater of the extinct volcano or into some deep neighboring crevasse. That would also explain the "dance" in the air, which would have been started by weight shifts of the mass in the air and the crosswind. (Professor Jekams reported that an annoying wind was blowing that day.) Turning partially on themselves (the propulsion band), those enormous masses were doubtless subject to the violent phenomena of gyroscopic precession. Like gigantic tops the aircraft spontaneously oscillated in the air in order to dampen the forces disturbing their hovering above the mountain receptacle.

4. See Gerald Heard, *The Riddle of the Flying Saucers* (London, Caroll and Nicholson, 1950). By applications of the well-known laws of electrophysics, Heard seriously thought that he had solved the mystery, or rather the various mysteries, of the UFOs. (Coming from the two moons of Mars, piloted by a sort of superintelligent bee, they had been carrying on a discreet strategic reconnaissance of the earth for at least a couple of centuries.)

5. See Donald H. Keyhoe, *The Flying Saucers Are Real* (New York, Fawcett Publications, 1950); *Flying Saucers from Outer Space* (New York, Henry Holt and Co., 1953); *The Flying Saucer Conspiracy* (New York, Henry Holt and Co., 1955).

6. The French ufologist Aimé Michel—a fanatical supporter of Plantier and the author of *The Truth about Flying Saucers* (New York, Criterion, 1956), a book especially rich in reports

of UFO sightings throughout the world—calls this mechanical reduction in the force field "decentering" and explains it as follows: This reduction "would be accomplished by means of a movable screen, which would nullify or attenuate the effect of the field on the surface covered by it. Since the ionization effects would vary according to the field strength, the position of the screen would be *visible from the outside*—to any observer on the ground, for instance. The spot in question could be seen quite clearly on a photograph taken on July 18, 1952, by the geologist Fregnale in the vicinity of Lake Chauvet" (p. 204). Simple reasoning reveals that the explanation has no basis: if the aircraft, engine, and passengers are permeated by the force of the field, only a miraculous and very special substance can disengage them from its influence. Moreover, the "Plantier screen" reminds us of the solution Wells thought up in *The First Men on the Moon* to regulate and render inactive his famous "cavorite." He, however, was writing an adventure story, and in an adventure story anything goes. Although ufology has for the most part become a frivolous science or science fiction, UFOs are certainly not subjects limited to novels. The Plantier screen has, therefore, the same scientific basis that cavorite and Newtonium have. In fact, starting from the assumption of new transuranium substances produced in physicists' laboratories, one American ufologist proposed some years ago that the synthetic element capable of neutralizing the earth's attraction be called Newtonium. "An element that is still completely unknown to us," he hastened to add, "but undoubtedly well known to our Brothers in Space for some time." While waiting for our brothers to decide to let us in on the secret of their productive process, it might be a good idea to call the hypothetical antigravity element with the more appropriate name of Unobtainium, as the technicians of the U.S. Air Force University in Maxwell, Alabama, ironically proposed for this sort of futuristic chimera. *Cf.* also Dr. D. C. Peaslee, "The Nonexistence of Gravity Shields," *Science* (Washington, Vol. CXXIX, No. 1292, 1956).

7. See Frank Scully, *Behind the Flying Saucers* (New York, Henry Holt and Co., 1950).

8. For a detailed treatment of this incredible case see Menzel, "The Little Men from Venus," Chapter XII in *Flying Saucers*.

9. Despite the Chilean authorities' ban on the publication of the photographs, which is still in effect, this sighting led the American ufologist Gray Barker to launch the "Antarctic Theory," which hypothesizes that the extraterrestrial explorers had chosen that remote part of the planet far from prying eyes for their way-station. See Gray Barker, *They Knew Too Much about Flying Saucers*, (New York, University Books, Inc., 1956).

10. And in fact the letters XF (which in 1950 stood for "experimental fighter") with a numerical designation greater than a unit did not even belong to the Navy but to the Air Force! In addition, the real XF-50 was an old experimental model produced by Grumman, with a piston engine, a propeller, and a lengthened nose; in other words, a modified Grumman Skyrocket.

11. *Cf.* Gert W. Heumann, "The 'Flying Pancake,'" *Air Pictorial* (London, February 1959, pp. 51–54).

12. In February 1951, Professor Liddel, publishing his theory in *Look,* pointed out that launches of Skyhooks had always been kept secret, and that the first balloons of this type had been released in 1947, precisely when the first flying saucers also appeared. A truly perfect coincidence. These statements immediately received the unconditional approval of military circles, which for obvious reasons could not support the adherents of the extraterrestrial source theory.

13. See H. T. Wilkins, *Flying Saucers on the Attack* (New York, Ace Books, 1967).

14. See George Adamsky and Desmond Leslie, *Flying Saucers Have Landed* (New York, British Book Centre, 1953).

15. See C. C. Wylie, "Those Flying Saucers," *Science* (Washington, No. 3057, July 31, 1953, pp. 124–126).

16. As suggested by the American ufologist M. K. Jessup, for whom the "saucerians" are the inhabitants of a number of artificial satellites that have been in permanent orbit for centuries at the neutral point of gravity between the earth and the moon. See his *The Case for the UFO* (New York, Citadel Press, 1955). After two decades of tight military secrecy and a decade of profound ufological studies of Mars and Venus, the planets which were first proposed as the most probable starting bases for the UFOs, we now have, with just about as much foundation, the following: Saturn or its principal moon Titan; Jupiter's third satellite, Ganymede, populated by people who are said to live on bacterial cultures now being depleted; the remote twin to earth, Uranus, or some other of the still unknown "dark planets" that perhaps gravitate beyond the orbit of Pluto; an earth belonging to the hypothetical planetary cortege of Wolf 359 or the extragalactic planet Clarion, ruled by an admirable matriarchy; the moon with its legendary troglodytes; lunar caverns where Nazi scientists who evaded capture by the Allies have their last refuge; other Nazi survivors developing their final "secret weapons" in the frozen Antarctic or in the solitude of remote regions of Patagonia or, again, in the impenetrable forests of the Gran Chaco or the Mato Grosso; the unplumbed depths of Time, the Fourth Dimension, with future Humanity that now explores its most remote past; the "wanderers of space," that is, the inhabitants of the destroyed planet Hsiu-chiu, a part of whom reached the earth in prehistoric times and populated present-day China; the star space explorers (sideranthropoi) who left the star Proxima Centauri centuries ago; the research voyagers hailing from Macrocosmos, a complex of "stellar systems" forming an organic whole of which our solar system is but a living "atomic cell"; the immaterial Ethereans living in the Fifth Dimension or in the burning shell of the sun; the Uranians coming from the outer edges of our planetary system or a highly evolved pre-Flood humanity (of the Atlantan or Lemurian or Tyrhennian race) that escaped its fate by flying into space; the biblical fallen angels; the descendants of the Incas who took refuge in impenetrable recesses of the Peruvian Andes with the secret of a primordial form of superenergy

obtained from volcanoes; the mythical "Children of the Red Earth" living beneath the Amazon jungle; the Hindu telemobile, the *duracapalam* launched into Hyperspace by mental energy and in behalf of a mysterious oriental sect. . . . And the list of these delirious ravings could be continued at length. When there are no concrete details that permit us to make a sound evaluation of the facts, any discussion, whether serious, semi-serious, or facetious, can without distinction aspire to the honor of being an "hypothesis."

17. *Cf.* Leonard G. Cramp, *Space, Gravity and the Flying Saucers* (New York: British Book Centre, 1955) and Dr. Erwin Stambler, "Anti-Gravity: Fact or Fantasy?" *Aviation Age* (New York, May 1957), pp. 26–31.

CHAPTER 3

The True Story of Project Blue Book

At the beginning of June the A.T.I.C. was forced, albeit unwillingly, to face the "big flap" of 1952. In Pentagon jargon, according to Edward Ruppelt, a flap is a condition, situation, or mental state of a group of persons that is characterized by an advanced stage of confusion which has not yet reached panic proportions.

In fact, a flood of reports engulfed the A.T.I.C. experts. By December 31 there were 2018 reports, not counting sightings that were reported only to local newspapers and those from foreign countries. Were the American people—indeed, the whole of humanity—perhaps showing unmistakable signs of progressive mental imbalance? Or were flotillas of disc-shaped space ships really intensifying their exploratory missions?

Even the high command of the U.S. Air Force had to take the problem seriously, simply because some of the detailed reports ("good UFO reports") had come and were continuing to come from far-off Korea, where military operations were taking a somewhat critical turn. More than one American pilot had encountered fast, silvery spheres or flaming aircraft with the strange roundish shape, and radar installations in Japan, on Okinawa, and in South Korea had repeatedly picked up unknown objects flying at high speeds. Comets? Self-propelled devices that the Russians had supplied to the Chinese and North Koreans? Or were they the notorious UFOs that serious people had relegated to the realm of fantasy?

No intense meteor activity was reported in June. The Aquarids shower (July 28) did not coincide with the bulk of the sightings reported, and, as we know, meteors are extremely punctual. Well, then, were the aircraft devices manufactured behind the Urals? The Air Force regarded this possibility with deep-seated skepticism. How could Russia, which was just taking its first steps in the area of modern aeronautics, have already developed such things?

Nevertheless, those "things" continued to crisscross "Western" skies, sorely trying the patience of those who should have been able to puncture the myth, which was particularly galling to the U.S. Air Force because it threatened its proclaimed air supremacy at a time when Soviet MIG-15 fighters on the Korean front had demonstrated that they were superior to the American planes.

The content of the reports was often disconcerting and sometimes even annoying. Different witnesses rarely gave the same descriptions of the UFOs: they were shaped like a ball, or they looked like falling stars, or they were flying triangles or rhombuses, or they floated in the air like jellyfish, or they were shapeless . . .

With justifiable consternation the A.T.I.C. personnel wondered how it was possible for a mechanical, metallic device not to have a well-defined and definite shape. How could it change so rapidly from a jellyfish into a comet and then into a sphere and a rhomboid and finally just fade away into something without any definite contours?

A "GOOD UFO REPORT"

One event in particular attracted the experts' attention. It took place on July 14 in Virginia, a few miles from Newport News, near Norfolk. The eyewitnesses were two veteran pilots of Pan American Airways, W. B. Nash and W. H. Fortenberry.

At 9:12 P.M. six large, silvery discs, proceeding horizontally in echelon, with the lead ship (or presumed squadron leader) on the bottom, appeared over the horizon and were soon within a mile of a DC-4 which was flying to Miami at an altitude of about 8000 feet. The objects were perfectly circular from plane view, and about seventy-five feet in diameter; they appeared to be enveloped in large reddish halos that at times changed to orange streaked with red, and they glowed like red-hot coals.

With the aid of a Dalton Mark 7 computer, the American pilots calculated that the formation was flying at a speed a little better than a thousand miles an hour.

Having evidently sighted the DC-4, the leading disc suddenly slowed and its glow dimmed markedly. The two farthest discs continued at high speed, catching up with the lead ship, as if their order to execute the maneuver had been received a bit late. At the same instant the lead ship flipped over on its edge and changed course. Immediately the five other discs imitated it in unison, clearly revealing their conformation—that of a sort of shallow cone with a maximum width of about fifteen feet in the center.

After another abrupt change in direction—of more than 150 degrees—their light grew brighter as if due to a sudden increase in propulsive force, and in fact they quickly removed themselves from the path of the DC-4, resuming their horizontal position and their curious echelon formation.

Moving westward, the formation was joined by two other discs that had been hovering at a lower altitude during the whole of the strange maneuvers, as if waiting for some specific command. In the few seconds during which they speeded up to reach the formation, they gave off a red glow that was brighter than usual.

Suddenly all the discs went dark, and a few seconds later, when they became bright again, the eight machines appeared in an even line. At this point, accompanied by a series of short, regular, blinding flashes, the formation climbed for about 3000 feet and finally disappeared rapidly toward the west.

"They are piloted!" some newspapers wrote. "Or at least many of the ships must be piloted, and the probability that this is correct increases the bigger the machines get."

In addition, some ufologists called attention—correctly, for once—to the fact that the evolutions the discs went through seemed to rule out the possibility that they were radio-controlled or had special electronic sighting or repulse devices. For with the radio impulses traveling at the enormous velocity of 186,000 miles per second, the craft would have had to be spaced at intervals of about a hundred yards or so; if not, carrying out strictly simultaneous maneuvers would have been impossible. For if, let us suppose, the receiver of one of the discs had not been properly tuned, the delay in the answering maneuver would then have had to show up during successive maneuvers also. Instead, as we have seen, the discs flipped on their edges in unison.

UFOS OVER WASHINGTON

On April 17, 1952, near the Canadian air base of North Bay in Ontario, several "red spheres" flew by at supersonic speeds and subsequently crossed over some of the southeastern states at the same high speeds.

The next day air defense headquarters for the eastern United States released a statement to the press from Newburgh, N.Y., saying that the detection system had developed a "pattern of unknowns in both the northeast and northwest which appeared potentially dangerous." An alert had been ordered when unexplained vapor trails were sighted at a high altitude near Nome, Alaska. Later, the period of emergency was lifted after the "unknowns" were identified.

No details were furnished as to the identification. Who had involuntarily caused that—fortunately groundless—fear that aggression was coming from the sky? And with what kinds of machines? And for what reasons?[1]

This haphazard approach to vigilance, if we can call it that, on the part of the American authorities did not, however, last long, and a foretaste of what was to come took place on July 17.

That night the radar installation at the Denver airfield sent its exploratory beams into the sky and caught a distant group of "things" moving along the horizon at a speed of nearly 3000 mph. Alerted by radio, Captain Paul L. Carpenter, flying an American Airlines DC-6, turned down his cockpit lights and waited. Shortly afterward four bright objects sped by at a fantastic speed. They were at his altitude, about 25,000 feet and a few miles off.

Three days of relative quiet obtained and then "incredible" things happened—incredible to the men at the A.T.I.C.

At 12:40 A.M. on July 20, the radar screen at the C.A.A. traffic control center in Washington, D.C., revealed the presence of eight unknown objects flying at about 100 to 130 mph in the vicinity of Andrews Air Force Base, in Maryland, about fifteen miles southwest of the capital. From time to time the radar blips showed that the objects shifted course rapidly, often moving against the wind, and that when they climbed, they rose absolutely vertically. The possibility that it was a squadron of jet fighters could, therefore, be ruled out. Toward one o'clock the blips disappeared as suddenly as they had appeared (that is, they moved out of the area covered by the radar beam), only to reappear some minutes later in the northwest, over the capital.

The controller on duty then informed Senior Controller Harry G. Barnes. He was skeptical concerning these moving lights in particular and UFOs in general. At the time he supported the ideas of Professor Menzel, author of a clever if useless theory that the saucers were "mirages caused by thermal inversion." Barnes insisted on personally checking the radar apparatus and found that it was functioning perfectly.

During this interval the control tower at the National Airport also got a fix on the mysterious apparitions and computed their speed, finding that *one of them had flown through the upper stratosphere for about eight miles at the astonishing speed of 7200 mph.*[2]

Some of the lights suddenly seemed to swoop down over the

White House, the Capitol, and the Pentagon, areas prohibited to overflights. A number of people working on the outskirts of the airport later agreed that there was a large, round glowing object followed by others flying at higher altitudes, all variously colored and flying toward the south.

A WELL-GROUNDED SUSPICION

Two jet fighters that were immediately sent out from New Castle, Delaware, ranged through the sky over Washington unsuccessfully looking for the "lights." But they meanwhile had disappeared from the radar screens, probably because they rose vertically to a very great altitude when the fighters arrived. After the fighters returned to the base the lights reappeared, "dancing in the air like young deer."

At this point Barnes had the distinct impression that *the mysterious visitors were able to hear and understand him when he radioed the pilots to intercept the objects,* because more than once the UFOs darted away as soon as he gave their exact position.

Receiving a radio message about the strange things in the sky, Captain H. Dermott, who was piloting a civilian plane toward the capital, caught sight of an intense white light of vaguely globular shape following him at a distance in the dark. Then when it "saw" that the plane was coming in for a landing, the shining phantom sped off at a high rate of speed.

Strange things were also seen from the ground. At 5:30 a radio engineer named E. W. Chambers watched the evolutions of five huge, clearly circular objects that "shone like headlights in fog" and crisscrossed the sky in a loose formation over the outskirts of Washington. For no apparent reason they suddenly climbed and disappeared in the night. It was then—that is, shortly before dawn—that the squadrons of luminous bodies finally disappeared from the radar screens as well.

During the next two days there were no local reports of UFOs, but during the night of July 22–23 a number of objects passed over several states in New England, giving off a silvery glow in the moonlight. For three days there were no new sightings; but at 9:08 P.M. on July 26 the sky over the District of Columbia was again favored with stratospheric incursions.

Twelve unknown objects suddenly arrived from the northeast and the radar of the C.A.A. control center picked them up lazily cruising at about forty miles an hour, an unusually low speed even for ordinary aircraft—stalling speed, in fact.

At first the C.A.A. staff thought a swarm of weather balloons had been caught by a current of air and were accidentally crossing over the city. They were soon disabused of this notion. The pilots of a plane that happened to be flying by radioed that the "balloons" flew off rapidly as the plane approached, almost as though they were afraid they would be attacked. Besides, they weren't balloons, but white-hot objects.

Again the base at New Castle fielded a pair of jets that sped toward Washington. The first one flew toward a white globular mass that was giving off a blinding brightness, but when the pilot came within a half mile of it the light mysteriously went out and he flew about in the dark looking for the elusive light.

At 10:30 the second fighter just as unsuccessfully followed three bluish globes; then he followed five others that had turned completely white in the meantime. As on the preceding Saturday, at dawn the UFO formation suddenly climbed away and did not reappear.

UFOS RETURN EN MASSE

On July 28 the radar screens in the capital caught no evidence of any unknown object. The scene of the new story this time was the Great Lakes area, near the Canadian border. At 2:30 A.M. Ground Control Intercept(G.C.I.) radar at the Osceola military base in Wisconsin caught a number of shining objects of undiscernible shape flying at a slow sixty miles an hour in a loose formation at about 80,000 feet, east of St. Paul, Minnesota.

The enthusiasm of the pilots who bravely took off to hunt down the slow invaders soon changed to disappointment. As soon as they became aware that the jets had taken off, the UFOs accelerated in a few seconds to over 600 mph and easily outdistanced the American fighters, vanishing toward Canada. Everything returned to normal for that day.

And that day only. For between 1:30 and 6:00 A.M. on July 29 Senior Controller Barnes noticed with annoyance that the notorious "lights" were reappearing over Washington in numbers varying from eight to twelve at the same instant.

Flying at 100 to 110 mph, they swarmed about within a radius of about ten miles in the air space between Andrews Air Force Base and Herndon, Virginia.

At 3:00 A.M. the blips disappeared from the radar screens, and instead there appeared the characteristic blip of a large transport plane heading for the field.[3] Informed of what was happening on their course, the pilots of the Constellation could only report that the sky was utterly empty, although visibility at the time extended for a radius of at least fifteen miles. Again the craft had made themselves invisible by climbing perpendicularly into the stratosphere. They did not come down again, probably having completed their mission.

During the day isolated discs also appeared over other parts of the United States, and twice they overflew the experimental atomic center of Los Alamos, New Mexico, at a very high altitude.

The A.T.I.C. thus was able to collect a conspicuous body of evidence that had been set down by observers free of any sort of censorship. Other equally accurate and important evidence came at the beginning of August.

The lunar eclipse of the night of August 5–6 had been over for a few hours when a large number of UFOs giving off the usual changing light again crossed over Washington. A spokesman for Andrews Air Base later declared that they had been observed "unmistakably" on local radar screens shortly before midnight, flying about for a considerable time before the eyes of a large crowd of observers, and that the fighters that were sent up from two fields in the vicinity had unsuccessfully tried to intercept the shining objects. But they were flying too high and too fast.

These nocturnal appearances of moving, lighted objects were, in any case, about to come to a close, at least over America. Early on the morning of August 20, the radar screen at Congaree Air Base in South Carolina picked up the track of a very fast UFO about sixty miles away. Flying a perfectly straight course and covering seventy miles in a minute (over 4000 mph), this late-appearing UFO showed how eager it was to regain its base. It was the last to be seen in that series of sightings.

Since the UFOs had not dropped anything explosive or damaging to the interests of the United States (*i.e.*, neither bombs nor subversive propaganda sheets), the public once again quickly forgot them, and the newspapers gave their time and attention to the many leaks concerning Project Ivy, which was preparing the first American H-bomb.

Thus the A.T.I.C. could proceed undisturbed in winnowing out all the material it had collected. Besides, even outside U.S. Air Force circles, the hypothesis advanced by the astronomer Donald H. Menzel a few months before was then receiving some favor.[4] The idea that the UFOs were only mirages caused by temperature inversions had come along at the right moment. Everything was accounted for, and all the lights—disembodied, of course—that had appeared over Washington during those summer nights were nonchalantly explained as balloons reflecting the moonlight or as recurrent mirages. After all, according to the most reliable local meteorologists, masses of cold air from Canada had reached the environs of Washington a number of times during that period, thus creating "the proper conditions for temperature inversions."[5]

POLICY GAPS IN THE A.T.I.C.

One does not know whether to believe the Air Force's top-ranking officers when they repeatedly profess their ignorance of UFO matters. It is certain, however, as Captain Ruppelt states so frankly in his volume on the work of the A.T.I.C., that at the beginning Project Blue Book did not deviate a fraction of an inch from the policy directives that had shaped the previous fruitless military inquiries.[6]

In fact, the staff reexamined all the intelligence reports on the Nazis' latest aeronautical experiments in order to establish whether the further development of any of these projects could have resulted in a type of aircraft having precisely the characteristics ascribed to the flying saucers. The essential data were then submitted to the aerodynamics experts at the Wright Field Aircraft Laboratory and to the best-known aircraft designers for their judgment, along with the anxious routine question: "Could the Russians have further developed these ideas?"

"No," they were reassuringly answered in each instance. "At present there is no possibility of making flying machines that can maneuver in the air like the UFOs."[7]

The Air Force's Aeromedical Laboratory added the weight of its authoritative opinion: "If piloted aircraft of this sort were constructed, the human body would not be able to withstand the violent accelerations reported by various witnesses."

The personnel at the A.T.I.C. boasted of being the immediate successors if not the heirs of the Air Matériel Command T-2 Intelligence Office, a secret organization that during the war had developed "highly efficient methods for getting all kinds of technical information on enemy aircraft production." But if the UFOs were really space ships commanded by a race of supermen, or, even worse, beings completely different from ourselves—as Captain Ruppelt quite properly suggested—all the ingenious procedures that T-2 had worked out would have been perfectly useless.

From the specific point of view of the UFO question there was, however, another and much more serious gap in the powers and conduct of the A.T.I.C. It continued, in fact, to concern itself with *enemy* aircraft production or, to spell it out, with the United States' only large potential enemy, the Eastern bloc. And what about the *other* world powers? England, for example? Only statesmen have the power to form alliances and issue ultimatums. Military men, however, have the indelicate and difficult but necessary duty of knowing everything about *every*one, for today's friend may, through unusual circumstance, not be tomorrow's or he may even go over to the camp of the adversary.

It is astonishing, therefore, that in reviewing German war inventions the A.T.I.C. did not remember that certain inventions were missing from the list of booty of German inventiveness that had been transferred to the United States. These inventions had been lost track of since the earliest days of the Nazi defeat.

To cite a few examples: Where were the designs of the gigantic A-14 multistage torpedo rocket? Or the blueprints for the piloted, rocket-engined *Triebflügel?* Who got hold of the plans of the "H.M.B. radio-immobilizer," whose heavy and still unperfected machinery was destroyed by the Germans themselves at Frankfurt-am-Main, just as it was to receive its first field test, because of the sudden collapse of the Rhine front? The working model of the first rocket turbine powered with liquid air and the anti-radar *Feuerball* device that had already been secretly used in battle were also both missing from the list. Again, how can anyone seriously think that the meticulous German researches on the "control of the boundary layer in its application to high speed aircraft" would not have found someone capable of recognizing its value?

To judge from appearances, then, in 1946 the experts of the A.T.I.C. had not divined the importance of British statements —exceedingly brief but, be it noted, *official*—mentioning that certain new types of "frighteningly fast" airplanes that would "astonish the world" were in an advanced state of preparation. The A.T.I.C. should have indexed, weighed, and analyzed these statements word by word.[8]

A good investigator would not have missed *the special significance of all those reports that showed that the UFOs consistently flew a general course in the direction of western Canada.* Is it possible that they were completely in the dark as to the "rumors" that had been circulating years before in Ottawa, Toronto, and Vancouver about the erection of aircraft centers in the semipopulated, forested areas of western Canada? Obviously when one hides something so carefully, one is hiding something important.

In any case, at the beginning of August 1952, 40 percent of the reports that reached Project Blue Book were stamped "unknown."

The contributions from certain foreign areas (France, England, and South America), where American military attachés collected reports of local flights for the Air Force, were not insignificant. Nevertheless, Captain Ruppelt says that these reports were neither investigated nor considered, because Blue Book had its hands full with its own. This was a strange attitude. While denying categorically that the UFOs were aircraft built somewhere on earth, the A.T.I.C. wanted to limit the sensational phenomenon of the UFOs (real or imaginary) to the United States.

The best sightings—best because of the wealth and novelty of the details reported—had been and would continue to be precisely those from foreign countries. The A.T.I.C. rejected them deliberately. Given the irrational basis of the investigation, the "big flap" was doomed to turn into a big flop.

RADAR DOESN'T LIE

"Flying discs: radar's gone crazy too! U.S. Air Force experts have established that the bright images mistaken for mysterious flying machines are produced by a rare but natural phenomenon of atmospheric refraction," an illustrated weekly proclaimed in August 1952.

Actually radar hadn't gone crazy. Instead, people who did not believe that the UFOs existed irrationally and hastily tried to pass radar off as error-prone in order to buttress their own inability to interpret observed facts correctly. Indeed, radar was too smart for that; it allowed a photographic film to register one of its UFO blips—strangely enough, for the A.T.I.C. experts—that had precisely all the characteristics of the UFOs, which, in any case, had already been photographed a number of times.

Ufologists, who are not extraordinarily subtle, accept all the material furnished by a score or so of episodes as authentic. Science rejects the lot. The attitude of the U.S. Air Force remains that of the "Fact Sheet" distributed to the press by the Department of Defense at the beginning of 1954 concerning certain "unusual aerial phenomena," which concludes with the following unqualified negation:

"The Air Force does not possess photographs which prove the

existence of 'flying saucers.' Because still photographs can be so easily faked, either by using a mock-up or model against a legitimate background, or by retouching the negative, they are practically worthless as evidence. Innumerable objects, from ash-trays to wash basins, have been photographed while sailing through the air. Many such photos have been published without revealing the true identity of the objects.

"More attention is given to moving pictures of unidentified flying objects since they are more difficult to fake. However, only a very few movie-type films have been received by the Air Force and they reveal only pinpoints of light moving across the sky. The Air Force has been unable to identify the source of these lights. The images are too small to analyze properly. Since ownership of these films remains with the persons taking them the Air Force is not in a position to give them out. The owners may do with them as they please." Too fast and furious, O iconoclast!

Captain Ruppelt had, in fact, among other things, subjected two fragments of movie film known as the "Montana Movie" and the "Tremonton Movie" (called the U-Film in A.T.I.C. circles) to the photographic laboratories of the Air Force at Wright-Patterson and of the Navy at Anacostia.

The first had been filmed by Nick Mariana, manager of the Great Falls baseball team, on August 15, 1950. Two large white lights had rapidly crossed a cloudless sky, one above and behind the other. Since it turned out that some F-94 fighters had flown over the other side of the city, the experts of Project Grudge—set up to continue the work of Project Sign, which had been dissolved—filed away the report, stating that it had been produced by reflections from the exhausts or the wings of the fighters. A kind of artificial parhelion.

Reexamined in 1952 at the request of the Pentagon, the hypothesis that the fighter planes had anything to do with the production of the phenomenon collapsed for various reasons. The true nature of the two moving spots remained unexplained, but as compensation the report was returned to the files, this time labeled "unknown," and so became part of the few bits of evidence of UFOs officially recognized as such.

The second film has a more complicated story. On July 2,

1952, Warrant Officer Delbert C. Newhouse was taking a trip with his wife and children in Utah. Some seven miles from Tremonton he caught sight of an irregular formation of shining, circular objects whirling about in the sky at a very high speed. It took him only a few seconds to stop his car at the edge of the road and aim his 16-mm Bell and Howell movie camera fitted with a telephoto lens in the direction of the UFOs.

THE INVESTIGATION OF THE U-FILM

The dozen blue-white objects flying west in an irregular but compact formation occasionally carried out strange maneuvers in the sky. Some seemed to pair up edge to edge for a short time; others seemed to be flying in tight circles, darting out to the edges of the formation or catching up with the leaders. Suddenly one of them reversed course sharply and drew away from the group, passing almost directly above Newhouse, who filmed it several times.

The attention of a considerable number of generals, admirals, and G.S.-16 men focused on the Tremonton film, and they flowed into Kelly Air Base in Texas, where the staff of the U.S. Air Force intelligence had their headquarters. A secret, high-level conference was held, and the pictures on the movie frames were identified as all sorts of things: balloons or known aircraft, reflections of the sunlight (for at 11:10, when the film was made, the sun was almost directly overhead), or a shower of meteorites, migratory birds, or gulls, a scientist present having reminded everyone that a species of white gull was native to the Great Salt Lake area. The term "spacecraft" was mentioned briefly, but merely in order to rule out any hypothesis along that line, and to be put in the same category with nonexistent supersecret airplanes of either American or Soviet manufacture that had the characteristics attributed to UFOs.

After countless showings of the film, no single view prevailed. Those bothersome spots vaguely resembled many things, but no single known thing in particular. Some of the assemblage complained that the film was without details and points of reference. The methods of the Navy photography analysts were criticized on the grounds that they had not used the densitometer correctly, and Newhouse found himself charged with having, perhaps unwittingly, changed the sequences of the film. After which, the film was rejected as documentary evidence of the existence of UFOs.

Captain Ruppelt did not, however, admit that he was beaten and he made a wise decision—to have a chat with Newhouse. The conversation lasted for two hours and brought out an interesting particular: When Newhouse and his family saw the UFOs for the first time, they were close to the car. "If they had been the size of a B-29 they would have been at 10,000 feet altitude," he said. And he added that they looked like "two pie pans, one inverted on the top of the other."

By joining two bodies having approximately the shape of pie pans, we again get the already reported characteristic biplanar structure of the flying saucers.

THE END OF PROJECT BLUE BOOK

In November 1952 Captain Ruppelt asked the Air Technical Intelligence Command for permission to release the films to the press. General Garland forwarded the request to the Pentagon for approval.

No films and no statements to the press, was the reply, even though the scientists whom the Department of Defense had sent to Kelly Air Base a few months before had suggested that the most likely explanation for the white spots on the U-film was that they were Salt Lake seagulls.

The seagull theory, continued the Pentagon's letter of refusal, was too weak. In addition, a new approach to keeping the public informed would be employed from now on. And in fact the periodic releases known as "Fact Sheets" did appear, quickly bogging down the whole affair.

Captain Ruppelt, who firmly believed that he had material of the greatest importance in his hands (could they really be space craft?), had repeatedly asked that his staff be increased. *At no time did it have more than ten active members*, many of whom were continually absent on trips all over the country to collect or check on reports. Requests to have special movie cameras set up in areas where UFOs were frequently sighted and to have experts in electronics, meteorology, photography, physics, and mechanics assigned to the project were turned down. It became very clear in the autumn of 1952 that the Air Force intended to write *finis* to Project Blue Book.

In fact, instead of strengthening the project, the Air Force decided to turn direct investigation over to a specialized intelligence operational unit, the 4602nd Air Intelligence Squadron. This substitution was at first passed off as a collaboration between the two units.

In December the somewhat embittered Ruppelt asked to be transferred to other duties and in April 1953 the staff was reduced to two members, Lieutenant Bob Olsson and Airman 1st Class Max Futch. Nevertheless, Ruppelt remained officially in charge until September, when, with "a simple ceremony on the poop deck of one of the flying saucers that I frequently have been accused of capturing, before a formation of the three-foot-tall green men that I have equally frequently been accused of keeping prisoner," he turned the office over to his successor, resigned from the Air Force, and went to California to work for Northrop Aircraft as a research engineer.

With this melancholy farewell, Project Blue Book virtually ceased to exist, and all the documentary material on the UFOs —more than four thousand reports—was buried in the files of the public relations office of the A.T.I.C. After the organizational matters were settled, a brief press release announced the transfer of power.

AIR FORCE DECEPTION

Ruppelt had directed Project Blue Book with passion and perseverance, though more than once he had given the distinct impression of being shackled by outside directives. In all probability the highly placed supporters of the project had created it specifically to put an end to the newspapers' and public's demands for information by gradually convincing them that the UFOs did not exist.

On May 8, 1952, after a long and detailed briefing on the project, Air Force Secretary Thomas K. Finletter had only a vague general comment to make: "You're doing a fine job, Captain. It must be interesting. Thank you."

This lukewarm interest in a subject that obsessed much of the country made it very clear that Captain Ruppelt, who had thrown himself into the investigation seriously, had completely failed to carry out the secret (or possibly merely implied) premises of the project. No wonder, then, that a few months later the Air Force began to press to have the project dropped.

On the other hand, the exceedingly small number of men assigned to the project certainly did not justify the outcry raised against it by both the press and ufologists, who frequently charged it with hiding the truth and, in effect, weaving a kind of conspiracy against the "Brothers from Space." The small and exceedingly busy staff of military ufologists simply could not have done that even if they had wanted to.

As for the A.T.I.C., it then got ready to put an end to the whole "UFO problem," and in its report of August 1954 declared: "The Air Force would like to state that no evidence has been received which would tend to indicate that the United States is being observed by machines from outer space or a foreign government. No object or particle of an unknown substance has been received and no photographs of detail have been produced."[9] This press release said in effect that the flying saucers were a myth, if by that term we mean something different from mistakenly identified natural phenomena.

When Project Blue Book was deprived of authority, science became the moral heir to the UFO problem. The Air Force would have been very happy to have the whole thing forgotten, but since people were still occasionally "seeing something" and getting excited about it, if science wanted to get into the act, then the Air Force had nothing against it. After all, hadn't past experience guaranteed that science would be a trusty ally?

Suspecting trickery from that part of science which was serving the military, Professor A. Aula, an Italian expert in aerodynamics, in a radio talk in 1954 spoke about certain nations that were secretly in the vanguard of progress. The United States repeatedly denied that it merited the honor of being in this vanguard until the first Sputnik removed America's comfortable laurels and Washington began to release a blizzard of statements on its formidable missile system. But United States policy on the UFOs never wavered.

Indeed, on January 1, 1955, the remaining staff of Project Blue Book (two members) was ordered to turn control of direct investigation over entirely to the 4602nd Air Intelligence Squadron, an organization created during the Second World War for the methodical interrogation of captured enemy airmen and subsequently charged with the study of "simulated problems"—for example, airborne invasion of hostile elements, the identification of preparations for an air attack on the United States, and so on.

As had been foreseen from the start, the decision had a double result. First, the now long inactive Project Blue Book was ditched. Second, the 131 sightings reported in the first six months in which the two units worked together, plus all the previous material, were so thoroughly studied that the percentage of "unknowns" suddenly dropped from 20 percent for 1952 and 9 percent for 1954 to 3 and 1.8 percent respectively. This computation was arrived at in 1960 with the reevaluation of the 6312 reports collected by various military and civilian bodies, beginning with the notorious first sighting of 1947, which cost the U.S. Air Force so much money in committees, conferences, investigations, and counterpropaganda in the press.

In reproducing the final official bulletin (Fact Sheet No. 812, dated July 21, 1960), the American newspapers added a comment that closed the matter: "Flying saucers totally debunked!"

In fact, for over five years since then, the American press—imitated by its sister publications throughout the Western world—no longer demanded to know the truth about the UFOs and limited itself to reporting briefly and without comment the increasingly rare news of sightings of unknown flying objects, which had been supplanted in public interest by the more sensational, more visible, and less mysterious space exploits.

Finally the U.S. Air Force could consider that it had won its long battle against the UFOs.

NOTES

1. UFO formations had, however, already previously appeared over the northern states without attracting press attention because of the small number of witnesses. In fact, on April 11, 1952, while launching some weather balloons, meteorologists at the Minneapolis Air Base were looking through the theodolite and followed a flight of "unknown aerial objects that moved in the stratosphere, reaching frightening speeds in a matter of seconds."

2. Other radar measurements of one of the objects moving at a high altitude established its speed at 4500 mph. In addition, it was observed that during some of the abrupt maneuvers one of the UFOs accelerated from 125 mph to 500 mph in only four seconds, while other objects seemed to reverse their direction sharply in seconds. For a more detailed recounting of these sightings see Major Donald H. Keyhoe, *The True Report on Flying Saucers* (Greenwich, Conn., Fawcett Publications, 1967), pp. 51 and 95–96; or the exhaustive and well-documented report of R. C. Borden and T. K. Vickers, *Preliminary Study of Unidentified Targets Observed on Air Traffic Control Radars* (C.A.A. Technical Development Report No. 180, Indianapolis, May 1953).

3. Blips, in radar jargon, are the responses received, that is, the band of radio waves bounced back by some object impervious to the waves. In the same jargon "angels" are pseudo blips, or the false pictures produced by some natural phenomenon (temperature inversion, storm centers, highly electrified clouds, hail clouds, and so on) that can influence the radio bands and that show up on the screen as irregular or evanescent spots, generally stationary.

4. See Menzel, *Flying Saucers,* p. 139 and especially pp. 300–310.

5. Major Keyhoe writes about this in his second book on the UFOs (*Flying Saucers from Outer Space,* p. 100): "For the next two weeks I talked with Barnes, Ritchey, Copeland, and most of the other Control Center men. Though they had cooled off, some were still bitter about the Air Force inversion answer. For years they had been guiding airliners through fog, snow, and rain without an accident. When the weather turned sour, thousands of lives were in their hands. As expert radar men, they were proud of their record—a record that depended on their ability to analyze and track blips in a split second. Then, overnight, they had been, in effect, called fools—deceived by a simple atmospheric condition they'd known for years. 'Every man in here knows temperature-inversion effects,' Barnes told me. 'When an inversion's big enough, it picks up all sorts of "ground clutter"—water tanks, buildings, shore lines, and so on. But anybody can recognize it. You'll see huge purplish blobs, *but nothing like those things we tracked.* In the six years I've watched the scopes, absolutely nothing—high-speed jets, storms, inversions, or anything else—has ever caused blips that maneuvered like that. And we've had identical weather many times.'"

6. See Edward J. Ruppelt, *The Report on Unidentified Flying Objects* (Ace Books, New York, 1956).

7. See the Department of Defense press release of April 27, 1949: "The possibility that these flying objects may be foreign aircraft was also taken into consideration, but the reported speeds are so much greater than those of any kind of airplane that we have technically approached to date that only an accidental discovery *so new that it has only now been reached* could sufficiently explain them."

8. Perhaps they had done so and the information was later simply forgotten, thanks to the postwar crisis in the British aircraft industry—the civilian portion thereof, of course. And

perhaps in the euphoria of the recent victory—which had virtually lifted the United States to the political leadership of the entire world—those in military circles allowed themselves to relax slightly in their investigations, convinced that they had now made war impossible thanks to their exclusive possession of the atom bomb.

9. *Cf.* Leon Davidson, *Flying Saucers: An Analysis of the Air Force Project Blue Book Special Report No. 14* (Ramsey, N.J., Ramsey-Wallace Corporation, 1967) and Lawrence J. Tacker, *Flying Saucers and the U.S. Air Force* (New York, Van Nostrand, 1960) p. 164.

CHAPTER 4

Mysterious Night Lights
Over the Rhineland

The clock in the plane read 8:25 P.M. when a "strange red light" appeared some ten miles off. The first person who saw it was the hostess, Gloria Hinshaw. It glowed in the night far to the rear, looking like the landing light of a fast interceptor.

The Trans World Airlines DC-3, en route to Chicago, was flying over the outskirts of Goshen, Indiana, at an altitude of about 2000 feet, and her captain, Robert Adickes, was checking the flight plan when the alarmed hostess reported that a very fast-moving light had climbed to the altitude of the airliner and was now pursuing it. Indeed, it had almost overtaken the plane.

The co-pilot, Robert F. Manning, immediately looked out

the side window and gave a startled exclamation. Although the plane was flying at about 175 miles an hour, the mysterious shining object was then overtaking it at a speed of at least 400 miles an hour, gradually, however, losing altitude.

"It's going down. . . . But the light is getting bigger and brighter! . . . It's bright orange, like a ball of red-hot metal. . . . It looks like a giant pinwheel rolling down a slope. . . . It's gone!"

A few minutes went by and the bright object again appeared toward the rear of the plane. Visibly slowing down and its light markedly decreasing in intensity, it began pacing the plane about half a mile away.

Nervously handling the controls, Adickes banked to approach the unknown object, but even before he cut the original distance in half, the invader began an unexpected maneuver: suddenly the underside of the object grew brighter and the UFO seemed to veer over on its edge and leap back, quickly reestablishing its distance.

"It veered away from us, as if it had some sort of radar-repulse mechanism," Lieutenant Manning observed with surprise.

Captain Adickes tried three times to approach the UFO, and three times the object moved back from the unwanted approach by veering over on its edge again. For a short while, however, the American pilots were able to observe it edgewise, and in the flight report dated April 27, 1950, they wrote that when viewed from the bottom it was perfectly circular in form, with a maximum thickness at the center equal to about a tenth of its diameter, which was probably a little more than fifty feet.

After the third sudden edgewise withdrawal, the flaming body took off northward, passing over South Bend and diminishing rapidly into the distance until it disappeared entirely.[1]

The Adickes report raised a basic question: did the UFO have some sort of automatic anti-collision mechanism? In principle it did not seem that the idea should be excluded. During night bombing raids on Germany, the Allies themselves had used such mechanisms widely.[2]

THE "MAGIC EYES" OF INFRARED

The British had made notable progress in liaison techniques that employed invisible infrared radiations, through their development of a very light high-tension storage battery, thanks to a clever application of the old Zamboni pile.

During the year 1942 the R.A.F. had mounted infrared "headlights" and receivers on its night fighters and they proved to be very useful—so useful, in fact, that the Germans became aware of them, for they allowed the British pilots to recognize one another during convoy missions. Subsequently, when the R.A.F. was equipped with its first radar-guided cannons, the infrared apparatus was also mounted in bombers so that they would be able to identify their convoy planes by night and open fire only on the enemy fighters.

With the thoroughness that characterizes their scientific research, the Germans had also considered the military applications of "invisible light."

The *Spanner* was a reflector that was supposed not only to pick up radiations from the exhausts of enemy engines, but, by illuminating the objective from a distance and receiving its reflection like a radar receiver, to trace the invading aircraft successfully even if too great a distance or an unfavorable position of the exhaust with respect to the reflector masked normal radiation. The technical authorities of the Luftwaffe judged the apparatus to be highly efficient but too bulky to be installed in its night fighters; the *Spanner* was therefore shelved, and the experience was profitably used in the construction of the Gaertner infrared phototheodolites for anti-aircraft rocket stations and in the project to develop the antiradar automatic search mechanism known as the *Feuerball*.[3]

In addition, during the year 1944, Section D of the Deutsche Forschungsanstalt für Segelflug (D.F.S.), of Ainring, near Salzburg, was working on various apparatuses for infrared night television using a network of ultrasensitive thermocouples that would permit distance vision even through clouds.[4]

When Albert Speer, the Minister of War Production, assumed the reins of the entire German war economy (August 1944), the highest priority was given to a D.F.S. apparatus (a small number of which were built in the plant of the Viennese firm Kepka Werke) equipped with a simplified type of photoelectric "magic eye" inserted in the center of a parabolic scanning mirror. This apparatus was also supposed to be mounted in the cone of the Enzian antiaircraft rocket, but just then the war suddenly took on a catastrophic rhythm.

After crossing the Po, the Allies forced Field Marshal Kesselring's divisions to surrender, and moving up from the south the British Eighth Army occupied the still undefended recesses of the Alpine Redoubt, which was then under construction. There, among hundreds of inventions of inestimable value, the men of the Eighth Army's T Unit found a number of pieces removed from the mysterious *Feuerball* together with the Enzian rocket and its deadly fuse, the minuscule Mücka detector, which was supposed to enable the pilots of the very fast night fighter jets to "see" their squadron mates by means of infrared lights mounted on their wing tips and tails.

The war ended but research continued. In fact, in 1948 the American Air Force experimented with a bomb (V.B. 6 Felix) whose trajectory was regulated by an apparatus sensitive to the heat given off by the target (ships, factories, petroleum refineries, steel mills, urban areas).[5]

In addition, they found on the drawing board items that a number of years later would result in the Sidewinder air-to-air missiles (similar to the British Firestreak), which were supposed to seek the hottest point in their cone of action: either the exhausts of aircraft engines—but only if the plane was attacked from the rear (wasn't that what the "strange red light" over Goshen did?)—or the propelling nozzle of a jet plane or missile (it was probably a rocket of this sort that downed the American V-2 over Russia), or the sun, if they were launched by mistake at a target against that star.

All this was well known at the Air Matériel Command, and the grotesque wall of secrecy that surrounded new military designs being separately worked out by the three American services was equally well known. Could the "ball" over Goshen have been some radio-controlled device belonging to the Army or Navy? The Pentagon immediately clamped the lid on such suspicions. A denial was also issued to the press. Then American newspapers "rediscovered" the Foo Fighters.

THE "KRAUT BALLS"

A former flying officer, who had been in the intelligence section of the Eighth Air Force during the final days of the war in Europe and did not wish to be named, apparently because he was still working in some section of the U.S. Air Force, declared to the New York press:

"It is quite possible that the flying saucers are the latest development of a 'psychological' antiaircraft weapon that the Germans had already used. During night missions over western Germany I happened to see on several occasions shining discs or balls that followed our formations. It was well known that the German night fighters had powerful headlights in their noses or propeller hubs—lights that would suddenly catch the target, partly in order to give the German pilots better aim but mostly in order to blind the enemy tail gunners in their turrets. They caused frequent alarms and continual nervous tension among the crews, thereby lowering their efficiency. During the last year of the war the Germans also sent up a number of radio-controlled bright objects to interfere with the ignition systems of our engines or the operation of the on-board radar. In all probability American scientists picked up this invention and are now perfecting it so that it will be on a par with the new offensive and defensive air weapons."

Then other flyers who had taken part in the opening of the second front also reported to the press that toward the end of the hostilities, in the area between Hagenau in Alsace-Lorraine and Neustadt an der Weinstrasse in the Rhine Valley, there were certain phenomena that oddly resembled the present-day reports of flying saucers. Convinced that they were faced with a new German secret weapon, the American flyers called them Foo Fighters (fire fighters, from the French *feu*, fire) and, jokingly, "Kraut balls." Subsequently, something similar but on a far smaller scale was seen by bomber crews over the Japanese islands.

Former war correspondent R. Palmer, for example, has related how one of the Foo Fighters followed an American plane over the Rhine Valley for about eighteen miles.

The incident began at 10:00 P.M. on November 23, 1944. Lieutenant Edward Schlueter of the 415th U.S. Night Fighter Squadron, stationed at Dijon, was flying a heavy night fighter toward Mainz. After carrying out a large-scale diversion along the northern edge of the Black Forest, the pilot began to follow the long ribbon of the Rhine. At about twenty miles from Strasbourg, Lieutenant Fred Ringwald, an Air Force intelligence officer who was taking part in the mission as an observer, glanced out the side window of the darkened cockpit and saw in the distance about ten small balls of reddish fire flying in formation at an amazing speed.

"I wonder what those lights are over there in the hills," Ringwald said to Schlueter.

"Probably stars," the pilot replied.

"I don't think so."

"Are you sure they're not a reflection from us?"

"Positive."

Puzzled, the pilot looked hard at the lights, which were now coming straight toward his plane. Without further delay, he radioed the American ground radar station:

"There are about ten Heinie night fighters around here, in the sky. Looks as if they are chasing us, and their speed is high."

"You guys must be nuts! Nobody up there but yourself," replied the radar station.

The radar observer, Lieutenant Donald J. Meiers, then got on the plane's radarscope to scan the fiery balls, but although the danger zone and the entire sky in the vicinity was scanned, there was no evidence of enemy aircraft: "Sure, no enemy planes showed up on the screen! And yet those red lights. . . ."

They continued to glow in sinister fashion a few miles off. Schlueter moved toward them at full throttle. As if they had foreseen the attack, the glow of the bodies rapidly dimmed, and without changing position, after a few moments they became completely invisible. The American plane crossed that part of the sky without encountering any moving body.

No more than two minutes went by and the globes, glowing red as before, reappeared but somewhat farther off, as though regrouping for a counterattack. Instead, six minutes later, after having completed a very long glide, they vanished into the night toward the German rear behind the Siegfried Line.

At this point the plane's radar began to give evidence of serious malfunctioning and the pilot had to give up his train strafing for the night.

Discussing what had happened during the flight back to the base, the flyers came to the conclusion that what they had seen were experimental devices (which explained the malfunctioning of the radar) on the order of the small multi-colored rockets that earlier used to be fired at German anti-aircraft batteries in order to confuse their aim during the great night bombing raids. Since they had not been able to identify the lights with any degree of certainty, and since the lights themselves had given no indication of aggressive intention, the flyers decided not to mention them in their flight report to the Dijon command for fear of being considered lunatics or victims of war neurosis.

REPORTS AND RUMORS
ABOUT THE FOO FIGHTERS

On November 27, 1944, two pilots, Henry Giblin and Walter Cleary, encountered an enormous, burning orange light in the vicinity of Speyer. It was flying at about 250 mph about 1500 feet above their fighter plane. The radar station in the sector again radioed back the equivalent of "Nuts!" when the pilots queried the presence of this threat.

The plane's own radar almost immediately began to malfunction, and they had to return to base. A detailed report— the first acknowledgment in official form—confirmed the existence of the inexplicable lights, and the two men who reported them became the butt of many jokes.

Subsequently other flyers encountered the mysterious Foo Fighters, but having learned their lesson from the fate of their colleagues, they never mentioned them in their flight reports.

Pilots McFalls and Baker were the ones who broke this imposed silence. They too were from the 415th Squadron, and their very short but detailed report forced Air Force intelligence to consider the matter seriously:

"At 0600 [on December 22], near Hagenau, at 10,000 feet altitude, two very bright lights climbed toward us from the ground. They leveled off and stayed on the tail of our plane. They were huge bright orange lights. They stayed there for two minutes. On my tail all the time. They *were under perfect control* [by operators on the ground]. Then they turned away from us, and the fire seemed to go out." The rest of the report was censored. Apparently it went on to mention the plane's radar and its sudden malfunctioning.

Two nights later the same pilots were flying over the Rhine when they were "attacked" by a glowing red ball that suddenly "changed into an airplane which did a wing over! Then it dived and disappeared." Additional censored lines.

Knowledge of these facts, which were being increasingly repeated, finally caught the attention of military publications. During the last days of December 1944, stories were leaked to the *American Legion Magazine*, which published the personal opinions of several U.S. Intelligence officers and suggested that the Foo Fighters were radio-controlled devices that the Germans sent up to baffle the radar of the night raiders. Picking up the story, the newspapers dug up Hitler's threatening speeches boasting of the imminent use of certain secret weapons capable of compromising or at least delaying the Allied victory.

In an effort to dissipate apprehension, on January 1, 1945, the science editor of the Associated Press, Howard W. Blakeslee, gave a radio talk in which he accepted the official view of Intelligence and assured his vast audience that the balls of light reported by flyers over France were simply St. Elmo's fire—natural and spontaneous lights produced by mutual electrostatic induction by the very craft flying the missions. And since the lights were immaterial, radar could not pick them up.

Echoes of these inconclusive discussions reached the American bases in France that were directly concerned with the question. Then the pilots themselves, most of whom had already been flying for a number of years and were quite familiar with St. Elmo's fire, decided to clear up the mystery.

The crew of a bomber that for a short time was being followed at a distance by an irregular formation of about fifteen fiery balls then reported that each of them gave off a strange light that went on and off at intervals and seemed to be related to clear variations in speed. At a certain point "one by one the balls approached so close that they almost touched the wings. They were huge, spinning balls, and for a short time we felt an intense sensation of heat." Naturally, the plane's radar ceased functioning.

The pilot of another Flying Fortress also reported that he had encountered a fiery ball over German territory. He was so ridiculed by his comrades, who declared that he had seen the celebrated Rhine maidens, that he was almost convinced that he had seen nothing at all when, two nights later, while flying back to the base, he saw a fiery mass similar to the one that had caused his discomfiture moving a few miles off. Aided by the fact that their paths were converging, he decided to fly right up to it. When he was a few hundred yards from the Foo Fighter, he heard a strange sound, like the "backwash of invisible planes." He continued on his flight path and the flying fire seemed to go out or to fly off. Resuming his interrupted flight to the base, the pilot saw the same shining, motionless ball at a high altitude off in the distance.

The suspicion that a German counteroffensive was imminent in Alsace to complement the one in the Ardennes led the Allied authorities to a close check of the most insignificant Nazi activities.

On January 12 several bombing squadrons simultaneously reported to the command at Dijon that they had seen the balls of light; some had seen one, others two, still others four or more. In the following months the reports on the Foo Fighters —and they were all alike in content and conclusions—formed a voluminous dossier that justified opening a special investigation, but it was at once noted that the balls showed no aggressive intentions, and since the territory over which they were operating had been occupied, the investigation was shelved toward the end of April 1945.

From the very beginning, the British showed not the least interest in the phenomenon. No hint of the facts recounted above appeared in the British press. But, in fact, Section T of British Intelligence was looking into the matter.

In early May, cruising on a free mission near the eastern edge of the Pfalzerwald, where French and American forces were still wiping out one of the many small pockets of isolated German units, yet another pilot from the 415th Squadron saw five orange balls in the distance proceeding in triangular formation. This was the last episode in the series. After the war was over, the Foo Fighters were forgotten for five years.[6]

Undoubtedly some of these manifestations could have been induced by the spontaneous, intensified production of natural phenomena, not electrostatic as Blakeslee had it but electro-atmospheric (ball lightning), arising out of the change of the German rear lines (as well as parts of Japanese territory) into a vast brazier and out of the violent daily movement of the land and the air above it.

But the Germans had brought into action various war devices that, examined one by one, could explain many of the things the American pilots had reported. For example, the Germans launched fluorescent balloons of moderate size. Released in the vicinity of the presumed point of ballistic contact between the raiders and the interceptors, they were supposed to fool the escort fighters and cause them to break away from the formation, thus permitting the attacking fighters to speed into the bomber formation.

Whole series of balloons were used to lift all kinds of shapes and sizes into the air in order to fool Allied radar by altering the apparent conformation of the land they were flying over. The shapes of the little lakes of Wannsee and Müggelsee, which were basic points of navigational reference, were frequently moved about in this manner.[7]

In addition, the Germans repeatedly sent up their Aphrodites, special black balloons that released sheets of tinfoil during enemy raids in order to confuse Allied radar.

Finally there were the first German jet and rocket interceptors for day and night combat, with their well-known white-hot circular exhausts and special fighting tactics; blueprints for these were subsequently sent to Japan in large transport submarines from a collapsing Germany.

THE ANTIRADAR FEUERBALL

With the news of the third massive appearance of the flying saucers, in 1950, the Foo Fighters reappeared on the scene, this time cited by ufologists as proof that Martian observers were present in the skies during the last war.

Since the idea of extraterrestrial observers clashes with the most elementary horse sense, let us rummage about for a while among the German secrets of the last days of the war, with special reference to that category of secrets which, for reasons of military expedience, even today preserves in whole or in part its shadowy and malefic character.

In the autumn of 1954, in Oberammergau in Bavaria, the O.B.F.—an experimental center run by the Luftwaffe—had completed a series of researches into electrical apparatuses capable of interfering with the operation of an engine up to a maximum distance of about a hundred feet by producing intense electromagnetic fields. If the ignition system of a plane's engine could be shortcircuited, the plane would be bound to crash. In order to make the invention a practical proposition, the German technicians proposed to at least triple the radius of action of this weapon, but when the conflict ended, researches along those lines had been barely sketched out.

In the meantime, as a by-product of these researches that could be put to immediate use in the war, another center, run by Speer and the S.S. Technical General Staff, had adopted the idea of employing "proximity radio interference" on the very much more delicate and hence more vulnerable electronic apparatuses of the American night fighters.

Thus a highly original flying machine was born; it was circular and armored, more or less resembling the shell of a tortoise, and was powered by a special turbojet engine, also flat and circular, whose principles of operation recalled the well-known aeolipile of Hero, which generated a great halo of luminous flames. Hence it was named *Feuerball* (Fireball). It was unarmed and pilotless. Radio-controlled at the moment of take-off, it then automatically followed enemy aircraft, attracted by their exhaust flames, and approached close enough without collision to wreck their radar gear.

The fiery halo around its perimeter—caused by a very rich fuel mixture—and the chemical additives that interrupted the flow of electricity by overionizing the atmosphere in the vicinity of the plane, generally around the wing tips or tail surfaces, subjected the H2S radar on the plane to the action of powerful electrostatic fields and electromagnetic impulses (the latter generated by large klystron radio tubes protected with special antishock and antiheat armor).[8] Since a metal arc carrying an oscillating current of the proper frequency —equal, that is, to the frequency used by the radar station —can cancel the blips (return signals from the target), the *Feuerball* was almost undetectable by the most powerful American radar of the time, despite its nighttime visibility.

In addition, the builders of the device hoped—and their hopes were fulfilled—that when the Allied flyers, not knowing their nature or purpose, noticed that the fiery balls were apparently harmless, they would not fire on these enormous-looking (because of their large halos of fire) "inoffensive" devices for fear of being caught in some gigantic explosion. More than once, in fact, as they fearfully watched those huge lights close in, the American pilots thought that some German technician on the ground was perhaps getting ready to push a button and cause the Foo Fighter to explode.[9]

Project *Feuerball* was first constructed at the aeronautical establishment at Wiener Neustadt, with the help of the Flugfunk Forschungsanstalt of Oberpfaffenhoffen (F.F.O.) in so far as radio control of the missile was concerned (but *was* it really a missile?).[10] One person who saw the first short test flights of the device, without its electrical gear, says that "during the day it looked like a shining disc spinning on its axis and during the night it looked like a burning globe."

Hermann Göring inspected the progress of the work a number of times, for he hoped, as in fact it happened, that the mechanical principle could later also be used to produce an offensive weapon capable of revolutionizing the whole field of aerial warfare.

When the Russians began to press on toward Austria, the construction of the first Fireballs was apparently continued by a number of underground plants in the Schwarzwald that were run by the Zeppelin Werke.[11] The klystron tubes were supplied by the section of the Forschungsanstalt der Deutschen Reichpost (F.D.R.P.) of Aach bei Radolfzell on Lake Constance, and later also by the F.D.R.P. section of Gehlberg, whose products, however, were not as perfect as those delivered by the F.D.R.P., a fact that caused a number of Fireballs to be used simultaneously in formation.[12]

THE JÄGERSTAB

After the "miraculous" failure of the July twentieth attempt on his life, Hitler was convinced that divine providence favored him; in August 1944, despite serious reverses in the field, he refused to admit that the war was now lost. He threatened harsh measures against anyone who dared speak of defeat, and in the military conference held on September 1 at Rastenburg he astonished the few generals who remained faithful to him with certain mysterious allusions to "the magnificent opportunity offered by the coming winter, with its fogs, snows, and long nights," which would finally bring the Allied operations to a halt. Through bitter experience he was well aware of the fact that the rigors of winter would stabilize all fronts, saving Germany for the moment. He was quite right, but, allowing himself to be carried away by excessive euphoria concerning that "magnificent opportunity" —or perhaps by an inner, growing desperation masked by euphoria—he ordered his generals to undertake the Ardennes winter counteroffensive. Because it was conducted with a forced economy of means, this maneuver could not achieve its objectives and ended by giving the *coup de grâce* to the exhausted German army.

At the same time Hitler's hopes for complete cessation of Allied aerial activity on the Western Front were disappointed. On the heels of the advancing troops, Allied service units had in fact set up field radar stations in the French rear, which by now was equivalent to the German border. These stations furnished the fighter and bomber formations with various kinds of information on the thin German defenses.

But the worst blow to Hitler's hopes was struck in October, when an enormous British air raid reduced to rubble the great radio jamming station that had recently been constructed on the Grosser Feldberg in the Taunus range. This station, equipped with the finest German devices, was built in an area from which it was able to protect the industrial regions of the Ruhr and the Saar, whose production, together with that of Silesia, had become vital to the prosecution of the war.[13] From that moment on, German skies, which had already been inadequately defended for some time, were completely opened to the enemy's so-called saturation bombings—in the last quarter of 1944 they accounted for 80,000 victims—and to the great air offensive against German transportation and communication designed to choke her war production at the source.[14]

To support the preparations for the Ardennes offensive and hinder the Allies from bringing up extensive supplies of troops and matériel along the Rhine axis by night, the Fireballs were thrown into action prematurely, and under the pressure of events unfavorable to the Germans, they were unable to have a decisive effect.[15] In addition, their development and subsequent use had paralleled the vicissitudes of German aeronautical production.

Notwithstanding the terrible Allied bombardments, German factories had continued to produce arms of all sorts, particularly air weaponry. In September 1944 they reached the amazing record of 4103 aircraft, but the greater part of this number never even flew because of the chronic shortage of fuel. The planes were destroyed on the ground at the airfields or during rail shipment from the factories to the flying fields.[16] The foundations for this undeniable but thoroughly useless achievement were laid down two years before.

Beginning in 1942, in order to meet the by now obvious

hreat of a long war against a powerful bloc of enemies, the German Air and War Production Ministries had encouraged very kind of proposal and experiment in the field of jet proulsion and related matters and had permitted a part of the egular assembly lines to be converted. Increasingly feeling the veight of Allied air mastery, the various services and techical groups each began to exert direct pressure on manuacturers and ministries in order to receive the lion's share f the allotments. The metropolitan air defense—supported rincipally by the air ace General Galland—requested fighter lanes, especially jet fighters, in order to halt the air raids vhich were mounting to a crescendo and reducing the country o ruins. The Heereswaffenamt (Army Weapons Office) worked ecretly to get fighter-bombers and antitank planes for the astern Front. Uncertain what to do and soured by the ailure of "his" Battle of Britain, Göring wanted heavy ombers, mostly to support his imminent retaliation with V-1s nd V-2s and restore the now eclipsed prestige of the Luftwaffe, nd thereby his own. Hitler wanted nothing but bombers, in rder to pay the British back in their own coin for the pound-ng that he had to take with angry impotence, and to give air upport to the various counteroffensives that he was planning n paper. The most powerful leaders in the party and the ropaganda office took Hitler's side, declaring that the United states, too, was ripe for a "good lesson."

In this atmosphere of senseless differences and disillusioned y Göring's many empty promises, Hitler acted as a clumsy nediator and irreparably delayed the production of the ex-ellent ME-262 jet fighter, which was already well advanced.[17] Nevertheless, the production of conventional fighters was at he same time speeded up, although not to the degree de-nanded under the circumstances; indeed, in February 1944 he Jägerstab (Fighter General Staff) was set up and achieved formidable increase in the single-engined ME-109 and FW-90 interceptors.

In April, Dr. Sauer changed the Jägerstab into a real re-rmament office (Rustungsstab), and for the first time civilian uthorities interfered officially in questions that had always een the province of Luftwaffe officers.[18] The Rustungsstab

set up an immediate program of emergency production, a
though it also gave a free hand to the development an
implementation of new projects so long as they did not i
terfere with the realization of the base program.[19] This pla
which would certainly have restored Germany's air supremac
at least over her own territory, was accepted only in part, an
in the final analysis this was the reason it failed.[20]

By means of complicated internal maneuvering Görin
sought to reestablish his shrunken authority, and by Octob
he succeeded in launching the Wehrforschungsgemeinschaf
a kind of research weapons pool of particular interest to th
air arm. But he had to accept the unwelcome presence in i
councils of Professor Osenberg, a high functionary und
Minister Speer, and finally of the extremist wing of the regim
the dreaded S.S. The S.S.'s fighting formations in the ranks c
the Wehrmacht had meantime grown to the proportions of
small army, battle-hardened and obviously destined to gro
even larger if circumstances permitted.

S.S. DOMINANCE

Once he had consolidated his power and in 1934 got rid of th
opposition of part of his collaborators through a bloodbath
Hitler dissolved the original storm troopers (the S.A.), wh
had become unreliable. He replaced them with a permaner
organization, the Gestapo (Geheime Staatspolizei, Secre
State Police), which created a black uniformed militia, th
Schutzstaffel (Elite Guard), later better known simply a
the S.S., and infamous for its political terrorism and its cruelt
in the death camps.

An offshoot of the same command, but organized for othe
purposes, was the Waffen S.S., the military body that fough
side by side with the army. It was quite apart from Himmler'
political militia, but it was tending to transform itself into a
kind of gigantic national militia. When the war broke out, th
Waffen S.S. Korps accepted into its ranks large numbers o
ardent young Nazis, who received a mixture of military an

political training and then, formed into autonomous S.S. divisions, took part in the military campaigns, distinguishing themselves not only for their admitted courage but also for the bloody reprisals they carried out in occupied territory.

The slow backstairs intrigue that the highest S.S. leaders engaged in in order to assume the reins of military operations began in 1943, when so many fronts were broken through that it became clear that the "inevitable victory" was neither so close nor so inevitable as Doctor Goebbels' political oratory would have one believe. But the right time came only with the unexpected assassination attempt of July 20, 1944, which revealed the latent enmity between part of the Wehrmacht and Nazism and resulted in a large, grim harvest of victims. It was the same antagonism that in Italy had set the monarchy against Fascism, but in Germany—given the time, place, and circumstances—the rival forces acted according to a *kolossal* plan, one that was really typically German.[21]

Furious at both the insult and the danger he had been in, Hitler turned control of planning, construction, and in some cases even the use of the "new weapons" over to the S.S.—without, however, taking away all authority from his ministers. Previously the S.S. had exercised only a more or less hidden control in this area to prevent production slow-downs, sabotage, and treason.

Reichsführer S.S. Himmler named Dr. Heinz Kammler, a Gruppenführer (Lieutenant General) of the S.S., the director of secret war production, which now included the famous V-series flying bombs and rockets. The effects, which from all reports were relatively beneficial to the Third Reich, were soon visible. The famous V-2 torpedo rocket, with its final bugs still not eliminated, was dragged—and that is exactly the right word—onto the launching areas and fired on London in salvos despite the bewilderment and resistance of the directors of the experimental center at Peenemünde. The S.S. wanted weapons, not promises. And in order to impose its growing authority in that sector, it requested and got control of the launching and even the firing of the bombs.

Another important skirmish in the S.S.'s growing intervention in the conduct of the war was its manifest interest in certain unusual weapons that promised dangerous but certain victories.

In August 1944 the Bachem firm in Waldsee began its project for a single-seater, rocket-armed, rocket-engined fighter, the Bachem 8-349-A.1, which was completed in record time. Called the *Natter* (Viper), this was a vertical-take-off plane controlled by a metal pylon.[22] In the spring of 1945 the firm received the following orders: for the Luftwaffe, 50 machines; for the S.S. Air Arm, 150 machines. The S.S. seemed bent on surpassing the Air Force in the defense of the Reich![23]

Then, since the weapons for active defense were delayed in leaving the underground assembly lines in the requisite numbers, the S.S. Technical General Staff prepared its own radar and radio antiaircraft interference units. By the clever use of "artificial objectives" and antiradar apparatuses that it had commandeered while still in the experimental stage, it succeeded in confusing the flight officers of the Allied bombers. But the greatest success of their most trusted technicians in this sector was without doubt the whirling antiradar airplane, the Fireball, which they had launched in squadrons and were still able to keep fairly secret until the very end.

To understand the rest of the story better, we must understand that the S.S. had a number of scientific research and testing centers that are best described as "private." One of the oldest of these was located in Grossendorf, where rocket studies were carried out under Captain R. Engel. Another center for similar testing was in operation at Jenbach, in Austria. A third and very well equipped center, and perhaps the most important of all, was also in operation in Austria, in St. Aegyd, a small city north of Vienna. Although it went under the name of the Kraftfahrtechnischenlehranstalt (K.T.L.) —in other words, a public technical institute, or a polytechnical school, for the S.S.—in the last days of the war it was in reality mostly concerned with unusual applications of jet propulsion and the first gas turbines for all sorts of war vehicles such as tanks, motorboats, gliders, and other such offensive vehicles. At the beginning of 1945 the S.S. high command moved the institute because it was located too far east. It took fifty trucks packed with documents, projects, blueprints, and experimental apparatuses and models to move the center to Sulzheim and the surrounding villages by night. It resumed operations on April 8, but a month later the British experts of the T Department were rummaging about in that precious heap of papers.

THE INDUSTRIEKONTOR

The full power that had been given to General Kammler also opened the door for the S.S. to those governmental and private centers that at first had resisted direct collaboration. Thus the Forschungsinstitut of Lindau am Bodensee, which was conducting researches into liquid air and "special weapons" only a short distance from the Black Forest, fell under S.S. control. Likewise the various departments of the Kaiser Wilhelm Institut; the remnants of the famous Baltic experimental center of Peenemünde, which had been evacuated to Kochel, Garmisch, and Oetzal in Bavaria; the research and development departments of industrial firms; and the laboratories of universities and technical institutes.[24] Nevertheless, the S.S. was unable to enjoy all the advantages from the new situation that it would have had earlier: namely, complete industrial and economic control of the whole nation. The links between the various centers and between the centers and the factories became increasingly precarious. Evacuating entire industries and setting them up again in underground quarters required time and manpower that was out of all proportion to what was available.[25]

Notwithstanding the self-sacrifice of the fighting men, the disciplined resignation of the civilians, the iron regimentation of the workingman, and the pitiless slave labor extracted from an immense number of war prisoners, the situation got worse and worse. In the east, Russian armies were already trampling the edges of German soil, while the Anglo-Americans were hammering deeper and deeper into Germany not only with the giant air raids but also with the intensive use of saboteurs, who were even more dangerous than the bombs because they struck silently and penetrated the underground laboratories, interrupting vital research.

The job of putting the industries and the new experimental centers underground (in order to save time and transport facilities, these two areas tended to be treated as one) had, until October 1944, been arranged between the competent government offices and the individual firms or directly between the latter and various private excavation contractors. Subsequently it was unified by Speer under a state enterprise, the Industriekontor G.m.b.H. (Industry Office), which controlled who was to use the underground complexes and the contractors under the Todt organization, which had the job of adapting already existent caves or excavating the underground facilities.[26]

The manpower (political and war prisoners) for the job of excavation was supplied and overseen by the S.S. It was therefore inevitable that in the end the S.S. would take over control of the entire operation. Indeed, it operated certain areas of industry for its own ends, ousting the Industry Office and taking over from Todt. Sometimes it took them over for reasons of private speculation, other times in order to better hide secret laboratories of particular interest to the S.S., like the one in Linz St. Georgen, in upper Austria. But the usual ideological differences and the well-known intransigence of the new bosses so delayed the work that in December 1944 only three-fifths of the underground facilities had been completed.[27]

General Kammler apologized to Himmler for this partial failure, pointing out in his defense the unfavorable progress of the war and the shortages of machinery, fuel, and manpower. Strangely (but perhaps there was some sort of secret understanding), Reichsführer S.S. Himmler did not take it badly; he did not fire or threaten his subordinate. With a red pencil he wrote in the margin of Kammler's report simply: "*Sehr gut*" (Very good).[28]

In fact, most of the establishments that had been set up underground during the course of the previous spring were already operating in or would soon be operating in the German rear lines, and Himmler grew more and more enamored of what he called the "Bavarian Redoubt," out of sheer chauvinism, for it was to include the Austrian Tyrol and the Italian Dolomites as well.

The southern Reich was not overlooked. S.S. technicians and Speer's trusted functionaries, though they both acted independently, had transferred or were in the process of transferring the better part of the scientific equipment for the rearming of the Wehrmacht to the south and they set about feverishly to get it into operation again.

OPERATION ALPINE REDOUBT

Following the complete reorganization of February 1, 1945, Speer, who was under secret surveillance and in some cases even forcibly subordinated to the S.S. Technical General Staff, assumed direct control of carrying out all the research and implementation of new projects, which were chosen and developed with a speed that seems miraculous to anyone unfamiliar with the means of coercion employed in the final phases of the war. The fundamental objective of the Nazis was, however, to speed up work on the so-called Operation Alpine Redoubt. But at this point we must introduce, in a necessarily condensed form, a bit of history prior to the above, for a final judgment on the aims and events of this controversial operation has a bearing on the *likelihood of a German origin —"paternity" would, perhaps, be too strong a word—for the new secret methods of propulsion that in later years would be manifested with the appearance of various types of UFO.*

The history of Nazi Germany is well enough known from its beginning to its end. We know how and with what means Hitler took power and we know in the most minute detail that "warlord's" victories and defeats. Although disagreeing on certain particulars, various authors have described how he swept both himself and the Third Reich into the final tragedy. Nevertheless, except for the unsuccessful Ardennes counteroffensive and the detailed picture of purely military operations, the period between the intensification of the Anglo-American heavy bombing raids and the battle of Berlin is not yet perfectly known. Fragmentary bits of information throw only a few flashes of light on the varied and complex aspects of the titanic industrial effort that Nazism made in order not to succumb.

In fact, of the numerous revolutionary "new weapons" that the Germans developed in that period, we know only those—fortunately, they comprise the majority—that fell into the hands of all, or at least more than one, of the four occupying powers. And little or no information on the enormous labor required to put German industries underground has been placed before the public at large, for the retention of the data collected by various Allied commissions, notwithstanding the more than twenty years that have passed since then, offers a textbook lesson in military secretiveness.

"I will win the Battle of Time!" Hitler proclaimed as he took leave of the experts from the Party and the Waffen S.S. who were planning their resistance in the south of the Reich. Now it is a historical fact that he lost that battle without ever having fought it when he decided not to leave his Berlin bunker, but no official report has so far illuminated that particular incident of the Nazi twilight, thus leaving the field free to the personal opinions of the writers of war memoirs.

In his book *A Soldier's Story*, the commander of the United States XII Army, General Omar Bradley, declares, for example: "I was eager to clean out the Ruhr and with every division that could be spared from that task push on to the Elbe and Mulde. Once we had closed to that river line, I would spread two of my Armies behind it and turn southeast with the third, down the Danube to link up in Austria with the Red army then nearing Vienna. After having completed that movement we would have cut off the enemy's retreat into his National Redoubt. . . . Months before, G-2 had tipped us off to a fantastic enemy plot for the withdrawal of troops into the Austrian Alps, where weapons, stores, and even aircraft plants were reported cached for a last-ditch holdout. . . .[29] Troops for the Redoubt, we had been told, were to come primarily from S.S. units and a swift check of the battle order on both our and the Russian front revealed a suspicious concentration of S.S. divisions on the southern flanks. Not until after the campaign ended were we to learn that this Redoubt existed largely in the imaginations of a few fanatic Nazis. It grew into so exaggerated a scheme that I am astonished we could have believed it as innocently as we did. But while it persisted, this legend of the Redoubt was too ominous a threat to be ignored and in consequence it shaped our tactical thinking during the closing weeks of the war."

Hanson Baldwin, author of *Great Mistakes of the War,* is another skeptic, although in his final sentence he partially admits the existence of the Redoubt: "[Eisenhower's] overemphasis on the 'National Redoubt' [was], it is now clear, mistaken. Intelligence failures again played a part in this mistake;[30] the 'National Redoubt'—fortifications and supplies supposed to have been prepared by the Nazi S.S. formations in the German-Austrian Alps for a last stand—was grossly overrated in our estimates. We learned later that relatively little work on the 'Redoubt' had been done; the scheme was more an idea than an accomplishment."

In *Top Secret,* Ralph Ingersoll, an American liaison officer at S.H.A.E.F., gives a version of the facts much more in line with German intentions: "Bradley was complete master of the situation, . . . in full command of the three armies that had broken through the Rhine defenses and were free to exploit their victories. Analyzing the whole situation, Bradley felt that to take battered Berlin would be an empty military victory. (It was not known at the time that Hitler was to make his last stand there.) The German War Department had long since moved out, leaving only a rear echelon. The main body of the German War Department, including its priceless archives, had been transferred to the Thuringian Forest, and an advance echelon was already near Berchtesgaden to prepare for a possible last stand in the mountains.[31] Berlin had been almost blown flat and was contributing practically nothing to the German war machine. The same Thuringian Forest that hid the German High Command was also known to be Hitler's secret factory area.[32] Moreover, Bradley felt that if he drove northeast from the Frankfurt gap to Berlin, he would be simply squeezing the German Army southward, forcing it to just where the Nazi Party leaders might want it to be. In the south the German Army had ideal terrain for a last stand."[33]

One final quotation, but this one is decisive, for it comes from a British source and is therefore much better informed in "secret matters," thanks above all to the information collected by Intelligence Service and S.A.S. agents who in the final days had daringly operated in the very area of the then abuilding redoubt:

"When our invasion armies were threatening his 'Fortress of Europe,' Hitler promised that if the German people would only hold out, and give him time, German scientists would provide them with new weapons which would change the course of the war.

"Again when the Reich was crumbling under the final onslaughts from West and East, Nazi propaganda laboured to create a vision of the Southern Redoubt, an inner fortress from which in a few months Germany would strike back with terrible weapons which would snatch victory at 'one minute past twelve.'

"In these respects they were not entirely lying. In the course of two recent visits to Germany, as leader of a technical mission for the Ministry of Aircraft Production, I have seen enough of their designs and production plans to realize that if they had managed to prolong the war some months longer, we would have been confronted with a set of entirely new and deadly developments in air warfare. . . .

"There is some reason to believe that Hitler had been promised atomic explosives by October of this year, and if Germany had been first to use them the idea of changing the whole course of the war from a small base in the south German mountains is by no means so far-fetched" (according to Sir Roy Fedden, in *The Nazi's V-Weapons Matured Too Late*, London, 1945).

It would be superfluous to quote the few other remarks that can be found in the memoirs of the actors in the final assault on the Greater Reich. These quotations, all having about the same degree of vagueness of content and differing in their conclusions, constitute the entire "literature" that exists today on the controversial question of the Alpine Redoubt. It will be worthwhile, however, to examine the sequence of events that preceded the Alpine Redoubt.

THE TRUTH ABOUT THE ALPINE REDOUBT

Just before the surprise Ardennes offensive, Allied propaganda was making much of the continual military reverses of the enemy and proclaiming that 1944 would be the year in which the Germans would be pushed back home. Indeed, after the Anglo-American D-Day invaders had disastrously broken through the "invulnerable" Atlantic Wall, the German armies had had to yield immense territories running from the whole of France to central Italy, from three-quarters of the Polish plains to the whole of Rumania, from the spontaneous evacuation of the Balkans to the forced evacuation from Finnish territory adjacent to Norway, which was still under firm control but now isolated and inactive.

The area of *Europa Festung* (Fortress Europe; *i.e.*, the various continental countries that had been occupied since September 1939, and that the Nazis boasted of having transformed into an armory of men and weapons that would guarantee their inevitable victory) had been virtually reduced to the territory of the Reich itself, with a few border areas of foreign soil soon destined to become a battlefield on which the Germans would try to stave off the collapse of Nazism.

The Vaterland Plan sprang from the premise that the ideal bastions of the great German quadrilateral would withstand the shock of enemy offensives until the various secret weapons that were supposed to reverse the fortunes of the war could be got ready. These weapons were variously called weapons of revenge, victory, or desperation, depending on whether Nazi leaders, German soldiers, or the Allied General Staff were referring to them.[34]

Mindful of the recent attempt on the Führer's life, and despite the liquidations that followed it, a small group of important leaders in the higher spheres of the Nazi Party were still worried about new treacheries hatching in the so-called "generals' clique" in the Wehrmacht, and they did not care to run irretrievable risks. Moreover, various contretemps—changes in plans of construction, bombardments, sabotage, political interference, lack of special raw materials and petroleum, decentralization and putting industries underground—kept postponing the development and production of the new weapons to an increasingly indeterminate future.

For this reason, while more and more private, ultrasecret feelers for a separate armistice with the Western powers were sent out without the Führer's knowledge, the possibility of being forced to give up most of the national territory was being studied. Of course, the land would be defended foot by foot and would be stripped of all war and industrial installations that could in any way help the invader, as the Soviets had previously done so successfully.

After the sensational climax to the Battle of France, among the many who began to doubt Hitler's farsightedness was the Gauleiter (regional president) of the Tyrol, Franz Hofer. He was rightly fearful that the Anglo-Americans would immediately launch the final Battle of Germany in order to try to bring the war in Europe to an end as soon as possible. With the strength of their air mastery and the exceptional mobility of their armored forces, they would easily swarm over the vast flatlands of northern Germany.

The hasty reactivation of the West Wall—the famous Siegfried Line, which had been inactive since 1940—seemed to him inadequate to stop the enemy onslaught after the poor showing offered by the far better equipped Atlantic Wall. The Rhine is, of course, a broad and deep river, but the far broader English Channel had not stopped the invaders! It was necessary, then, to think in terms of some natural barrier that would be more efficacious than a mere river and where one could form a bridgehead and hold out until the day when large numbers of the secret weapons could be employed. Given its central position with respect to the crumbling fronts, the formidable complex of peaks, valleys, and glaciers of the Alps appeared to be, if not the only, certainly the best adapted for a long-drawn-out stand. Besides, by a fortunate coincidence— if it could be called that—the direction of march of the Allied armies advancing on the French, Polish, and Italian fronts in the late autumn of 1944 made it almost certain that the German armies, retiring according to plan, would all converge precisely in the Alpine area.

Judging by the technical and military resources of the time, this was an ideal region in which to attempt prolonged resistance, provided the necessary defenses could be got ready in time. And it would also be the ideal place from which the victorious—as Hofer saw it—counterattack could be launched when the situation was ripe.

From private sources among his friends in the upper ranks of the S.S. and the Party, he had come to know about the proposal to evacuate the Italian peninsula secretly—which, it was rumored, Marshal Badoglio himself had suggested in August 1943. He had also learned that a number of generals commanding combat units had repeatedly requested that a kind of East Wall be constructed in the rear, running unbroken from the Baltic to the Black Sea across Polish territory, in order to immobilize the Russian front until hostilities could be ended in the West.[35] Moreover, he had for years followed with ill-concealed annoyance the work that the Italian army engineers were doing back in 1941 to complete the Littorio Wall, a chain of forts and communication trenches that in part dated back to the First World War and were aimed toward Austria.

But the impulse for the final working out of his *Alpenfestung* (Alpine Redoubt) plan came to Hofer from his knowledge of the measures that the Swiss had adopted in order to resist possible aggression. These measures had principally taken shape in the preparation of a great National Redoubt in the mountains of the southern part of the Confederation. The information secretly furnished by pro-Nazi members of various Swiss National Socialist cultural associations that, with German support, sprang up between 1938 and 1941 provided a detailed rundown of the various preparations: blocking mountain passes, mining tunnels and bridges, planning extensive destruction of roads and highways to prevent the movement of traffic outside the National Redoubt, building makeshift airports, digging trenches, camouflaging communication trenches, and transforming new tunnels into storehouses for food, arms, ammunition, medical supplies, and fuel.[36]

If little Switzerland with its limited resources, working seriously and diligently before the Normandy landings, was able to protect itself so well that the Germans were finally dissuaded from undertaking such a chancy adventure, could not big Germany with its far greater resources do the same thing? Or, even better, protect itself against the Allies' inevitable attack in depth?

After the Italian armistice, Hofer, now suddenly appointed Gauleiter for the South Tyrol and Reichstaatshalter (civilian high commissioner) for the pre-Alpine zone of operations, had extended his political jurisdiction to the Italian provinces of Bolzano, Trento, and Belluno. This development made it possible for him to gain more exact knowledge of the military possibilities of the Italian side of the Alps.

Inspecting the Littorio Wall installations, he immediately saw that only simple detail modifications were required to alter it successfully for a defense against an army approaching from the Italian plain. But since at that time it was unthinkable that the Littorio Wall should be reconstructed in order to meet an attack from the south, the whole complex of forts, caves, and tunnels, which was especially well developed in the area of the Dolomites, was quickly transformed in the spring of 1944 into a sort of arsenal for Marshal Kesselring's army. After his successful defense of Cassino, however, Kesselring decided not to abandon the peninsula.

Like many other minor leaders on the Nazi Olympus, Hofer was completely in the dark about Hitler's hopeful but highly secret plans for a counteroffensive in the Ardennes. He believed, not without reason, that the Wehrmacht's new divisions, with their reduced and demoralized effectives, and the very formation of the Volkssturm, that sort of people's militia made up of fifteen- and sixty-year-olds (the "army of grandfathers and grandsons," as Allied propaganda derisively put it), could only be a mask for reorganizing a "real" army far from the deteriorating fronts and rear lines.

THE HOFER PLAN

In November 1944 Hofer delivered a long memorandum, the *Alpenfestung Unternehmen*, to Bormann, asking him to show it to the Führer. Maps, photographs, and geostatistical data demonstrated the possibility of quickly creating an enormous camp, complete with communication trenches, in the Alps, in order to concentrate and reequip the remaining forces, principally elite troops and the Waffen S.S. The original sketch of the plan restricted the area of the "fortress" to the mountainous territory of western Austria, with a few edges projecting into the Po Valley to make use of installations already in existence.

The shock perimeter—taking advantage of the long Swiss border that the Allies would not, he thought, violate—beginning with the Ortles massif, would follow the Littorio Wall (rebaptized *Süd-Wall* for the occasion), excluding the high eastern plateaus to avoid possible encirclement from Croatia. Bordering the Hohe Tauern range, running along the Salzach River up to and including Berchtesgaden and then proceeding westward along the spurs of the Bavarian Alps until it reached the southern tip of Lake Constance, the gigantic defensive ring would have practically encircled, except at the Voralberg and part of Salzburg, the entire Gau (district) of the Tyrol, in which Hofer exercised, according to rumor, a personal dictatorship.

To carry out the plan with all the speed that the circumstances demanded, he offered the Nazi Party about 70,000 Austrian construction workers, already enrolled in the Labor Front and especially expert in building in mountainous terrain and in bombproof constructions, to add to the 250,000 prisoners that would be available if the work of putting industries underground in the remainder of the territory of the Reich were, as proposed, halted. Because of their familiarity with the area, the 30,000 men of the *Tiroler Standschützen*, the Tyrolean Territorial Militia, were to act as a police force and be responsible for defense against invading paratroopers in the rear areas of the Redoubt.

We don't know quite why Bormann considered this emergency plan to be "mad and defeatist" and refused to present it to the Führer. Perhaps he genuinely believed that the military situation was about to be reversed with the imminent resumption of German offensives on the French and Belgian fronts.

The reception of the plan by the highest political levels of the secret services was equally negative. S.S. Gruppenführer Walter Schellenberg, who had—secretly, of course—opened armistice negotiations with the Anglo-Americans, opposed the plan in a number of ways, tacitly approving what Bormann had done, for he was afraid that if this project, which was judged to be completely useless insofar as obtaining a favorable armed solution of the conflict was concerned, were carried out, it might prejudice the outcome of his secret negotiations. Indeed, to take advantage of the inevitable gaps in Allied intelligence, some of the information presented in Hofer's memorandum was cleverly manipulated and falsified by German counterespionage experts—the AMT VI, under the direction of Schellenberg himself—and then circulated among Allied informers who sent it on to Allied headquarters in Paris, thereby nourishing the fear of prolonged German resistance. By rattling this skeleton, Schellenberg hoped both to speed up the negotiations and to get more advantageous surrender terms from the Allies. It was doubtless a very clever trick, but the Allied formula of "unconditional surrender" rendered it useless from the start (except for the "mysterious" postwar rescue of a number of Nazi personalities with somewhat compromised histories).

When the winter offensive in the Ardennes—which began to peter out because of a shortage of planes, firepower, and gasoline—finally failed, the tormenting question of the defense of the national territory (already violated in Aachen and east Prussia) once again became the prime concern. While Dr. Goebbels on Radio Berlin was entreating the soldiers to resist at all costs because something sensational was in the offing, Bormann, under the pressure of unfavorable events and cleverly maneuvering so as not to be held responsible for his obstructionism, allowed the head of national security, S.S. Obergruppenführer (General) Ernst Kaltenbrunner, to report to Hitler the Allies' concern about the defensive possibilities of the Alpine Redoubt.

A discussion between Hofer and Hitler was immediately arranged. The Führer became convinced, albeit reluctantly, of the utility and urgency of the operation. Then and there Hofer was charged with seeing to the defensive reinforcement of his district on the basis of the facts contained in his memorandum, the plan of which, however, would have to "undergo certain modifications in order to increase its efficacy."

THE MILITARY CONFERENCE
OF JANUARY 27, 1945

The modifications were subsequently spelled out during one of those daily meetings that took place at the Führer's headquarters, which had been moved under the Berlin Chancellery.

It was January 27, 1945. In addition to the ever present darlings of the regime—Göring, Goebbels, and Bormann—twenty-five officers from the General Staff of the Wehrmacht and an unrecorded number of unidentifiable S.S. "experts" were also present. At first Hitler discussed aimlessly and at some length certain indications that had appeared in the neutral press concerning a coming rupture in the Allied camp and the consequent possibilities of offering a separate peace with Germany, in order to thwart the danger of Soviet occupation of eastern Europe. After finishing his absurdly optimistic political overview, the unconquerable warlord made it clear, however, that should the Anglo-American demands prove to be unacceptable, the alternative suggested by Gauleiter Hofer should be seriously considered. This would either induce the stubborn Western Allies to take milder counsel or enable Germany to continue the war in the unfortunate case that the Allies did not propose to reverse the front. The second part of the meeting was in fact dedicated to examining and perfecting the secret plan.[37]

Gauleiter Friedrich Rainer, High Civil Commissioner for the coastal zone of Croatia, was assigned the responsibility, which remained on paper owing to the swift development of events, of extending the eastern frontiers of the fortress to the district of Carinthia, where atomic research was being carried on by a number of Viennese experts who had been evacuated to the south the preceding spring and were working under the supervision of the S.S. Technical General Staff. The defensive perimeter was also to include western Styria and most of Salzburg—the latter because of the possibilities offered by its intricate network of lakes and the numerous abandoned salt mines in the Saltzkammergut, some of which had already been used in 1944 to hide certain essential war industries.

The Alpine Redoubt thus came to include the following: Upper Bavaria, the Allgäuern Alps, the Vorarlberg, the Tyrol, Berchtesgaden, Salzburg, Carinthia, western Styria, Trentino, and the Dolomites—much too large an area, considering the crucial factor of time. Other minor "islands," either for a last-ditch stand or for holding up the gigantic Allied pincers movement on Germany and causing confusion, were set up in Norway, the Harz Mountains, the Böhmerwald, the Bayerischerwald, and the Schwartzwald.[38]

In spite of the well-known conformism in the Hitlerian entourage, there were nevertheless some differences of opinion. The Chief of the General Staff of the Wehrmacht, General Jodl, was flatly opposed to the idea of fortifying the areas bordering on the Swiss frontier, fearing an unfavorable reaction from the Swiss government. (He later reiterated his view in a personal letter to Himmler.[39]) In the end it was decided to furnish that delicate sector with tiny prefabricated concrete forts, called *Kugelstände*, which would be dug into the earth by night in such a way that they would be practically invisible even from quite close.[40]

After the general plan of operations was laid out—including a plan for the simultaneous withdrawal of fighting units and the assignment of special jobs to various persons attending the conference—Hitler made it clear as he was leaving that if the deteriorating situation made it necessary, he would assume command of the Alpine Redoubt on April 20, the day of his fifty-sixth birthday.

UNDERGROUND AIRFIELDS AND FACTORIES

In order to protect the north-central edge of the fortress, which ran along flat land for a certain distance west of the Ammersee, it was decided to construct three gigantic underground airfields in the Iglingerwald in record time.

What with the coming of vertical take-off, this Cyclopean enterprise will probably remain unique in the annals of military engineering. It was planned by the Führer as a corollary to the decisions taken with respect to the Alpine Redoubt. Headed by Speer, the principal persons in charge of war production were called to the Berlin Chancellery. Hitler discussed in detail the "U Plan," which the Todt engineers had prepared fourteen months earlier. This plan provided the blueprint for putting the factories of the vast Messerschmitt aircraft complex of Augsburg, which had already been hard hit by Allied bombardments, completely underground.

The modifications made necessary by the new war situation dealt principally with the extension of the enormous roof so that it would also cover the runway opposite the opening of the original construction in order to protect the jet fighters at take-off and landing, since it had been noted that at these times the planes were so vulnerable that their superiority in the air over ordinary enemy fighters was virtually canceled.

For several years no fewer than 120 ammunition dumps of the Waffenamt had been operating completely undisturbed in the Iglingerwald, camouflaged with topsoil and planted with bushes and pines. This circumstance, together with the possibility of being able to use some of these bunkers as advanced forts, weighed in favor of choosing the same locality. The go-ahead was given, first for the excavation of the underground areas and then for the erection of bombproof armor consisting of concrete reinforced with millions of steel rods.

The northern portion of Construction No. 1 was supposed to hold the assembly lines for the ME-163 jet fighters and the ME-262 turbine fighters, with a combined projected production rate of 900 units a month. In this same area, and enclosed by a thick vertical block of concrete, were also installed the tools for repairing and refitting the aircraft, which were normally kept in the southern portion. In the center a cement runway would permit the ME-163s, with their short runs, to take off, while for the ME-262s, with their longer runs and auxiliary rocket boosters for take-off, it was planned to lengthen the runway outside and protect it with the bombproof canopy.[41]

The S.S. summarily selected the prisoners who were still capable of heavy work from Dachau and neighboring concentration camps. In all, the S.S. collected more than 20,000 laborers and quickly brought them to the new grouping center of Kaufering. Hidden by thick trees and working mostly by night—one of the aims of the increasing appearance of the Foo Fighters (alias *Feuerbälle*) was to hamper Allied night reconnaissance, which was fanning out dangerously close to Bavaria—these masses of ill-fed unfortunates, bitten by the winter cold, finished the excavation of the first airfield in the second half of February.[42]

With the work still proceeding under cover of darkness, cement for the foundations began to be poured on March 1, but a time study then showed that the work would not be completed until the first part of August. Construction on the other two airfields, side by side about a mile away, was slowed down in order to concentrate most of the workers and material on the first, and so improve the schedule.

One of the secondary airfields was supposed to serve also as the operating base for the pilotless rocket fighters in a state of advanced preparation at the Messerschmitt factories in Oberammergau, and for other revolutionary types of antiaircraft weaponry "related" to today's UFOs that were being developed by the Zeppelin Werke under contract to the S.S. Technical General Staff but were still not ready for large-scale use.

On the southern boundary of the Redoubt, which was especially protected by the jagged slopes of the Italian side, the attention of the German General Staff focused on the Dolomite caves, which could be further developed quickly and easily.

Nevertheless, in an area that should have been only a neutral strip, maintained as a kind of no man's land by the constant deterrent barrages characteristic of positional warfare—which was precisely the type of warfare that the Redoubt entailed—the Germans continued to operate, and indeed, to develop, right up to the end what their accidental discoverer (an officer of the Eighth Army) justly called "two of the most ingenious war factories in Europe." They "operated within 100 yards of the Allied Armies for several months, yet were never discovered, even though Allied aeroplanes passed over the area almost every day."[43]

The seventy-four tunnels of the highway on the west side of Lake Garda, which had been dug out of the living rock overhanging the lake, had been transformed under Speer's orders into an underground complex for the assembly-line production of piston engines and propellers for aircraft. In operation since the fall of 1944, the plant was put under the care of technical personnel from Fiat. In the six tunnels of the eastern branch of the same highway, that is, on the opposite shore of the lake, and similarly well camouflaged and protected, the Caproni industrial complex was busy turning out aircraft parts (air frames, fuselages, and other parts).

A tiny narrow-gauge railway (slightly under thirty inches) was constructed directly on the highway surface and connected the various tunnels with one another. It was so well camouflaged that it was almost invisible at a few yards' distance. Besides, the tunnels' protection even in the improbable case of being spotted from the air was perfectly insured by the mountains above. Most of them were in fact dug under a solid layer of rock sixty-five to a hundred feet thick.

The original industrial complex was supplied mainly by carefully camouflaged boats that linked it by night with Riva, Desenzano, and Peschiera, so that in case of necessity it could be totally isolated from the Po Plains.[44] This plant was supposed, consequently, to become the only supplier of conventional planes for the forces occupying the Redoubt, while jets would be supplied mainly by the underground factories in the Bavarian Alps and others that were already in operation in the planned "resistance island" in the Harz-Thuringerwald, in other words, by the enormous underground complexes of Nordhausen and Kahla.

In addition, the seven northern tunnels on the western side of the Garda highway in the area of Limone, which were still hurriedly being got ready at the time of the armistice, were earmarked for the production of certain special weapons that were about to be released from their final test phase at the experimental center of the Hermann Göring Institut (L.F.A.) in Riva del Garda.

In spite of the fact that its further development was not carried out, it has been demonstrated that in January 1945, for at least a part of the Nazi hierarchy—those inclined toward war to the last man—the Alpine Redoubt project became a dramatic alternative. In spite of the difficulties caused by the military situation and the culpable, lukewarm zeal shown by political leaders, an extremist minority of second-echelon leaders tried, in fact, to translate the Redoubt into reality. They began by transferring the most recent war inventions still in developmental stages to the Redoubt, where they would later be manufactured on a large scale and used to support the final counteroffensive. The reports of the British Intelligence Technical Staff on electronic, atomic, aeronautic, and rocket applications of Nazi science that were written immediately after the war, and that traced German industrial activity during the first quarter of 1945, frequently contain such significant annotations as the following: "Documents removed [or destroyed] by the S.S. before its retreat toward the Bavarian Alps," or "Plans [or models] removed by S.S. men to the mountain areas in the south of the Reich."

Nor was that all. Beginning at that moment certain secret devices that still required a few months or more of experimentation were used against the Allies in order to gain time and buttress those absurd hopes of a second chance.

NOTES

1. *Cf.* the following report from the American press on October 29, 1953: at 2:00 A.M. during night-flying exercises over Hempstead, Long Island, the pilots of two F-94 jet fighters sighted a large, motionless object glowing whitely some miles ahead. One of the fighters attempted to outflank it. But perhaps the occupants of the object spotted it, for the strange machine suddenly turned in a tight circle that would intersect the flight path of the pursuer. Already flying at full speed, the fighter tried to approach more closely by increasing its speed in the turn to a dangerous point, but the UFO continued on its intersecting line. The machine "allowed" itself to be followed for eight minutes, then it climbed at supersonic speed and disappeared. The two pilots were inclined to think that it was "some new revolutionary kind of invention, directed by something or someone that maintained visual contact with us and

had on tap speeds and powers beyond any plane known in the United States." But it is more probable that what was involved was mainly greater maneuverability as a result of the different flight dynamics of the saucers.

2. The four-engined British Lancasters in operation over the Continent in 1944 carried no less than 1200 pounds of radio and electrical equipment, subdivided into fifteen different apparatuses—for communication in flight and on the ground with the crew and the different planes in the command, for blind flying, scrambling, ground-control approach (G.C.A.), flight toward the objective (G.E.E.), radar scanning of the territory being flown over (H.2.S.), in-flight survey of the direction-finder bearing, identification of enemy planes (I.F.F.), and radar sensing of the attacking enemy (A.I. Look-follow), in which the locating apparatus is locked in on the intercepting plane and follows its movements as long as it remains within the effective radius of this small auxiliary radar. Finally, there was the Mountain Goat, a sonic indicator of fixed and moving objects; it was later replaced by an electronic anticollision device that not only signaled the nearness or approach of any stationary or moving obstacle that could endanger the flight of the bomber, but also revealed the formation of distant storm clouds.

3. In 1943 the *Spanner* already provided an extraordinarily clear picture—greenish, as with all equipment of that type— within a radius of fifteen miles and was fairly efficient up to a maximum radius of eighty miles. Beyond that the picture quickly went out of focus.

4. Combined Intelligence Objectives Sub-committee, *German Infrared Telescopes* (Report No. CXXXI-37, London, H.M.S.O., 1947); British Intelligence Objectives Sub-committee, *German Bolometers* (Report No. 215, London, H.M.S.O., 1947).

5. In spite of fair results, the project was temporarily dropped because the "search head" was not sufficiently reliable.

6. A recent book exhuming these apparitions merits a few lines of comment because it gives a further sample of the wild thought patterns of ufologists. See Vincent Gaddis, *Mysterious Fires and Lights* (New York, Dell Publishing Co., 1968), pp. 25–27. The author writes: "The foo fighters that followed and teased World War II planes were tenuous, luminous balls or spheres that acted like curious, playful animals.

"The suggestion that some UFOs may be animals—*i.e.*, life-forms or animate creatures indigenous to rarefied atmospheres or possibly space itself—may seem fantastic at first. Actually it is a logical theory that answers many questions about the behavior of some UFOs and strange lights.

"I have a friend, Curtis Fuller, who is president of two publishing companies. A friend of his, who for obvious reasons prefers to remain anonymous, is a top biologist at Wright-Patterson Air Force Base, Dayton, Ohio, headquarters of the Air Force's UFO investigation, the Air Matériel Command, and a number of scientific development projects.

". . . our biologist suggests that some UFOs are space creatures—a form of life new to man that may feed on pure energy, and has adapted itself to living high in the atmosphere."

The eminent biologist had, however, been preceded along this path by other eminent investigators who, with minor modifications, had put forth the same absurdities, although with fewer "scientific" details and consequently with less success. John P. Bessor "states that he evolved the theory in 1946 and presented it to the Air Force in July, 1947. An officer in the Press and Radio Section, in acknowledging the submission, said it was 'one of the most intelligent theories we have received.' . . .

"[Bessor] thinks at least some of the things we call UFOs usually make their appearance after some sort of disturbance like volcanic eruptions, earthquakes, or atomic explosions. 'Whatever they are,' he adds, 'I suspect they just come down to look us over. I believe they are harmless or we would have had trouble with them long ago.'" Apparently they "come down to look us over" in order to discover the causes of the disturbances; that is, to investigate us and our activities—and then take some kind of action with respect to the people causing the disturbances?

Gaddis' book lists various people who have thought up such theories, impartially giving each his due. It remains, however, to establish why in the world these "stratospheric dragons" or Foo Birds chose to dog American fighters and reconnaissance planes operating in the very limited southern sector of the French front.

7. See Combined Intelligence Objectives Sub-committee, *Interrogation of Professor Scherzer of the B.H.F.* (Report No. XXXII-87, London, H.M.S.O., 1945).

8. By way of keeping the secret while it was still in the project stage, the name *Feuerball* was also given to a ground radar apparatus constructed by the Post Dienstelle F of the German Ministry of Posts, which was actually used in the war—apparently in defense of the refineries of Leuna—even before the flying mechanism was perfected.

9. In fact, it was not an imaginary danger. The Foo Fighters did contain a strong explosive charge to destroy them in flight in case serious damage to the automatic guidance system made it impossible for the operators to control it. It seems, however, that during the time they were last seen, at least one American flyer opened fire on a Foo Fighter from a safe distance without succeeding in shooting it down, although he had it well within his sights. A convincing detail, this, especially in view of the fact that under the armored covering of the Foo Fighters there was a thin sheet of aluminum attached to it (but electrically insulated) that acted as a switch. When a bullet pierced the exterior covering, contact between the two sheets was established and the consequent closing of the circuit that operated the maximum acceleration device of the craft (generally in a vertical direction) caused the Foo Fighter to fly off, taking it out of the range of further enemy fire.

10. The F.F.O. was an important government institution in operation thirty miles south of Munich with about eight hundred technicians conducting research in the fields of high frequency, guided missiles, radar, infrared radiation, and electronics in general. It was under the direction of Professor

Dieckman until the autumn of 1944 and under Dr. Ahrens afterwards.

11. Before it was decentralized in the Schwartzwald, the Zeppelin Werke had already done secret work in the field of radar. It had built parabolic reflectors for ground radio position finders, attracting the attention of the Intelligence Service and so of the R.A.F. to its Friedrichshafen factories near the Swiss border. (The first heavy bombing raid of sixty four-engined Lancasters was expressly ordered by Churchill on the recommendation of the Central Interpretation Unit, Photographic Intelligence, and took place on June 20, 1943.) The British Intelligence Objectives Sub-committee reports of British investigation committees in Germany (1945–1946) on the Zeppelin Werke's production are still classified documents.

12. For information on the German klystron tubes see Combined Intelligence Objectives Sub-committttee, *Establishments of the Forschungsanstalt der Deutschen Reichpost* (Report No. XXX-1, London, H.M.S.O., 1946).

13. The radio-jamming devices installed on the Grosser Feldberg also operated in the field of the shortest waves, covering all the wave lengths used by the Anglo-American apparatuses for radar scanning of the terrain over which they were flying and for long-distance control of the course of their bombing formations (the H.2.S., Oboe, Rebecca-Eureka). Through the usual spy channels the news reached London that the first examples of the Roderich radio jammer, which represented the best that German radio technology could produce, had arrived at the center. These apparatuses—designed by the Austrian branch of the Ferdinand Braun Institut, in Gaisberg bei Salzburg, and built by Siemens—simultaneously covered the two shortest enemy wave lengths (nine and three centimeters), constituting a serious obstacle for bombers that operated over most of western Germany. The R.A.F.'s photographic aerial spotting and 120 four-engined Lancasters wrote *finis* to the matter. (For further information on the Roderich, see Report V of the Combined Intelligence Objectives Sub-committee,

Institutes of the Bevollmächtiger für Hochfrequenz-Forschung [Report No. XXXI-137, London, H.M.S.O., 1945].)

14. The Tedder Plan, which was an additional support to the offensive that had been in action for some time against German fuel production, went into action, in fact, in the first weeks of November, after Germany had been divided into nine zones in which the total destruction of all transport was to be gradually effected. This proscriptive policy reached its culmination on February 22, 1945, when—within the framework of Operation Clarion, which was designed to break any Nazi will to resist to the bitter end—9000 planes swarmed over Germany, destroying over two hundred rail centers. Thus the entire production of the last two months of the war, which was about to be sent to the front or to assembly plants, was destroyed or lay unused in freight cars on torn-up roadbeds. This operation virtually guaranteed the collapse of the German war machine.

15. Although they had many well-equipped planes, in the fall of 1944 the German night-fighter squadrons entered into action only in defense of major objectives and without much success because they were short of fuel and nearly always "blinded" by the British antiradar devices, which members of the 100th Bomber Group operated with extraordinary skill. After the Grosser Feldberg was bombed, the low technical efficiency of their night fighters forced the Germans to throw all the electronic defense devices of the *Feuer* series (which was still in the experimental stage) into action prematurely. In addition to the *Feuerball,* this meant its ground operated equivalent, the Lorentz-Siemens *Feuermolch* (Fire Salamander)—a device designed by the technicians of the Irschenberg branch of the Ferdinand Braun Institut—and of the *Feuerland* (Fire Land), a subsidiary device manufactured by Blaupunkt in Berlin-Wilhelmsdorf, for jamming radio communications on board. According to Dr. Gunther Breukopf of Blaupunkt, it is doubtful that the *Feuerland* was used by any front-line units, while from the British intelligence reports on German industry we learn that during the last months of the war no fewer than fifty *Feuermolch* devices were in use on the Western Front.

They were destroyed one after the other by the personnel to whom they were issued on precise instructions from the S.S. Technical General Staff.

16. Altogether "38,000 aircraft of all types" were built in 1944, a figure never achieved in any other war year. In the month of September alone, "3013 single-engine fighter aircraft, newly built or repaired," were delivered to the German fighter branch. ". . . And this after a year of systematic raids! In the summer of 1944 alone the Allies dropped 18,500 tons of bombs on the German aircraft industry. After the 'Big Week' [February 19–25, 1944: Operation Argument], which was supposed to be the death blow to our armament, Speer had contrived the reconstruction and the dispersal of the industry. So far it had been concentrated in twenty-seven larger works arranged on production, technical, and economical lines. Now it was spread over 729 medium and very small plants. Some were situated in tunnels, caves, or disused mines, some were hidden in forests, ravines, and villages. . . . The unbelievable difficulties of bringing air armament to such heights by 'home industries' are impossible to describe. . . ." See General Adolf Galland, *The First and the Last* (New York, Ballantine Books, 1967, pp. 192, 237–38). The attrition in aircraft and the reduced production caused by the military defeats were, however, absolutely appalling. In the summer of 1944, following the Allied landings in Normandy, the Luftwaffe lost on the average 5000 planes a week, either through bombardment on the ground or in air actions covering the retreat. Thus in August it had a force of 1500 fighters. In spite of intensive production, in January 1945 only 2000 fighters were delivered to the flying detachments.

17. It has been historically established that after the heavy British night raids during the spring of 1942, Hitler refused even to consider Field Marshal Milch's proposal to strengthen the fighter building program, ordering instead that all priority be given to bombers for reprisal against England. General Galland (see Chapter 28, "The Jet-fighter Tragedy," in the book cited above) declared that in mid-1943—after an exhilarating test flight in one of the preproduction ME-262s and

the forwarding of a detailed report to Hitler—he had hoped the Führer would change his foolish stand, but when "the next days passed without any news or orders from above," he "had an idea that our hopes for a quick development of the German jet fighter would not be realized. Hitler had refused to give his sanction. He had already conceived a great distrust of Göring and the Luftwaffe, and wanted to convince himself personally about the soundness of our proposal. He told Göring—and not without justification—that the Luftwaffe had disappointed him too often in the past with promises and announcements of technical innovations and improvements. The heavy bomber, the HE-177, had been promised him not later than 1941, and even today no one could foresee when this aircraft would go into action. The fact that he did not call any member of the Luftwaffe to the conference of experts that he held showed how great Hitler's distrust really was. He even forbade their participation. [Göring] took this obvious affront quite passively. . . . [Hitler] ordered that the technical tests of the ME-262 should be continued with a few prototypes, expressly forbidding any kind of preparation for mass production. This far-reaching decision was taken without the agreement of the Supreme Commander of the Luftwaffe. Thereby the production of the ME-262 [which had already experienced a delay of nearly a year as a result of Hitler's personal order in the autumn of 1940 to suspend the research—because, according to him, the war was about to end with the "inevitable" surrender [of the British] received a further delay of six months. . . . I believe that in this way about eighteen months were lost in the development of the ME-262. . . ."

18. Sauer was director of the Armament Office under Speer.

19. At the time of the armistice there existed, in fact, some 138 different projects involving flying bombs designed for strategic bombing, tactical use, antiaircraft and antiship fire, and, to remain in the strictly aeronautic field, over seventy types of jet planes, built in restricted production runs, as prototypes or, mostly, merely designed by various firms and institutes controlled by Speer.

20. See General Galland, in the book cited in note 16: In April 1944 the program for emergency aircraft production was shown to Göring, who was in the Obersalzberg. "Bomber production had been curtailed, and the production of many other types was to be stopped. Night and day fighters were to be made as one unified type, which also had to meet the requirements of the other branches of the Luftwaffe. The quantities which were planned were absolutely adequate to the Anglo-American aircraft production. I was present at this memorable conference. I had the impression that Göring listened to Sauer's disquisition with a premeditated attitude, on Hitler's orders. He . . . replied immediately with many and definite objections. The radical curtailment of the bomber program, especially that of the HE-177 and JU-88 and their further development, was regarded by him as impossible and he rejected it; on the contrary he demanded an increase and a guarantee of a minimum production of 400 HE-177 and 500 Junker bombers a month. This was, of course, possible only if the originally planned fighter production were heavily cut. Speer's fighter program was changed according to Göring's directives and came into force eight days later in its diluted form. . . . The production of bombers went on at an increased rate. They could not prevent the raids on our synthetic petrol plants which started a little later, as a stronger fighter force could have done [by bombing airstrips in England and liberated France]. In the end there was not enough petrol for the test flights of the bombers when they came from the assembly belt; they had to be wrecked on the benches where they had been built [in order to recover material that could be reused]. The Anglo-American air force crossed the bomber off the German armament plans." The same technological and strategic idiocy—disastrous because it reflected, if indeed it did not come directly from, the highest political source—kept even the field of German radio location, which might have wholly outclassed the adversary's, in a constant state of inferiority with respect to the Anglo-Americans. On August 8, 1942, General Wolfgang Martini had unsuccessfully requested scientists working on high frequency waves to prepare radar apparatuses that would work on centimeter waves. It was only when a British four-

engined plane equipped with one of the first H.2.S. radars was shot down in the vicinity of Rotterdam during the night of February 2–3, 1943, that the General Staff experts were convinced that centimeter waves were deciding the outcome of the war. As with the jet fighters, the "counteroffensive" waged by German radio scientists was now also hamstrung because it was "too late," and the ingenious *Feuerball, Feuermolch,* and *Roderich* devices were only palliatives that could not improve a situation that had become desperate (*cf.* Caius Bekker, *Radar-Duell im Dunkell*).

21. See J. Nobecourt, *Le dernier coup de dés de Hitler* (Paris, Robert Laffont, 1962), Chapter II: "The politicalization of the Wehrmacht had, however, begun before July 20th. During the winter of 1943–1944, Martin Bormann was, like Himmler, conducting a personal campaign through his leadership of the N.S.F.O. (Nationalsozialistischen Führungsoffiziere, Party workers assigned to the army as 'political commissars'). After July 20th he had the ranks and prerogatives of combat officers conferred upon them. Their official job was to verify the officers' degree of Nazi fervor, but in reality they worked solely to extend the personal influence of Bormann in the land forces. [The Luftwaffe was Göring's "fief;" the Navy was traditionalist and did not put up with political interference.] Allied only in appearance, in the summer of 1944 both he and Himmler aimed at the conquest of power after their common enemies—Göring, Ribbentrop, the Wehrmacht generals, and their direct supporters—were progressively eliminated."

22. Combined Intelligence Objectives Sub-committee, *Natter Interceptor Project* (Report No. XXX-107, London, H.M.S.O., 1945). Because of an aerodynamic defect, the first test flight of the *Natter* ended in a disaster that brought about the death of the pilot, Lothar Sieber, but about a month later over Hannover on March 29, 1945, during the only attack made with the *Natter* craft—officially called the Bachem BP-20—Sergeant Ernest Hemmer piloted one of the first preproduction models against a formation of four-engined Liberators and succeeded in downing two and damaging a third.

23. The S.S. Air Corps had been formed in November 1944 with 150 volunteers—who became known as S.O.M. (*Selbstopfer Männer, i.e.,* Self-sacrificers)—taken from the ranks of the Waffen S.S. and sent to the special training center of Friedenthal, run by the famous Colonel Otto Skorzeny, to be instructed in piloting the Reichemberg flying bombs (modified V-1s) against special objectives, with a (theoretical) possibility of escape before impact. Göring and Goebbels had enthusiastically approved the formation of this body, impressed by the actions of the Japanese Kamikaze. In October they had also supported with similar fervor the proposal of Colonel General Keller, commander of the Nationalsozialistichen Flieger Korps (National Socialist Aviators' Corps), to form assault squadrons composed of young men drawn from the ranks of the Hitler Jugend and equipped with the jet turbine HE-162 *Volksjäger* then under construction. Full-scale preparation of this "People's Fighter" having been delayed by technical difficulties, it was then decided—despite the outspoken hostility of Fighter General Galland and War Production Minister Speer, on the grounds of humanity and of the doubtful utility of the proposal—to use those sixteen-to-eighteen-year-olds, who had no serious military or flight training, in a series of desperate actions to support the air defense of Germany itself and the counteroffensives being planned for the Western Front. A number of aircraft firms were urgently asked to submit bids for the immediate preparation of light, simplified emergency planes, very fast but inexpensive, since they would be built mostly of wood, and relatively efficient though not very safe. Among the plans approved and in part already realized (but only in the prototype stage, of course) by April 1945 were the following: air-towed glider-bombers, tiny rocket interceptors (the Junkers JU-EF-128 *Wally*), assault planes (the JU-EF-126 *Elli*, derived from the V-1 and the ME-328 Messerschmitt with a double pulsejet), and rocket-engined glider fighters (the ME-P-1104 and the Heinkel HE-P-1077 *Julia*). In addition there were revolutionary types of piloted antiaircraft bombs and "flying rams," the latter designed to break off the tails of enemy bombers by ramming into them at high speed, without, in theory at least, harm to the pilot, who would be

nclosed in a heavily armored cockpit (the rocket interceptor
Arado AR *Flugstosser,* the Zeppelin plane-slicing rocket
fighter, the Daimler-Benz DB-P-5 disposable fighter with a
ramjet engine and auxiliary rockets similar in appearance to the
flying bombs, and a modified version of the *Natter*). In addition to blocking the slaughter of the boys, the end of the hostilities fortunately prevented the S.S. Air Corps from being
enlarged by enrolling these units, akin in duty and ideals, and
from putting its semisuicidal plans into action.

24. Since it had been granted full powers, the high command
of the S.S. secretly began to set up the S.S. Technical General
Staff, modeled on the official body with the same name that
Speer had created at the beginning of 1944 to plan war production and that had replaced the old system of ministerial orders
to industry with the principle of direct military-industrial in-
terdependence. Speer's Technical General Staff gathered into
a sort of "industrial high command" the best talents from industry and technology, with long manufacturing experience, to
whom the needs of the various armed forces were directly
presented for immediate solution. It was made up of twenty-
one special committees that controlled the production of raw
materials and the distribution of work through twelve liaison
offices. The entire technical body was comprised of some six
thousand engineers and experts of various sorts (consultants),
each one a specialist in a particular area. As a result, the whole
bureaucratic compartmentalization existing between industries
was broken down, along with manufacturing secrets and
monopolies on patents and special processes, thus making
available to all the firms manufacturing a given product any
and all experience and progress achieved by any of them
individually. Despite the delays caused by frictions that
stemmed from by-passing ministerial ranks and stepping on
the toes of powerful interests, the system in general worked
quite well, and production became uniform throughout the
nation, assuring identical products, interchangeability of parts,
and stable production figures even during the heaviest phases
of the Allied bombardments. In addition, very often some
technical discovery that had previously been held exclusively

by one factory and was turned over to one of the specia
committees was now not only mass produced but furthe
improved by some other factory in the same field. (For exam
ple, the Junkers firm produced a markedly improved versio
of Messerschmitt's famous ME-163 rocket-engined fighter, th
JU-263.) We have no information on the structure and compo
sition of the S.S. Technical General Staff under Gruppen
führer Hans Kammler, which doubtless had a smaller sta
than and far different aims from Speer's organization. Neverthe
less, from certain documents collected by the American "Alsos
Mission (an organization created to carry out the preliminar
sifting of industrial and scientific—particularly atomic—in
formation about Germany and German-occupied countries)
it appears that during the war Kammler's group held its meet
ings at the S.S. command in Northeim in Hannover.

25. The slogan that was current in Nazi circles at the begin
ning of 1945 was that it was necessary to win "the Battle o
Time." Because of a whole series of erroneous technical an
military decisions that the Führer imposed, the Allies won i
instead. To better understand the unfolding of subsequen
events, let us examine a few examples of measures that cam
too late or that were counterproductive and thereby lost pre
cious time. Only in the fall of 1943 was the entire textil
production in the Reich stopped and the factories converted t
arms manufacture. On the basis of an agreement betwee
Speer and Bichelonne, Minister of Industry in the Vichy gov
ernment, French textile manufacturers had to work exclusive
according to German orders, thereby freeing German plant
for arms production, which was being decentralized in orde
to escape bombardment. Thus some Berlin factories makin
radar apparatus were immediately evacuated to the textil
plants in southern Silesia and part of the machinery that sur
vived the attack on the Zeppelin Werke found a temporar
refuge in spinning mills in the Black Forest. Other measure
contributed to the dispersion of the ball-bearing industry
Again it was only at the end of 1943 that plans were made t
move the giant Bayerische Motoren Werke (B.M.W.)—to
late to keep a considerable part of the machinery from bein

destroyed or lying unused for some time in the new locations. Besides, the move did not get really under way until the late spring of 1945, a delay that led to the S.S.'s arrest of Dr. Zipprich, the director of B.M.W., who was held responsible. (Nevertheless, his successor, Dr. Bruckman, later declared that in his view "the best system of decentralization still remains a strong Luftwaffe"!) *Cf.* Combined Intelligence Objectives Sub-committee, *Bavarian Motor Works* (*B.M.W.*), *A Production Survey* (Report No. XXX-80, London, H.M.S.O., 1945). Besides, these efforts to decentralize manufacturing plants often truly became labors of Sisyphus. For example, following the stepping up of air attacks and after stormy internal arguments aggravated by S.S. meddling, the gas-turbine section of B.M.W., which was originally located in the Berlin suburb of Spandau, was transferred lock, stock, and barrel to the underground plant of Wittringen in the vicinity of Saarbrücken, but the liberation of France in the fall of the same year (1944) forced it to leave the area and disappear into seven abandoned salt mines at Neu Stassfurt in Thuringia and in the Harz Mountains. *Cf.* Intelligence Objectives Sub-committee, *Gas Turbine Development: B.M.W., Junkers, Daimler-Benz* (Report No. XXIV-6, London, H.M.S.O., 1945). Another significant example from among many is offered by the chain removals of the Steyr-Daimler-Puch A.G., which manufactured Daimler-Benz high-powered aircraft piston engines on license, beginning in 1944. After the main plant in Steyr was bombed, the machinery was set up in the suburbs around Vienna, but air raids on Vienna were resumed, and in May the firm moved to the underground warehouse of a large brewery in Budapest. When the move was completed and the factory was finally getting ready to produce large numbers of the new DB-605-D engine, the Russians began their push toward Hungary, forcing the directors to retrace the steps of their evacuation until the original main plant in Steyr was started up again—which was achieved just before the final collapse. Naturally, the whole thing was accompanied by a notable drop in production. See British Intelligence Objectives Sub-committee, *Report on a Visit to Daimler-Benz A.G. at Stuttgart-Unterturkheim* (B.I. O.S., Final Report No. 35, London, H.M.S.O., 1946).

26. See Combined Intelligence Objectives Sub-committee, *Underground Factories in Central Germany* (Report No. XXXII-17, London, H.M.S.O., 1945).

27. Unimpeachable evidence is offered by General Galland, who writes: "Operation orders for the ME-262s now [in the first week of April 1945] changed daily. . . . The time of commissioners, special commissioners, ambassadors of the Führer, commissars, and special commissariats had started. All who were to increase production of the industry or to coordinate operations were appointed subordinate to each other, equal to each other, and over each other. From February until March the jet-fighter command went partly over to the SA. From their ranks came the so-called Commissariat of the Führer for Jet Aircraft, a general of the Waffen SS. Hitler had appointed him although Göring in his turn had appointed a Special Commissioner for Jet Aircraft."

28. See Samuel A. Goudsmit, "The Efficiency of German Industry," Chapter XV (pp. 214–231) in the volume *Alsos* (New York, Schuman, 1947).

29. William L. Shirer, the well-informed American historian of the Third Reich—see Chapter XXX, "The Conquest of Germany" in *The Rise and Fall of the Third Reich* (New York, Simon & Schuster, 1959)—wrote apropos of this: ". . . Eisenhower and his staff at SHAEF were obsessed at this moment with the urgency of heading southeast after the junction with the Russians in order to capture the so-called National Redoubt, where it was believed Hitler was gathering his remaining forces to make a last stand in the almost impenetrable Alpine mountains of southern Bavaria and western Austria.

"The 'National Redoubt' was a phantom. It never existed except in the propaganda blasts of Dr. Goebbels and in the cautious minds at Eisenhower's headquarters which had fallen for them. As early as March 11, SHAEF intelligence had warned Eisenhower that the Nazis were planning to make an impregnable fortress in the mountains and that Hitler himself would command its defenses from his retreat at Berchtesgaden. The icy mountain crags were 'practically impenetrable,' it said. 'Here, defended by nature and by the most efficient secret weapons yet invented, the powers that have hitherto guided Germany will survive to reorganize her resurrection; here armaments will be manufactured in bombproof factories, food and equipment will be stored in vast underground caverns and a specially selected corps of young men will be trained in guerrilla warfare, so that a whole underground army can be fitted and directed to liberate Germany from the occupying forces.'

"It would almost seem as though the Allied Supreme Commander's intelligence staff had been infiltrated by British and American mystery writers. At any rate, this fantastic appreciation was taken seriously at SHAEF, where Eisenhower's chief of staff, General Bedell Smith, mulled over the dread possibility 'of a prolonged campaign in the Alpine area' which would take a heavy toll of American lives and prolong the war indefinitely.

"This was the last time that the resourceful Dr. Goebbels succeeded in influencing the strategic course of the war by propaganda bluff." *Cf.* also Chester Wilmot's *The Struggle for Europe* (New York, Harper, 1952).

30. *Cf.* Wilhelm Hoettl (Walter Hagen), *Die Geheime Front* (Linz, 1950): "In autumn 1944 our central office in Berlin [the Gestapo] was informed of the existence of an American office in Switzerland that went far beyond the activities of a simple intelligence service. It turned out that it was run by the lawyer Allen Welsh Dulles . . . and his true activity had been camouflaged by accrediting him as the representative of Minister Harrison in Berne. . . . The men who ran the German Secret Service then tried to get in touch with this individual and succeeding in so doing thanks to support from a big Austrian businessman and the German air attaché in Berne. . . . For us Germans it was important at least to try to convince the Americans that for the future of Europe we should not give up vital parts of the territories of Germany and Austria to the Soviets. And so it was decided that the Americans should be informed of how Russia was doublecrossing her

Western allies by turning over certain documents containing concrete proof. Subsequently the basis of the negotiations shifted to a completely different sphere. For some time we had been informed that the Anglo-American General Staff was very much afraid of continued German resistance in the so-called Alpine Redoubt. According to the information gathered by the Allied secret services, this *réduit*, as the Swiss called it, comprised large areas of the alpine massif of northern Italy and of Austria as well as a strip of land of considerable size in front of it. With reason, Allied military experts considered that it was possible for the Germans to hold off the Allied armies for a long time from that position. In fact, it would not have been able to seize this alpine region turned into a sort of huge fortress without serious difficulty, even in the period of atom bombs and rockets, without using special mountain troops, of which the Allies were almost totally devoid in 1945. . . . In any case, the Allies' worries were without foundation. They had arisen because of the rumors that German propaganda had spread and also partly because our intelligence service had succeeded in getting some cleverly falsified documents into the hands of the Allied secret service."

31. In fact, the files of the O.K.W. were subsequently captured more or less intact by the Americans in the Tyrol and parts of the documents were later presented in evidence at the Nuremberg Trials in order to incriminate Wehrmacht generals who were strong Nazis. *Cf.* Helmut Greiner, *Die Oberste Wehrmachtführung* (Wiesbaden, 1952).

32. This alludes to the enormous underground complex of the Mittel-werke factories (referred to in the German documents of the time as M-Werke), which was in operation in the Harz Mountains on the edges of the village of Dora, near Nordhausen. It was formed of two broad parallel tunnels each a mile long and connected to one another by sixty-two transverse minor tunnels, giving a total of about twelve miles of underground installations. Shortly before the armistice this complex had begun large-scale manufacture of the V-2 rocket, the V-1 flying bomb, and several types of antiaircraft rockets

(principally the *Taifun* and *Föhn* types). With its four hundred yards of natural covering, the plant was virtually invulnerable to any aerial attack. In February 1945, the personnel and equipment of the Baltic experimental center at Peenemünde that had been evacuated was partially installed in the neighboring village of Bleicherode Ost, where the plans for the giant two-stage rocket-torpedo A-9/A-10, planned to be used for bombing the United States, were being speeded along. At first occupied by Assault Group B of the U.S. Third Armored Division on April 11, 1945, the zone and its priceless industrial complex were subsequently consigned to the Soviets on the basis of the Yalta agreement.

33. According to the strategic plan hurriedly worked out in February 1945, besides the Waffen S.S. and the paramilitary formations of the Hitler Jugend, what remained of the armies retiring on several fronts was also supposed to take part in the reinforcement of the Alpine Redoubt. These armies were: General Alexander Loehr's army from Greece, which was waiting on the Austro-Yugoslavian frontier; General Lothar Rentulic's army, which was bloodily confronting the Russians on the Austro-Hungarian frontier; Field Marshal Albert Kesselring's Army Group South, for some time dug in on the Gothic Line to guard the Po Plains; Field Marshal Ferdinand Schoerner's group of armies, which held out until the end of May in the mountains of Bohemia; and finally that of Field Marshal Gerd von Rundstedt, who was supposed to extricate himself from the Allied pincers in order to fall back to the Allgäuer Alps through the Black Forest. At the beginning of spring 1945, of the 300 divisions that the Wehrmacht had put in the field to oppose the 96 Anglo-American and 400 Soviet divisions, only 65 divisions, and most of those short of effectives and weapons, were available. A cautious estimate from Allied sources guessed that there were twenty remaining divisions in combat readiness that the Nazis could count on for the effective strengthening of the Alpine Redoubt. To this force, which would have to be reorganized and rearmed from top to bottom, would be added an indefinite number—perhaps twenty-five or more—of Waffen S.S. divisions and the very young soldiers of the

Hitler Jugend. In all, a ten- or twelve-to-one disadvantage for the Germans. They held, at least theoretically, that this discrepancy would be mitigated by their taking advantage of the natural barriers hindering the large-scale use of armored units.

34. For an opinion on the reality of the Germans' industrial hopes and possibilities, see Chapter IV of Nobecourt's *Le dernier coup de dés de Hitler*, under the section entitled "Le mythe des armes secrètes." For greater detail and a more extensive review of the new types of weapons (except for the various aeronautical and antiaircraft discoveries that are described in the present volume and that have until now been wholly or partially unknown), see Major Rudolf Lusar, *Die deutschen Waffen und Geheimwaffen des Zweites Weltkrieges* (Munich, J. F. Lehmans Verlag, 1958), p. 239; or Colonel Leslie Simon, *German Scientific Establishments* (Report P.B. 19849, New York, Mapleton House Publications, 1947), p. 228.

35. W. Hoettl (Walter Hagen) has reported that "militarily [in August 1943] the best solution would have been to evacuate the Italian peninsula and create a new defensive line that would follow the Alps and the Po River to the Adriatic. This would require only a minimal force, thereby making at least 300 or 400 thousand well-trained and well-equipped men available for the Russian Front. The passive aspect of the operation would have been represented by the loss of an ally, who was in any case greatly weakened and tired and whose industry was not absolutely essential to our war effort. [All this is correct, but it does not take into account the fact that Anglo-American air bases would be dangerously close to the southern borders of Germany.] Hitler rejected the plan, which appears to have been proposed by a high-ranking Italian officer with Marshal Badoglio's concurrence, declaring that 'it could only be the proposal of an irresponsible defeatist who had betrayed his friend and ally Mussolini.' Revised and presented with the recommendation of the head of the AMT-VI, Gruppenführer S.S. Walter Schellenberg, the plan caused Hitler to explode with fury, and the person who presented it—Obergruppenführer S.S. Ernst Kaltenbrunner, head of the Reich's se-

curity services—had a hard job defending the work and person of his subordinate. But in March 1945 Hitler confided to Kaltenbrunner that he was very sorry that he had not accepted the suggestions of the AMT-VI for a 'solution to the Italian question.' Indeed, this solution would have avoided or at least greatly retarded the serious military reverses on the Russian front, insuring that Germany would for some time still receive priceless Rumanian oil, and it would have anticipated much of the plan for the 'Alpine Redoubt.' "

36. The extent and nature of these defensive countermeasures were well known to the Germans as well, thanks to information picked up in Berne military circles by the Reich's ambassador, Koecher. From the outbreak of hostilities in Europe—at the time, that is, of the general defensive mobilization (September 2, 1939)—Swiss military authorities had made a plan for a National Redoubt in the Alps. The plan was being put into effect and strengthened during the course of the war in such a way as to guarantee at least a two-year period of armed resistance against any aggressive act aimed at the Swiss Confederation. The various preventive measures also included the methodical dismantling of factories, the supplies and machinery of which—already accurately inventoried by General Guisan —were to be destroyed, hidden, or transferred to the Redoubt in secret locations when the time came, according to their importance or bulk.

37. Through leaks that were, it appears, fostered by the promoter himself, some of those present were in reality already more or less familiar with the proposal. Indeed, without even waiting for the Führer's approval, a number of moves had been made to sound out the practical possibilities of the plan. Göring was particularly interested in the Berchtesgaden region, perhaps because he was already secretly thinking of going there when military collapse seemed imminent in order to replace Hitler in the government of the Reich and to negotiate with the Allies from a position of strength. Because of his well-known political rashness (which gives us further evidence of the level of organizational inefficiency reached by this baffling

personality who inexplicably allowed "his" Luftwaffe to be humiliated and destroyed after having so brilliantly created it), Berchtesgaden, together with the greater part of the Bavarian slope of the Alpine Redoubt, was from a military point of view practically defenseless, harboring only the villas of the Nazi bigwigs with their attendant S.S. men, and a few aircraft companies working on the development of truly revolutionary war discoveries. As for Himmler, he had sent a squadron of geologists from the Ahnenerbe—a sort of academy of sciences for the S.S.—to study the configuration of the mountains in the area insofar as they could be employed in a military defense system modeled on the Swiss National Redoubt. Finally, the staff of the army group operating in Italy, which for some time had been using the dumps in the Dolomite caverns, reexamined the possibility of adapting the military installations of the entire Italian slope of the Alps to resistance from attack from the Po Valley as an expedient in case the "Gothic Line" was broken through.

38. Because of its excessively open geo-strategic position, the Valtellina had been excluded from the plan for the Alpine Redoubt, although in the last days of the war the highest political and military leaders of the Italian Social Republic [Mussolini's government in the north of Italy, formed after he had been liberated by Col. Otto Skorzeny.—Tr.] had decided to make their own "Alpine Redoubt" there and carry on the fight while waiting for the military situation to be reversed, as the Germans promised. Without any genuine permanent fortifications, the Valtellina redoubt was supposed to serve mainly as a center for gathering together the Fascist formations being evacuated from the Po Valley.

39. The Swiss General Staff, which had a highly efficient intelligence network, had, in fact, reinforced the defensive measures in the area of the National Redoubt facing Germany, although after a careful evaluation of the information they had received, they judged the Alpine Redoubt plan as practically unrealizable, or at least as coming too late. Wilhelm

Hoettl reports that "the fact that in the final phase of the conflict a German center of resistance might arise in the proximity of the most delicate of its borders could constitute a serious menace for Switzerland. Especially when certain information obtained from S.H.A.E.F. circles gave them reason to believe that if the Germans were dug in in the Alps the Anglo-American General Staff would bring strong pressure to bear on the Swiss government to induce it to put its highly specialized mountain troops at the disposition of the Allies. Even if this belligerent act had been passed off as a simple, necessary police action, public opinion in neutral Switzerland would not have been able to accept it without serious internal conflict." These were well-founded fears, and they explain and justify the political conduct of the Swiss authorities which favored, with the discretion that the circumstances demanded, the approaches between the emissaries of S.S. General Karl Wolff and American Vice-ambassador Allen W. Dulles for the surrender in Italy of Army Group South (the so-called Operation Sunrise Crossword).

40. The *Kugelstand* was a hollow spheroid made of reinforced concrete weighing 3740 pounds, with an internal diameter of seven and a half feet, made by joining together six prefabricated parts, constructed according to the designs of the Bavarian firm of Dyckerhof and Widmann, which in November 1944 suggested to the Wehrmacht that these spheroids could serve as easily transportable small forts that could be buried, would not sink in marshy terrain, and were invisible to aerial reconnaissance. Despite their relatively thin shells (one and a half inches), the first experimental models were run over by heavy tanks without suffering any damage. Starting on December 4, twenty factories were supposed to produce them on a large scale with a monthly production of 2500 units per factory. Nevertheless, because of delays in every sector of war production, when the armistice was signed no more than thirty *Kugelstand* were in operation along the Swiss frontier in the Dornbirn zone. *Cf.* Section VII, "Fortifications," in the report by the C.I.O.S. Section Intelligence Division Office, *German*

Underground Installations, of General Interest (J.I.O.A. Report No. 3, Washington, September, 1945).

41. To determine the minimum length of the take-off runway, hasty tests were made with the Messerschmitt fighters at the air base of Fürstenfeldbruck, and when the Luftwaffe reported the data requested, the following dimensions were adopted: length of the canopy, 1056 feet; width, 439 feet; height, 146 feet; thickness of the canopy in reinforced concrete, 16 feet, with a further covering of topsoil to bring the total depth of the protective layer to 23 feet. Thus small oblong artificial hills would be created, heavily covered with grassy and woodland vegetation, surrounded by irregular layers simulating natural elevations in the terrain in order to baffle aerial reconnaissance.

42. The almost incredible efficiency in camouflaging the work and the constructions themselves merits special mention, though the Germans were aided in this by a number of heavy snows. Some Intelligence Service agents operating in the Oberbayern area had heard rumors of the project, which the officers of the U.S.A.A.F. intelligence attached to S.H.A.E.F. had called "a wild exaggeration." A number of aerial reconnaissance missions were flown for the extraordinarily well-equipped sections E (recognition of enemy camouflage) and U (underground factories) of the R.A.F. Photographic Intelligence Section of Benson, but the results were completely negative, although the territory between Landsberg and Kaufering was photographed foot by foot. In their final report the British experts declared: "If the aerodromes really exist, they are completely invisible from the air."

43. See M.G.O., "Underground Factories in Italy," *The Aeroplane* (London, Vol. LXX, No. 1818, March 29, 1946), pp. 370-371.

44. At one point the work force at the factory had numbered 10,000, but it later tripled with the further influx of a great number of prisoners of war. When the Allies occupied the zone, a considerable quantity of industrial and technological

material had been evacuated or hidden in the neighborhood, and some had been stolen or destroyed by escaping prisoners. Nevertheless, the material found in the plants and the complementary stores dug out along the Garda and in the neighboring Dolomites filled eight miles of freight cars.

CHAPTER 5

Revolutionary German Antiaircraft Weaponry

"The circular German fighter without wings or rudder suddenly overtook the four-engined Liberator, crossing its flight path at very high speed. When it passed in front of the formation, it gave off a number of little bluish clouds of smoke. A moment later the American bombers mysteriously caught fire, exploding in the air, while the German 'rocket' had already disappeared over the horizon."

This astonishing combat—if it can be called that—between the very latest type of interceptor and a group of Flying Fortresses that had detached themselves from the main group and were heading toward southern Bavaria took place within a matter of seconds in the sky over Würtemberg. The date is unspecified, but it must have been around the end of March or the beginning of April 1945.

A sketchy account of the event had been included in a report on the latest developments of the German aircraft industry written by a Gaullist French diplomat living in Switzerland. This report, together with other restricted documents, was destined for the Intelligence Service of the General Headquarters in Algiers and was clearly the work of an informer operating on the German side of Lake Constance.[1] In the same report there was even a mention of certain "methane antiaircraft bombs" that the Germans had experimented with on Lake Garda against another formation of Flying Fortresses, with results about the same as those of the first.

Intercepted by Italian agents, the report was deciphered by the S.I.D. (Servizio Informazioni Difeso, Defense Intelligence Service) in Castiglione delle Stiviere while the Allies were pushing to break through the Po Valley defenses. Shortly afterwards it made up part of the loot seized by Intelligence Service agents following the British Eighth Army.[2]

The event was not completely unknown to the Allied investigators. When Dr. Goebbels attempted to allay the fears caused by the terrible bombardment of Dresden by resuming his propaganda campaign promising that powerful and still unknown antiaircraft weapons would soon be in use, both the Intelligence Service and the O.S.S. managed to obtain a short report of a test made with the sort of weapon that could perhaps explain the mysterious disappearance of a dozen four-engined American planes during their flight into Germany from a British base. This report, which also seemed to come from an informer in Switzerland, reported in fact that: "*A strange flying machine, hemispherical or at any rate circular in shape, attacked them at a fantastic speed, destroying them in a few seconds without using any guns.*"

After the German surrender in May 1945, when the British examined the secret papers of the technical departments of certain factories hidden in the forested area of the Schwarzwald—another region earmarked as an "island" for a last-ditch stand—they discovered that some of the documents miraculously spared from the retreating S.S. units' destruction of papers concerned "important experiments conducted with liquid air as a power supply for certain new types of turbine engines capable of producing tremendous power outputs. At first the discovery led them to believe that a new system for powering submarines was under study,[3] but ancillary information about the construction of powerful apparatuses working on the principle of electromagnetic waves that would make it possible to exercise radio control at great distances, as well as photographs showing some parts of the new turbine, caused them to change their minds. Thus they got on the track of a preliminary preparatory stage for a new and very powerful type of armored, radio-controlled aircraft."[4]

Now, it cannot be denied that these bombs with their strange contents and that mysterious circular aircraft—armed, besides, only with tubes for spewing out a deadly gas that, blown against enemy planes with great force, caught fire from their exhaust flames and caused them to explode in the air —would certainly appear to noninitiates of military secrets to be the wildest science fiction, if proof to the contrary did not exist. Indirect proof, to be sure, but, one might say, irrefutable.

EXPLOSIVE GASES

In the spring of 1936 an odd story was making the rounds in international press circles. It was received with considerable skepticism and soon forgotten. After all, there had been a spate of similar stories before, dealing with death rays, superpowerful gases, disintegrating radiation, and other such weapons of the future. This one dealt with certain military experiments being carried out near the Hungarian border by an unnamed European power (but, for various reasons, it clearly appeared to be Austria). The experiments were being conducted with a colorless, liquefied gas, harmless to humans but lethal to engines.

The Italian press mentioned it, though under a misleading headline (ASPHYXIATED ENGINES?), reporting as follows: "While inventors of those famous ultrahighfrequency paralyzing rays appear from time to time in the newspapers declaring that they can short out the ignition system of any internal combustion engine from a distance, other inventors are trying other paths to achieve the same object, but with simpler and, apparently, more hopeful results. It is known, for example, that one foreign nation has been conducting experiments with projectiles containing a liquid gas that, when the shell explodes, forms a very extensive cloud that envelops the machine to be destroyed. Any engine whose carburetor breathes in the least amount of this gas will immediately and repeatedly self-ignite. This not only hampers the proper functioning of the engine but generally causes the pistons and connecting rods to break or the block to explode. A column of trucks is said to have been stopped by this gas from a distance of seven and a half miles with a deliberately inaccurate barrage, keeping about half the explosions at a considerable height above the road and off to one side. The gas used allegedly has the added advantage of being colorless, a very valuable characteristic for air defense. Finally, the fact that it is harmless to humans would encourage its use at low altitudes in warfare and for the defense of urban centers."[5]

The Anschluss that united Germany and Austria to form the Greater Reich came, and then came also the Second World War. But the explosive gas did not appear on the battlefields. Informers, secret agents, and prisoners nevertheless repeatedly confirmed after 1944 that a secret weapon of that sort was in an experimental stage.

Dr. Rosenstein, a Jewish collaborator well-versed in the problems of organic chemistry and with special competence in the production of synthetic gasoline, was the first to mention it. In the autumn of 1944 he was captured by the Americans and taken to Paris to be interrogated by members of the Alsos Mission. "The German chemists had succeeded in perfecting the formula for a new gas whose use would have caused strong vibrations and even breakage in aircraft engines," Rosenstein declared. "They refused, however, to employ it because it might possibly have adverse effects on the crews of the planes enveloped in it, and that, in turn, could have unleashed poison gas warfare, which was especially distasteful to the Führer."[6]

Independently of the research indicated by Rosenstein

(which seems directly related to the development of the old Austrian experiments that were reactivated in Leuna or Brüx), other experiments were going on at the R-Laboratory of the Luftfahrtsforschungsanstalt in Volkenrode. While working with various oxydizing substances in July 1944, Dr. Hans Friederich Gold, a chemical engineer working in the rocket division of the institute, discovered accidentally that if he mixed 2 percent of myrol with air, internal combustion engines immediately began detonating irregularly; an 8 percent mixture stopped the engines completely in a matter of seconds.[7]

Other information dealt with liquid and gaseous chemical combinations of terrible incendiary power.

Undoubtedly the basic fact supporting the credibility of the above-mentioned matters lies in the Allies' discovery during the progressive occupation of German territory of a number of special "projectileless cannons" which were principally to be used against aircraft.[8]

BLOWER CANNONS

According to the French military press immediately after the war, the land-based version of these cannons—called *Windkanone*—were constructed by "a Stuttgart firm under the protection of the Luftwaffe" (specifically, it appears, the government-run Hermann Göring Stahl Werke of Heerte, which at one time had also undertaken experiments on rockets and ramjet engines). That is, the factory was about thirty miles, as the crow flies, from the secret factories in the Black Forest.

The cannon had been designed to protect specific secondary objectives and to be used against low-flying fighter-bombers and any other kinds of low-flying plane, "in other words, whenever it is difficult to use the classic type of cannon with any success."

The *Windkanone* looked like a capital L turned upside down and was pointed toward the sky at an angle; tongues of flame instead of the usual shells shot out of the muzzle. It was constructed of a thick cast-iron tube about three feet in diameter and about thirty-five feet long. The short upper extremity, at right angles to the remainder of the tube, had a large nozzle on the end. In place of the normal breech, the weapon had a combustion chamber loaded with an explosive mixture (hydrogen and oxygen or ammonia) that, after being electrically fired, produced a strong wind from the nozzle pointed in the path of the plane. The violent displacement of air was supposed to bring down the plane, or at least render it unstable, at a maximum distance of about 650 feet.

Mounted on a railway car, the weapon could also be used from the mouths of tunnels to defend hilly and mountainous terrain which concealed important military objectives. For this reason it seemed to be the ideal weapon for passive air defense in the Alpine Redoubt. Practically, however, it proved to be inefficient, because the high speed of the planes themselves and the very short duration of the wind stream, together with the inherent problem of aiming the cannon, had a negative influence on the number of successful shots produced.

Since the cannon had demonstrated in tests on fixed targets that it was capable of shattering a board one inch thick at a distance of 650 feet, the *Windkanone* was then relegated to infantry use. It was hoped that if this bizarre piece of artillery was used against troops attacking along such obvious routes as valleys, bridges, and tunnels, it would blow them away like chaff. But the weapon could not be used even in this way, since it was unwieldy and consequently highly vulnerable to enemy fire.

The unused and rusted prototype was later found on April 28, 1945, on the outskirts of the Hillersleben testing grounds, some eighty miles west of Berlin, by members of the Intelligence Technical Branch (C.A.F.T.) of the 12th Army Group.[9]

The American experts also came upon a strange device mounted on a strong frame that raised it about fifteen feet from the ground. It was basically a sheet-steel cylinder welded along its eight-foot length and with a large internal crown nozzle at the upper end. At first mistaken for the head of a small vertical heater, it turned out to be the experimental model of the *Wirbelringkanone* (whirlwind annular vortex cannon).

This strange cannon—which was also called, somewhat prematurely, the *Himmelfeger* (Skysweep) by the German experimenters—had been sent to Hillersleben in the winter of 1944 from its original home in Kummersdorf. According to Professor Maas, this weapon "fired" a gas ring that spun rapidly on its own axis, a kind of miniature artificial cyclone. It was activated by a charge of compressed hydrogen and was capable of producing considerable damage up to a distance of about 1400 feet. The German technicians hoped that by increasing the dimensions of the "cannon" they would soon be able to scatter bomber formations flying at 15,000 feet, buffeting the planes so violently that they would be thrown off course and be easy prey for the fighters.

OTHER "WIND CANNONS"

The government factory that had constructed the wind cannon had also prepared two other types of projectileless weapon.

The *Wirbelkanone* (whirlwind cannon) shot about a hundred pounds of pulverized coal soaked in kerosene a distance of some hundred yards. Automatically ignited as it left the launching tube, this mixture, which burned for about half a minute, was supposed to eliminate such specifically land objectives as advanced platoons, isolated tanks, machine-gun emplacements, forts and so on. Because of the difficulty of getting the bugs out of the launching apparatus, this weapon did not have its baptism by fire either.[10]

Finally there was the *Vielfältigwindkanone* (multiple blower cannon), much smaller in size, which could be mounted on airplanes. The steel tube contained a number of smaller tubes with slanted vanes that broke the wind up into a series of rapid gusts. Internally ignited by a charge of special powder or a gaseous mixture, the gases expelled from the arrangement of nozzles at a muzzle velocity of about 3250 feet per second were supposed to strike the enemy plane and render it unmaneuverable.

To supplant the machine guns and cannons already mounted on the German fighters, the new weapon had to at least be able to damage seriously or, better still, to down the enemy aircraft. For example, it would have had to envelop the enemy plane in a cloud of incendiary or explosive gas so as to insure its certain destruction.

Since East Prussia was about to fall into the hands of the Russians, the designers of the blower cannon feverishly pushed ahead the working out of the technical principle, drawing on the results furnished by the tests that had previously been carried out at the Austrian experimental centers.

At Lofer, in the Tyrolean mountains, the Waffenamt had an institute that at one time was assigned to develop mountain artillery. In addition, the Technische Akademie der Luftwaffe (T.A.L.) was running a station for secondary research on aerial equipment in the same region. In 1944 Speer took over direct management of the two institutes, radically changing the type of research and experimentation they were engaged in.

Colonel Leslie E. Simon, the American investigator who visited the zone after the armistice (and after the British T Unit had passed through), reported that the two institutes were working on different and completely heterogeneous sorts of fantastic inventions.[11]

The fact is that the buildings had also served as the technical nerve center for a far greater complex of research workers scattered about and hidden in the area, and if some of these weapons appeared to be somewhat bizarre and impractical (as, for example, the "ultrasonic cannon"), others, had they been completed in time, would doubtless have caused considerable annoyance to the Allies.

One of these was called the *Luftwirbelkanone* (air vortex cannon) and thus seemed to be related to the blower types, but in reality the launching mechanism followed traditional ballistic patterns and it was the content of the shell that marked the advent of a new antiaircraft technique.

AN INSPIRING DISASTER

Dr. Zippermeyer, an Austrian researcher, got the idea of reducing the normal explosive charge to the minimum necessary to fracture the shell, which was loaded with extremely fine coal dust. The explosion of the shell thereby produced a small, fiery cloud that burned up in the air it passed through in a matter of fifteen seconds.

At Lofer preliminary experiments fully confirmed the possibility of destroying a plane in flight by causing the wings or rudder to fracture after being struck by the violent, fiery gust, but difficulties in establishing the proper amount of the charge (efficacy diminished with distance owing to the decreased final density of the "cloud") and certain unforeseen problems in timing the ignition phase caused the staff to consider replacing the solid combustible with a gaseous one.

While Dr. Zippermeyer was busy perfecting his antiaircraft coal-dust clouds, the technicians of the Institute for Ballistics of the T.A.L. began a decisive line of research on the physics of explosions in rarefied media.

Flak gunners had reported a number of times that the efficiency of barrages against high-flying invaders fell off sharply above 15,000 feet. The T.A.L. experts explained this shortcoming as resulting from the fact that the intensity and density of the spherical shock waves as developed by ordinary explosives fell off by 50 percent at 15,000 feet because of tamping flaws and through the action of mass defect itself and rarefaction of the air.

In order to verify the exact extent of the phenomenon, in October and November of 1943 a hundred prisoners of war transported with backbreaking work the wings and fuselages of German HE-111 bombers and four-engined American B-17s to the large T.A.L. experimental center at Zugspitzplatt, 10,000 feet above sea level. There the planes were subjected to the explosions of antiaircraft shells detonated at decreasing distances. New firing tables were computed for flak at the end of this unusual line of research.

Then, in the summer of 1944, a frightening series of consecutive explosions—with effects not unlike the American "saturation bombing"—devastated the synthetic gasoline refineries at Ludwigshafen. Although Allied propaganda immediately seized the opportunity to claim that the explosions were the result of successful delayed-action detonation of a new type of liquid air bomb-mine, the disaster had, in reality, been caused by the accidental escape of ethylene gas at the

Athelane recovery center, the explosion of which spread to the gas containers and the whole surrounding plant.

Among the experts on the commission of inquiry was a small special group sent by the T.A.L. The tragic incident provided the opportunity to "reconsider a proposal made some time before for the study of liquefied gas antiaircraft rocket bombs."[12]

T.A.L.'s huge institute in the Bavarian Alps, working together with the neighboring experimental center of Garmisch-Partenkirken (run by the Waffenamt), repeated the tests on the wings and fuselages of large planes, this time using small cylinders loaded with ethylene in both gaseous and liquid states.[13]

The shock wave of ethylene launched with rocket bombs having an explosive core (the Zippermeyer system) maintained its destructive level virtually unchanged even at altitudes considerably above 15,000 feet. But practically it was necessary to take into account the difficulties of loading and preserving the projectiles, the intrinsic danger of the gaseous material, which was supersensitive to shocks and temperature variations, and also the too rapid exhaustion of atmospheric combustion. Tests in flight with the first rudimentary models of the *Flugschnittel* (Flying Scythe) made it clear that it would be necessary to stabilize the explosive or to replace it with some similar substance.

In the end the second solution prevailed. It was suggested by the Luftfahrtforschungsanstalt of Vienna (L.F.W.), which for some time had itself been conducting interesting experiments on the explosive properties of liquefied combustible gases with the help of some Italian technicians who had a great deal of experience in synthetic combustibles.

Continuation of the work thus became practically the prerogative of the L.F.W., which had it carried out in its Italian branch at Riva del Garda.

SYNTHETIC FIREDAMP

In working with gases it was desirable to use those that were physiologically harmless, for international sanctions had banned the use of poison gases. The idea of liquefying a nonpoisonous gaseous combustible to make it so concentrated that when it instantly resumed its original gaseous state it would envelop and permeate military objectives had occurred to Italian scientists at the time of the rumor about the Austrian experiments. In other words, in 1936.

Acetylene, which remains liquid at $1°$ C. under a pressure of 48 atmospheres, was immediately discarded as being too sensitive to shock; methane too, despite the fact that it was coming more and more into use, did not seem to meet the requirements, since it remains in a liquid state only at $0°$ C. and under a pressure of 150 atmospheres. After examining a number of similar gases, the scientists' attention finally focused on a fifty-fifty mixture of butane and propane—a mixture typical of the methane homologs—which was not poisonous and had a calorific power slightly higher than even that of gasoline and a very low liquefaction point (between two and six atmospheres, according to temperature), which meant it could easily be stored in welded steel containers only a fraction of an inch thick. Since the heat of evaporation of this methane mixture is very low, once it was fired an almost instantaneous volatilization of the liquid could be counted on and every cubic foot of gas would have burned about twenty-eight cubic feet of air.

For various reasons—not the least of which were the small capacity of ordinary antiaircraft shells and the promising development of thermite incendiary bombs—the idea did not reach the experimental stage until 1942, and the armistice found Italian scientists carrying out successful tests on additives to increase the explosive qualities of the substance.[14]

If the background of these researches is little known today, the outcome is even less known. Nevertheless, doesn't it seem significant that the Gaullist diplomat described certain mysterious antiaircraft bombs as containing methane? The notorious firedamp of the coal mines is, in fact, nothing but a natural mixture of saturated acyclic paraffin hydrocarbons composed mainly of methane with small percentages of ethane, propane, and butane.

Since the liquefied combustibles possess the important property of spontaneously being self-pumping and self-mixing, the idea immediately developed that the propulsive part of the bomb could be fueled with part of the explosive material itself. For obvious reasons, rocket propulsion was abandoned and a project was sketched out for a flying bomb with a simplified turbine that recalled in appearance and function the *Turboproietto* (turbine projectile), an Italian antiaircraft device that never left the experimental stage, and to a small extent the propulsive system of the *Feuerball* antiradar aircraft.

In spring 1945 the scientists at the Riva del Garda center were also perfecting the manufacturing process for a ceramic material for turbine blades—similar to the German *Dug* (70 percent $Al_2O_3 \div 30$ percent Fe)—which gave promise of withstanding continuously and under enormous pressures temperatures of around $1000°$ C.[15]

The proposal to increase the size of the turbine bomb in order to transform it into a genuine airplane of an entirely new concept—using the temperature-resistant ceramic for the parts subjected to high temperature—was, however, put aside by the L.F.W., which already had various special projects in the course of development.

When the pool for aeronautical research that Speer started in 1944 and the S.S. then implemented brought together and unified all the inventions of the same sort, artificial firedamp immediately proved to be the ideal explosive for the little blower cannon that fired deadly gusts of gas—the "little bluish clouds" released by the strange circular fighter plane against the unfortunate four-engined Liberators flying in close formation.[16]

"THEY'LL DROP BY THE DOZENS"

The howling of the last siren that signaled the end of the air raid—one of many which were reducing section after section of Berlin to rubble—had only just ended when the correspondents of the neutral press were urgently summoned to the Reichsluftfahrtministerium (R.L.M.) for a message of the greatest importance. Normally Dr. Goebbels, the minister for press and propaganda, handled press relations, but this time Marshal Göring—whose prestige was declining sharply and who for some time had been keeping himself on the outer fringes of the Nazi world "for reasons of health"—personally wanted to reaffirm the policy of "reprisal" and the imminent advent of new kinds of air defense:

"And then their bombers will drop by the dozens, like sparrows under the hunter's gun," he concluded angrily. "Our fighter pilots will only have to press the trigger!"

The correspondents diligently wrote down everything that was said and took leave of the powerful personality, masking their growing skepticism. In fact, it was not the first time that spectacular countermeasures were announced, but the months passed and they never appeared.

The press conference took place toward the beginning of November 1944, just before the so-called Great Council of the Luftwaffe was convened at Berlin Gatow. The V-1 flying bomb had been in large-scale use against England since June, but this had not thrown back or even stopped the invasion forces. On September 8, 1943, the V-2 rocket bomb had made its appearance, but although it was certainly an extraordinary device, as the Allies themselves admitted, the Allied bombing raids continued.

And yet Göring was not lying. His angry impatience caused him to suggest that the weapons were closer to production than they actually were. In fact, the designers at the various government institutes had planned with special care every possible kind of scientific apparatus, system, and principle capable of conducting German technology step by step to the final realization of the ideal antiaircraft weapon: the supersonic fighter under remote television control.

Ever since the spring of 1941—that is, when the Luftwaffe understood that it had irremediably lost the "Battle of England"—its high command (O.K.L.) had been seriously considering the possibility of intensive bombardment of London by means of flying bombs and remote-controlled pilotless planes.

In order not to overload its own radio industry, which was already engaged in a heavy production, the Nazi authorities placed their first order for two hundred transmitters for airplanes with the Paris firm of S.A.D.I.R.-Carpentier, which was supposed to build them at the Puteaux factories under German supervision. After the plans were completed, sabotage and delays of all sorts became evident. A year later it turned out that hardly a single apparatus had been built.[17] Since this was a derivation from the prewar British E.M.I. transmitter, the Germans decided, on second thought, that the British were quite familiar with it and would easily be able to jam it. So they let the contract expire and in July 1943 approached the Lyons firm of Radio-Industrie, asking it to design a top-secret television receiver that could be installed in airplanes flying at an altitude of 40,000 feet. A team of German electrical scientists headed by Dr. Neiss remained at the Lyons factory for a long time, but sabotage and passive resistance on the part of the French again held up the work until the American troops arrived.[18]

Back home, of course, things went much better. Two large industrial complexes (Telefunken and Fernseh-Blaupunkt) had been investigating the possibilities in the military applications of television since 1939, in strict collaboration with the principal government experimental centers.[19]

TELEVISION-GUIDED BOMBS

The Telefunken laboratories were trying to perfect apparatuses for strategic use (that is, with a radius of action of about two hundred miles) and were working closely with the B.H.F., the Institute for High Frequency Studies.

Fernseh G.m.b.H. of Berlin, on the other hand, applied itself to apparatuses for tactical use. In 1939, with Professor Herbert Wagner of the Henschel aircraft company as a consultant, Fernseh undertook to develop a television installation that would enable pilots to control both planing bombs and rocket bombs after they were launched. The installation used a wave length of between seventy and a hundred centimeters and the images received appeared on a tiny screen about three inches square.

Beginning on June 10, 1942, an extensive series of laboratory experiments coupled with numerous flight launches was carried

out at the Hochfrequenzinstitut D.F.S. at Ainring in the Bavarian Alps, and in the autumn of 1943 this still experimental
equipment made it possible for the Henschel HE-263-A flying
bomb to sink the torpedo-boat destroyer *Egret* in the Bay of
Biscay and an American transport ship in the Gulf of Salerno.
The immediate countermeasures taken by Allied radio branches
had already been established for some time, thanks to data
furnished by espionage, and the Germans were forced to mod-
ify the guidance system.

Type B was used with modest success along the northern
coastline of France until this too was jammed.[20]

Type C was supposed to have an installation derived from
the preceding model, but with a cathode tube of 221 lines and
twenty-five pictures per second. It was developed by Section F
of the very active experimental institute run by the Postal
Ministry (F.D.R.P.). When the institute was transferred to
Aach-am-Bodensee in October 1943, however, the work was
temporarily interrupted.

Meantime, the Hochfrequezinstitut D.F.S. scientists had experimented with the apparatus for the Type D bombs, and in
July and October of 1944 they successfully carried out remote
control of shots against land and sea targets in Garz and
Karlshagen.

After the F.D.R.P.'s activities were resumed in full, it completed the plans for the *Tonne* project, and the new television
apparatus was ordered from Fernseh, which began series production at its factories in Obertanwald-bei-Reichenberg, in the
Sudetenland. But the Russians continued advancing, and in
April 1945 Fernseh moved to Taufkirchen in Bavaria, continuing to work on the *Tonne*, four-fifths ready for industrial assembly, as well as on one of Dr. Moller's projects, the *Sprotte*,
which had very recently been laid down. This project was
concerned with the development of a microtelevision camera
to be installed in the nose of an antiaircraft rocket to guide it
precisely to the center of the Allied bomber formations.[21]

At the beginning of 1945 the balance sheet of German radio-
television technology in the field of missiles read more or less
as follows:

In Bayreuth Dr. Rambauske, director of the Institut für
Physikalische-Forschung (I.F.P.F.), was completing an appa-

ratus for antiaircraft missiles, flying bombs, and naval air torpedoes for the Luftwaffe. Among other things, this apparatus offered the possibility of being able to supply periodic corrections to the "automatic pilot" of planes or boats, regulating itself by the light of the sun, a star, a lighthouse, or any other light source. Tested in autumn 1944, the device accurately guided a motorboat through a complicated series of remote-controlled evolutions on the Madu See, a lake in Pomerania. Nevertheless, it apparently aroused only very lukewarm interest in the technical circles of the Luftwaffe.[22]

At Ainring, the latest model in development promised to have an effective radius of action of twelve miles on land and sixty miles at sea. At the time of the surrender, however, it still needed at least another six months of work to perfect it and bring it to large-scale production. The laboratory for the military applications of high-frequency radio waves had also completed a remote-control system for bombs, rockets, and aircraft that "resisted all known enemy systems of 'jamming.'" This was the *Mosaik* project developed by Professor Folske from an idea that had occurred to him in 1943; in May 1945 it was ready to go into the preproduction run.

At Oberammergau, in addition to its radio and television researches, the Oberbayerische Forschunsanstalt (O.B.F.), under the direction of Dr. Konrad, was working on infrared detecting devices based on the principle of the bolometer. In reality a laboratory under the aegis of Messerschmitt, the O.B.F. was responsible for the study of a number of special projects that it was considered necessary and prudent to keep confined to the Bavarian mountains.

The antiaircraft *Enzian* missile, with an infrared automatic search head (project Madrid), was also included among the high-priority projects of 1944. The development of this missile had been divided up and distributed among the various government institutes equipped for that sort of research. The part dealing with the flight-control mechanism of the device had been assigned to the Reichenhall section of the D.F.S., which was responsible for aircraft equipment, through the subcontractor Holzbau-Kissing, A.G., of Sonthofen-im-Allgäu, which had also worked on the *Feuerball*.

In December 1944 the O.B.F. resumed control of the entire

research program on the *Enzian*, basing its decision on the greater local availability of the scientific equipment considered necessary for completing the work rapidly. But when the D.F.S. scientists arrived in Oberammergau to take part in the project, they learned to their consternation that the whole program had in the meantime been shelved. And yet test flights of the *Enzian* had been very encouraging and the device was well worth being completed in the shortest possible time.[23] What could possibly have been the reason for that apparently self-inflicted wound?

There were two good reasons.

In its underground factories at Nordhausen, the Henschel firm, which had always been relatively more concerned with missiles than with airplanes, was about to begin large-scale production of the excellent antiaircraft rocket, the *Schmetterling* (Butterfly).[24]

The other and perhaps even more decisive reason was that Messerschmitt, which had always been more concerned with airplanes than with missiles, had completed in the greatest secrecy the fighter plane that Göring had dreamed about for so long: the radio-controlled interceptor rocket plane.

PILOTLESS FIGHTER PLANES

Göring had repeatedly inspected the work in progress, following the explanations of the scientists with absorbed and enthusiastic attention and occasionally making suggestions of his own.

In the euphoria of the moment, reinforced by the thin, bracing air of the Alps far from the dismal rumble of war, a foretaste of the bitter surprise that awaited the enemies of the Greater Reich was already on his lips. And he thought that in order to insure that "thousands" of those fantastic fighters would be built, he would increase the productive capacity of Messerschmitt by giving it the support of "his own" Reimahg-Bau G.m.b.H.[25]

Two types of *Raketenflugzeuge ohne Pilote* (pilotless fighter rockets) were designed.

The *Krache* (Crack) was about sixteen feet long and armed with a battery of eight 55-mm R-4-M rocket projectiles. The *Donner* (Thunder) was armed with a rapid-fire MG-213/C.30 small cannon.

Both had the characteristic blunt, teardrop shape of the well-known ME-163 rocket-engined fighter. In effect they were the same machine partially redesigned to be pilotless and controlled from the ground through an elaborate television receiver installed in an armored console. Lighter at the end of a mission because of the ammunition and rocket fuel expended, the *Krache* would fall to earth under a huge tail chute. For the *Donner*, it was decided to try to land the craft on a belly skid, as with the original ME-163.

At the beginning of 1945 the O.B.F. completed the preproduction run of twenty examples. But unarmed tests against conventional German planes revealed at once certain secondary defects. These concerned the excessively high maneuverability of the craft. In fact, it was difficult to coordinate quickly enough the radio order to fire with the fleeting television picture of the target, which danced about a great deal because both hunter and target were in motion. In addition, the high speeds caused oscillations that reduced the number of hits to an unacceptably low figure.

The radical solution that was suggested was to make the firing control completely automatic. But it was now March 1945, only two months from the disastrous end.

GERMAN AUTOMATIC FUSES

The Lilienthalgesellschaft für Luftfahrtsforschung (L.F.L.) was an academic institution of the highest level set up to coordinate science and industry in the field of aeronautical research. At Ainring in December 1943 it held its large year-end congress for the elite in the German science of air weaponry.

Among the reports prepared for the event, one especially attracted the attention of those who had the thankless responsibility of handling the Reich's air defenses (and, of course, it also attracted the attention of British secret agents). The report was given by Dr. Hackemann, of the Waffen-Institut L.F.A. of Volkenrode. Entitled "New Methods of Research in Weaponry," it set forth for the first time certain technical principles destined not only to revolutionize the aiming and firing of aircraft-mounted guns but also to make the "search heads" of missiles and flak shells completely automatic.

Before the war there had been a good deal of talk about installing automatic fuses controlled by tiny electronic or electromagnetic devices mounted in antiaircraft projectiles. In 1939 the Swedish munitions firm of Bofors had designed a photoelectric cell fuse, but it was unsuccessful because of its extreme fragility. In spite of all their efforts, neither the French nor the Americans succeeded in perfecting really effective devices.

The British were more rational, and also luckier. In 1942 they secretly designed the famous radio fuse, the R-Proximity Fuse, which they had manufactured in the United States on a large scale. This fuse seriously hampered the German V-1 air offensive against London and in the autumn of 1944 finally knocked it out completely.

Behind the British in the time factor, during 1944 the Germans began to catch up with giant strides, aiming at high quality. Their automatic fuses sought, in fact, to exploit methodically, singly or in combination, all the physical phenomena that accompany the movement of a body in the air.

Thus at the F.D.R.P.'s institute for electronic research, Professor Hanle, who was working on behalf of the Luftwaffe, adapted the well-known Geiger counter, making a rocket fuse activated by ultraviolet radiations that to many Allied scientists seemed to be well ahead of its time. Elsewhere work was carried out on electromagnetic, acoustical, electroacoustical, photoelectric, and photochemical fuses.

The major bulk of the work on automatic fuses was, however, supplied by the Ernst Orlich Institut run by the Plenipotentiary Board for the Study and Application of Ultrahighfrequency Waves (B.H.F.). Located in Travemünde, near Danzig, the institute had also distinguished itself in the field of antiradar camouflage.[26] In 1943 it was moved to Wolfersdorf and Altenburg, in Thuringia, to escape the British air raids that repeatedly pounded the coast line and German islands in the

Baltic after the "discovery" of Peenemünde. At the end of 1944 it moved farther south, finding refuge in the Tyrolean mountains. Of the forty-six military applications of electronic projects that were completed or still being perfected at the time of the surrender, six dealt with the preparation of special proximity fuses.

The fuses developed under project *Kuhglocke* (Cowbell), which had been commissioned by Speer, were sensitive to the natural electrostatic fields that surround airplanes in flight.[27]

In a sense the Luftwaffe was running for cover when it commissioned Project *Pinscher* (Terrier), taking a leaf out of the British book to provide flak shells with short-wave radio fuses operating on a band of about six meters. Ground-tested in the late autumn of 1944, they proved to be efficient up to a distance of 160 feet from the target.

Knowing that the British were masters at jamming enemy radio apparatuses, in the summer of 1944 the Speer Commission also set up project *Marder* (Marten). The aim here was to control the explosion of the projectile by radio from a plane in flight or from a ground station within a radius of ten miles from the target. Control at this distance would avoid the danger of accidental explosions and prevent any possible electronic interference from attacking aircraft. But by autumn the new project *Wiesel* (Weasel) gave such promise of being perfected that it tended to supplant *Marder*, its principle having been reported as "very promising."

Project *Reineke* had been suggested by the Luftwaffe in the winter of 1943, shelved in 1944, and resumed, financed and speeded up by the Speer Commission, at the beginning of 1945. Its scientists were engaged in the study of the advantages offered by magnetic fuses, which were difficult to "spook" and did not have the danger of accidental or premature explosions.

Finally there was project *Isegrim* (Grumbler), which the Luftwaffe supported toward the end of 1944. Its aim was to revolutionize antitank techniques. Experimented on successfully toward the end of the war, the *Isegrim* was a device that automatically launched and detonated ordinary antitank rockets from a plane deliberately—or by chance, as during a night flight—flying horizontally at a low altitude directly over a

tank. The system worked because of the astonishing sensitivity
of the apparatus to weak variations in the local geomagnetic
field produced by the metallic mass of the target. The device
that launched the rockets was in this case mounted vertically
under the wings or inside the fuselage, with the launch muz
zles pointed down toward the ground. The plane had to fly no
more than fifty feet above the ground.

THE SPITFIRE AND BREECHLESS CANNONS

The same rocket launchers installed in the fuselage, but with
the muzzles aimed upward and controlled by a firing device
based on the principle of electrostatic fuses, was called the
Feuerspucker (Spitfire).[28]

Now the forward-fixed weapons—cannons and machine guns
—were destined to disappear from German fighters. The re
cently installed lateral-fixed weapons (the so-called *Schrägen-
musik* machine guns), which proved of doubtful utility, also
disappeared, as did the impractical electromechanically fired
rear weapons, which had the designers of the twin turbine
bomber Arado AR-234 studying the problem of remote-control
firing and the application to aircraft of special rear-view re-
tractable periscopes for aiming and firing at pursuing fighters.

Allied bombers had a number of fixed-forward weapons and
maneuverable guns in the back, tail, and belly blisters. But the
undersides of planes remained relatively unprotected because
of the physical impossibility of swinging the belly and tail guns
down ninety degrees. In the heroic days of dogfighting, attacking fighters preferred to fling themselves daringly and riskily
up at the bellies of enemy planes. The fighters could easily
have shot up the bellies of raiders and at the same time maintained a certain distance from their fire if they had had guns
that shot upward.[29] Downing enemy planes "by the dozen"
would have been child's play. The future—conditions permitting—seemed definitely to promise the arrival of guns with
vertical and lateral fire.

Nevertheless, rocket projectiles had the defect of a relatively
low initial velocity and were not nearly as accurate as pro-

jectiles fired from rifled barrels, although certain types with small stabilizers were being perfected in Stuttgart, Hillersleben, and Peenemünde (project *Pfeil,* Arrow).

Like a good Teutonic scientist Professor Hackemann had foreseen this problem too, though it was not really very serious. And so when the Allies occupied the L.F.A.'s Waffen-Erprobung W.2 at Volkenrode, they found a number of examples of 75-mm antiaircraft grenades with automatic fuses that could be fired from six-throated vertical cannons of the breechless type (*Sondergerät*) and with a firing control determined by a device sensitive to the natural electrostatic field of the huge bombers.[30]

The essential point in all these new weapons was the automatic control of firing. All the pilot had to do was fly a hundred yards beneath the bomber and the automatic firing mechanism would operate on the basis of the photoelectric, magnetic, or electrostatic principles.

Having given little encouragement during the course of tests, the first two efforts in this direction were shelved to await improvements in the apparatuses that provided the bearings.

The third type of control, coupled with a vertical cannon having multiple batteries, was very successfully tested against radio-controlled target planes at the Altenburg airfield in Thuringia. At the time of the armistice it required only a few detail improvements before being ready to send to the underground factories that were building hundreds of new fighters and their weapons. Everything had been planned with the greatest care. All contingencies had been taken into account. All . . . except the sudden breakthrough of General Patton's tanks into the Bavarian plains.

In Italy, the Gothic Line was still holding the enemy, and it held him until almost the end. But the defenses on the Oder and the bastions of the old Siegfried Line were falling at various points under the pressure of the gigantic forces that the Allies were putting in the field for the final battle.

The Remagen bridge over the Rhine, which had inexplicably remained intact, allowed the Americans to cross the Rhine in large numbers at the beginning of March. And this was the end for Germany, although certain high Nazi leaders under the influence of Dr. Goebbels' fiery fanaticism still hoped for a "last-minute miracle" with a blind faith that was close to madness.

The death of President Roosevelt had not given rise to a rupture between the Anglo-Americans and the Russians, as had been hoped. The combined land and air hammering of Germany continued, more implacable than ever.

During those apocalyptic days when Nazism was in its death throes, there appeared—only to disappear immediately among the best and longest kept secrets of one of the victors—the last and perhaps also the most amazing of all the flying machines that the Germans constructed toward the end of the war.

THE "BALL LIGHTNING" AUTOMATIC FIGHTER

Parallel with the formation of the special S.S. Air Corps, the S.S. Technical General Staff had not only espoused Marshal Göring's pressing demands for the preparation of the "decisive" fighter, but had implemented them by having all the aeronautic advances of the past two years sent to the industrial combine of the "G. Werke."

Thus the principle of the symmetrical circular aircraft was combined with direct gyroscopic stabilization; synthetic fire-damp was combined with the multiple-batteried blower cannon; a gelatinous organic metallic hypercombustible was combined with the total reaction turbine; television-controlled flying was combined with vertical take-off and landing; armor that was sensitive to small-caliber projectiles and radio control that was free of enemy jamming were combined with the active blinding of enemy radar; infrared search "eyes" were combined with electrostatic weapon firing. This marked the rapid development of the *Feuerball*, which finally became a weapon.

The *Kugelblitz* (Ball Lightning), which apparently for greater safety combined the electrostatic firing device with an analogous short-wave device manufactured by the Patent-Verwertungs Gesellschaft of Salzburg, lumped together in a single compact mass the wings, tail, and fuselage of ordinary planes, but it had nothing in common with them in either form or performance. It was the first example of the "jet-lift" aircraft.[31]

After a single lucky wartime mission, the *Kugelblitz* was subsequently destroyed by technical detachments of retreating S.S. troops, and thanks to the instructions that had been given to the investigators of the T Force by the exceedingly strict British military censorship, nothing else has come out since then.

Even if ufologists do not know it or refuse to admit it, the *Kugelblitz,* older brother of the *Feuerball* antiradar device, *is the second authentic antecedent of the present-day flying saucers and it is with them*—and with the other German devices of the same family (spinning bombs, lenticular bombs, ramming fighters, and flying spheres)—*that the true history or, if you like, the "prehistory" of the UFO question begins.*

The military finale of the matter, however, goes beyond the chronicle of aeronautics and belongs to the bloody story of the forties.

After the Remagen disaster, the Nazi general staff realized that it was not possible to resist the Allies' triple-pronged offensive much longer. Desertions in the commands and the pitiless repression of real or presumed desertions of soldiers under the pressure of continuous defeats had a disastrous effect on the efficiency of the Wehrmacht. Nevertheless, they did not produce the hoped-for breakdown of the German military machine, which continued to fight the Allies on a multitude of local fronts produced by the break-up of the marginal territories of the Reich, in a series of gigantic pockets that Hitler optimistically insisted on calling fortresses. These fronts had only the most precarious communications with one another and often had absolutely no communication with general headquarters, which were partly located in the Chancellery bunker in Berlin and partly evacuated to Thuringia and to even remoter Berchtesgaden.

In spite of the propaganda that had choked the air waves during the last quarter of 1944, promising a new year studded with military triumphs, the situation in the air and on the sea was just as desperate as that on land.

Reduced to a few submarines that had survived the defeat in the Atlantic, a couple of squadrons of torpedo boats, and the large ships hidden in Norwegian fjords, for many months the German navy lay more or less inactive at anchor under air attack while awaiting the new, so-called invulnerable submarines.[32]

In the air the Luftwaffe was being implacably destroyed, despite the new rocket and turbine planes, which were overwhelmed by the fire power and sheer numbers of the adversary. At dawn on January 1, 1945, the disastrous *Bodenplatte Unternehmen* (Operation Tile) that Hitler wanted as a support for the Ardennes offensive got under way. In this operation nine hundred planes—now an enormous number for the Germans—were thrown against the Allied airfields in the Dutch-Belgian sector. Three hundred sixty-four of them did not return to their bases, thus endangering the success of the subsequent operations. After that unlucky enterprise, the appearances of the Luftwaffe became even rarer because of the progressive breakup of the various combat units, which were nailed to the ground both by enemy air attacks and by the rapid depletion of their fuel supplies.

Toward the beginning of spring most of the German airfields were practically shut down. In view of the excellent results obtained by the dispersion of their industries, the Germans *in extremis* began to disperse the planes that were still left on their surviving airfields. A number of improvised airfields were set up in the thick pine forests of the Schwäbischerwald and the Bubesheimerwald which used nearby stretches of hastily camouflaged highway as dangerous airstrips. It was from one of these improvised fields that the first *Kugelblitz* fighter took off on its fantastic flight.

At the eastern tip of the ephemeral defensive arc set up as advanced protection for the Austro-Bavarian bastion, the great underground industrial complex of Kahla, in Thuringia, was transformed into a sort of dry-land aircraft carrier. The long cement strip of the ridge on the thickly forested summit served as the runway for the immediate testing of the prototypes that were being produced inside the hill.[33]

As the military situation worsened the weather improved, so

that new supplies of cement and trucks arrived, along with additional prisoners being evacuated from the north. Work on the U aerodromes, which had meantime come under the complete control of the S.S., was speeded up to a totally inhuman pace. Fourteen-hour work days, seven days a week, a five-mile daily walk to reach the work sites—such was the killing way of life of the slave workers. Naturally, the mortality rate soared. But this was of no concern to the promoters of the enterprise, whose only torments were caused by the obvious consolidation of the Allied forces on the western borders of Bavaria.

When the sudden advance of General Patton's army interrupted the work, the first airfield was already three-quarters finished. The other two were only half completed, and no important installations or plans were found among the abandoned constructions because of the final, rapid evacuation of the technical experts and the most skilled workers to the heart of the Alpine Redoubt.[34]

THE END OF THE ALPINE REDOUBT

Every attempt to push General Bradley's American troops back over the Rhine failed. On March 14, 1945, at the end of one of Hitler's usual military conferences and while the usual authorized spokesman was proclaiming that new weapons would soon be thrown into the battle, the Führer called a meeting of some high S.S. officers, the Gauleiters of the six southern provinces and all the generals who were still faithful to him. He ordered them to see at once to the immediate preparation of the Alpine Redoubt—time: not more than two weeks!

We have no record of the reactions of those present to that insane order. But we may assume that there were no objections, each one probably having already decided for himself the best way to save himself, outside and, if necessary, even against the Führer's orders.

According to certain information that the British picked up immediately after the war, the revival of interest in the Redoubt came about because a few days earlier artillery Colonel Hans von Schmückert had declared to Hitler that he believed it was possible to bring the first grenades containing 750 grams of "disintegrating explosive" under experiment in Austria to completion within a few months at the latest. If this matter, as was to be expected, came to the attention of the Allied command, they would be forced to throw all their reserves into the fight in order to isolate Austria and Bavaria and thus avert that danger.[35]

In the feverish search for the most extreme solutions to the retreat, the concept of isolated "fortresses" defended to the last man was extended to the principal cities of East Prussia and Silesia (Königsberg, Danzig, Breslau, and still others), condemning them to utter devastation in the hope of temporarily holding up the onrushing Soviet advance.

To complete the gloomy picture it should be remembered that on March 19 Hitler ordered the Gauleiters of the regions about to be invaded to carry out the criminal "scorched-earth" policy. The idea was to hamstring the occupying troops by methodically destroying not only military but industrial and urban installations with no regard for the most elementary requirements for survival of the civilian population. The order was subsequently revoked through the firm opposition of Speer.

The movement of the retreating troops became more and more difficult, however, because of the devastation of the German heartland by the Allied bombers. Whole units were wiped out in the big and little "pockets" that were created by the irresistible thrusts of Allied armor, galvanized by the foretaste of the German collapse. And the possibility of replacing all these losses, which was already minimal in January, disappeared entirely.

On March 27, S.S. Gruppenführer Kammler returned to the Berlin bunker after a long trip to Austria and the Bavarian Alps, where he had inspected the preparations for the Redoubt which had begun in February but had been carried out slowly because of the lack of specific orders. By questioning the military and scientific authorities in Austria who were directing the preparation of the "secret weapons" that had been chosen for the final resistance, he had learned from Commandant Petschek that the subatomic explosives could not be ready before the end of 1945.[36]

Although the plan for the Alpine Redoubt was by now practically unrealizable, in obedience to orders Himmler named S.S. Obergruppenführer Kaltenbrunner head of security police for southern Germany, and sent him to Innsbruck to organize the surviving S.S. forces that were streaming in. Himmler did not, however, trust Kaltenbrunner, fearing that he might make secret advances to the Anglo-Americans for a separate peace. He appointed S.S. Obergruppenführer Gottlob Berger as Kaltenbrunner's assistant—officially, but in reality to report on Kaltenbrunner's moves.

Among the other "special deputies" was the celebrated Colonel Skorzeny, the man of desperate situations, personally named by the Führer to the command of the special "Alpine Defense Corps," which, of course, had still to be formed.[37]

In April the collapse of German military and political institutions took on a catastrophic rhythm. The myth of the Alpine Redoubt was now only a faded memory to the bigwigs of the regime, or a pretext for deserting the dangerous "redoubt" of Berlin.

The final, irreparable reverse began on April 13, with the fall of Vienna. On the sixteenth the Americans took Nuremberg and headed toward Munich and Bavaria. On the eighteenth General Model's Army Group B, trapped and decimated in the giant Ruhr pocket, surrendered after a valiant eighteen-day struggle, leaving the Americans with 325,000 prisoners, including thirty generals. The armored divisions of General Bradley poured through that two-hundred-mile gap in the German defenses into the heart of Germany, driving toward Thuringia and the Harz.[38]

On April 25, advanced Russian and American patrols met at Torgau on the Elbe and Germany was cut in two.

Contrary to previously established plans, Hitler did not leave Berlin on April 20 to assume command of the Alpine Redoubt.[39] It seems that Goebbels and Bormann convinced him that Berlin was "the only position between the Elbe and the Oder that was really threatened by the Soviet advance and from which the counteroffensive to ease the Russian pressure would have to be mounted"! A magnificent whim that closed to Hitler the only remaining escape—to the tranquillity of the

Tyrol or to General Schoerner's Army Group strongly entrenched in the Boemerwald.

The last days of Hitler and of the Third Reich—masterfully pieced together and described by Major Trevor-Roper of the British Intelligence Service—are the quintessence of the farce, drama, tragedy, and chaos that culminated in Hitler's pistol shot and in the general surrender of the surviving German forces.[40]

The Alpine Fortress, then, took no military part in the war. It was overcome by the very events that had given rise to it. But its embryonic existence and the great mass of secrets that had been moved there in the first quarter of 1945 nevertheless engaged an army of expert investigators briefed by qualified bureaus of the various national secret services.

Interrogations of officials and designers, careful searches among the rubble of factories bombed by the Allies or mined by retreating S.S. units, in natural and artificial caverns, abandoned mines, the cellars of old castles and family homes, unused railway tunnels, river and lake beds, recently cut wooded areas, ruined churches and schools, new masonry, damaged cemeteries—nothing escaped the practiced eyes of the investigators. For the remainder of 1945 and much of 1946 tons and tons of blueprints, company papers, lists of researchers, laboratory models, memoranda, reports and notes that covered every sector of the war industry came pouring out of thousands of unlikely hiding places.

In concluding a review of German secrets that fell into American hands, Colonel D. L. Putt, assistant commanding officer for the Technical Information Service of the Allied Military Government, frankly stated in July 1946 that at the end of the war, despite the heavy defeat, German scientists and technical experts had left behind at Peenemünde, Brunswick, Wiener Neustadt, and elsewhere the milestones of new aeronautical developments and future air wars.

A self-evident truth (or a discouraging prospect) that justified the later development of certain unknown or still little known stages in aeronautical technology that were reached between the beginning of the prewar period and the end of the postwar period, and knowledge of which is indispensable in order to solve the mystery of the UFOs.

NOTES

1. Or perhaps in the entourage of the little known "secessionist government" of France formed by Jacques Doriot at Mainau or Lake Constance? This phantom government was supported by Himmler and Goebbels in opposition to De Brinon's "legitimate" collaborationist government, which moved to Sigmaringen after the liberation of Paris. Because of its unconditional support of S.S. policies, it enjoyed their special protection and it was confidently informed of secrets that even German military higher-ups were denied knowledge of.

2. See Professor Gianfranco Bianchi's 1962 observation after he had completed his historical research on the period running from July 25, 1943 (the date of Mussolini's downfall) to May 8, 1945: "The lawyer Paolo Porta, who was the Republican Fascist Party secretary for the province of Como and inspector of the Black Brigades in Lombardy, used Adolfo Belgeri, the head of the Political Investigation Office of the R.F.P. in Como, as a confidential courier to deliver secret political and military information concerning the Italo-Swiss frontier and internal Swiss matters to Mussolini at Gargnano on Lake Garda. A secret intelligence service had been set up on Swiss soil by the Italian Social Republic, which was not legally recognized by the Berne government."

3. This initial error had been prompted by examination of Dr. Dräger's plan for the construction of a diesel engine fueled with liquid oxygen for powering underwater craft that Dräger had first sketched out in 1936. A prototype was built by the Kreislaufbetrieb-Motor D.W. In 1943 the prototype was completed at the Forschungsinstitut für Kraftfahrt und Fahrzeugmotoren (F.F.K.F.) of Stuttgart-Untertürkheim with the collaboration of Professor Kamm and Dr. Ernst. Dubbed the Oxygen Recycle System by the Anglo-American investigators, the design was completely abandoned in favor of the Walter turbine functioning on hydrogen peroxide. The agents of the T Force Camp at Bad Gandersheim who examined the documents found in the G Werke factories—which were under the

technical supervision of the Henschel and Zeppelin firms and the administration of the S.S. Technical General Staff—imagined therefore that it was a recent resumption of those researches along new lines, *i.e.*, the laying down of a "compound" type of engine (diesel plus turbine).

4. G. Ventura, *Il radioplano ad aria liquida* (private communication to the author). The initial mistake had been further compounded by the detail that certain special turbine blades —the use of which was unknown to the German suppliers themselves and which in the specifications were required to have "highly polished surfaces"—were ordered from Kuhl, Kopp, and Kausch A.G. of Frankenthal, a firm well known for its working ties with the Kriegsmarine. See Combined Intelligence Objectives Sub-committee, *Visit to the Ludwigshafen-Mannheim Area: Torpedoes, Submarines and Naval Constructions* (Report No. XXX-44, London, H.M.S.O., 1945). In the hurried hunt for the whereabouts of the secret, T Unit agents interrogated the French scientist Georges Claude, the inventor of industrial processes for manufacturing liquid air, lengthily but apparently unsuccessfully. He was arrested in the autumn of 1944 at Nancy and released the following year. The charge was that he had collaborated with the Germans in the production and handling of liquid oxygen, which was actually used on a very large scale by the various types of German rocket engines. The first real clues were shortly afterward provided by the designs of a special pump of clearly aeronautical use found in the design studio of a subcontractor attached to the B.M.W. company in Allach that supplied components for the *Vergeltung* antiaircraft rocket. The factory of the subcontractor remained in a cavern of Wittringen in the district of Saarbrücken after the B.M.W. complex was later moved to the east. Perhaps some slight trace of that revolutionary type of aircraft (akin to the *Feuerball*) is to be found in the article "Deflex-Reaction Propulsion" (*Flight*, London, September 13, 1945), in which a certain Mr. F. Umpleby, perhaps having mistakenly interpreted the information he had received, expounded a theory concerning the improvement of jet engines that was based on faulty premises. His reply to the criticisms

that immediately flowed in from all sides (see *Flight*, October 18, 1945) ended with the following declaration: "The rocket referred to is, I suppose, the Oberth, a number of which were built and tested in Germany. They worked well but nothing much seems to be known about them. The writer has given these rockets some thought and investigation, and may give some results on the investigations later, if they should be of sufficient interest." But Umpleby did not, as he promised, publish the results of his investigations on those special and still unknown German "rockets."

5. These experiments led other powers to investigate what immediately seemed to be a promising defense principle. It is known, for example, that in 1937–1938 the Americans secretly carried out tests with "clouds of metallic dust" that was so fine as to be almost invisible but was highly abrasive and designed to speed up the natural wear and tear on engines. The tests apparently were unsuccessful. In addition, the United States also experimented with "poison curtains" to be spread in the air in order to create a temporary biological barrier against invading planes. This, too, proved unsuccessful.

6. See S. A. Goudsmit, *Alsos* (New York, Schuman, 1947), pp. 50–65.

7. This discovery led Gold to propose to the Luftwaffe an antiaircraft rocket loaded with vaporizable myrol, while another L.F.A. expert, Dr. Zeumer, concluded a number of successful tests with an antitank bomb like the one designed for the Heereswaffenamt. Indeed, the Heereswaffenamt immediately ordered a long series of tests which were to be carried out at the Spandau artillery range until the beginning of 1945. The experiments were not carried out because Spandau had to be evacuated under the threat of the Soviet advance. Myrol, which was manufactured on an industrial scale by the Schmidding firm at Bodenbach, was a mixture of methylnitrate (75 percent) and methanol (25 percent) extracted by direct nitration from liquid methanol. See Combined Intelligence Objectives Sub-committee, *Luftfahrtforschungsanstalt "Her-*

mann Göring," Volkenrode, Brunswick (Report No. XXV-2, London, H.M.S.O., March 1946), p. 14.

8. *Cf. "Quelques armes et engins bizarres," L'Armée Française* (III, 26, Paris, May 1948), pp. 3–6.

9. See Combined Intelligence Objectives Sub-committee, *Artillery Experimental Range: Hillersleben* (Report No. XXVIII-2, London, H.M.S.O., 1945), appendices 1 and 2, pp. 15 and 15A.

10. Conceptually related to the well-known flame-throwers, this weapon had already been carefully considered by the British from different and perhaps more rational constructional and operational approaches. Immediately after the war, Sir Geoffrey Lloyd made known certain details of the so-called "belt of fire," one of the secret weapons the British had excogitated in June 1940 to discourage the Germans from attempting an invasion of England. Still too inadequately armed to repel an invasion carried out by the means and methods of the time, the British possessed large stores of gasoline. Lloyd, who was high in the Fuels and Energy Ministry, believed correctly that with its terrible inhibitory power, fire could be transformed into a valid weapon of retreat. He approached Lord Hankey with his plan. Before the war Hankey had conducted experiments in passive defense with curtains of fire, taking off from the technique suggested by what he had read about the mysterious "Greek fire" in Gibbon's *Decline and Fall of the Roman Empire*. In June 1940 the first tests were made on the beach at Dumpton with a rudimentary catapult that hurled large drums of burning oil out to sea. These missiles (which later went under the code name of "Fougasses") were the beginning of "a frightful system of flame-throwers that was used not only to cause fire on the surface of the sea by means of the catapulted containers, underwater conduits and powerful jets of flame but also to defend strategic and tactical positions on the coastal hinterland. A chemical substance based on calcium that ignited on contact with water was pumped into the gasoline piping laid on the sea floor along with the fuel, thus

setting fire to the huge floating slick . . . special flame-throwing catapults mounted on ships hurled jets of fire 150 feet in the air against the dive bombers. This last was the only 'flame weapon' actually used against the enemy. The others never had a chance to see action." In fact, the Germans did not attempt an invasion for a number of reasons, not the least of which was fear of these deadly defenses after one test company made up of invasion troops dressed in asbestos clothing (which proved defective) ventured into a large oil slick that was set afire off the coast of France. Almost the entire company met a horrible end.

11. See Col. L. E. Simon, "Research in the Berchtesgaden Area," *German Scientific Establishments* (Report 19,849, New York, Mapleton House Publications, 1947), pp. 153–163.

12. See Hans Fritsche, *Hier Spricht Hans Fritsche*, 1948. On the subject of German secret weapons, the former political editor of Radio Berlin wrote: "It is in any case absolutely true that if the miracle weapons did not exist, we did, however, have new types of weapons that were not quickly enough— and in some cases were not at all—put into operation. I am not talking about the new antiaircraft homing weapons, or about the new explosive 'butardin,' which was discovered by accident after an explosion in the Ludwigshafen factory and which produced extensive annihilating explosions among close bombing formations. Both had still to be perfected [at the time of the German surrender]."

13. The choice of ethylene was motivated by the fact that this hydrocarbon possesses the very advantageous property of requiring a volume of air for combustion greater than that required by any other gaseous combustible.

14. Indeed, it seems that it was intended to include appropriate quantities of highly detonative substances, such as octane (C_8H_{18}), and others that were supposed to speed up the firing of the cloud in its final expansion, such as cetane ($C_{16}H_{34}$), both substances belonging to the same series of the fundamental components of methane.

15. See Combined Intelligence Objectives Sub-committee, *Development of Ceramics Materials for Use in Turbine Blades* (Report No. XXV-9, London, H.M.S.O., 1945), p. 13.

16. The history of the Zippermeyer system is not officially known. It seems, nevertheless, that at the beginning of 1945 tests of various types of grenades of somewhat complex content were being prepared. In one of these the explosive charge was thoroughly mixed with coal dust pressed into a very friable and porous agglomerate, whose interstices were loaded with a liquefied explosive gas. The "coal sponge"—a special type of *Schaumkohle* manufactured by the Heinrich Schmitt Werke K.G. of Frankfurt-am-Main and evacuated to Berchtesgaden —thus acted as a stabilizer, reducing the danger of handling the projectiles. It is said that from the beginning of 1944 Hitler followed these researches with particular interest, in the absurd hope of soon being able to use a powerful and regenerated flak in the passive defense of the Reich and thus supplant the fighter arm of the Luftwaffe that had so disappointed him because of Göring's empty promises.

17. See Combined Intelligence Objectives Sub-committee, *Radar and Controlled Missiles: Paris Area* (Report No. I/1, London, H.M.S.O., October 1944), p. 63.

18. See Combined Intelligence Objectives Sub-committee, *German Research and Development in the Radio Field: Lyon Area* (Report No. XI-7, London, H.M.S.O., November 19, 1944), p. 31.

19. See British Intelligence Objectives Sub-committee, *Photo-Surfaces: A Report on German Developments of Photocells, Electron Multipliers and Television Pick-up Tubes* (Final Report No. 530, London, H.M.S.O., 1946).

20. See Combined Intelligence Objectives Sub-committee, *Stassfurter Rundfunk: Stassfurt* (Report No. XXXII-88, London, H.M.S.O., 1945); or B.16: "Works of the High Frequency

Department D.F.S. (1939–1945)" in Deutsche Forschungsanstalt für Segelflug (pp. 107–115), Combined Intelligence Objectives Sub-committee Report No. XXXII-66 (London, 1945).

21. See British Intelligence Objectives Sub-committee, *Television Development and Application in Germany*, Final Report No. 867 (London, H.M.S.O., 1946), p. 20; and Combined Intelligence Objectives Sub-committee Investigator's Preliminary Report, *Draft Report on Investigation at Taufkirchen*, pp. 53–56 of the Combined Intelligence Objectives Sub-committee Report No. XXXI-38, *The I.T.T., Siemens and Robert Bosch Organizations* (London, H.M.S.O., 1945).

22. See Combined Intelligence Objectives Sub-committee, *Institut für Physikalische Forschung: Neu Drossenfeld*, Report No. XXVIII-41 (London, H.M.S.O., 1945), p. 13.

23. Shortly afterward the starting date for series production was reexamined and set for May 1945—a theoretical date, since the armistice overtook these plans. The only complete working models were later found at the experimental center of Lofer, in the Tyrol, which had functioned as the last center for the collection of new antiaircraft inventions.

24. In fact, the first antiaircraft salvo of "Butterflies"—to which Goebbels gave *in extremis* the propagandistic denomination of V-3 (*i.e.*, "Reprisal Weapon No. 3"), though it was not a true reprisal weapon but a purely defensive device—was launched with deadly effect on the Allied raiders exactly one week before the Nazi collapse. Assembly-line production of the rocket had been set up to furnish 3000 units a month, beginning in November 1945.

25. The Reimahg-Bau G.m.b.H. was a recently formed aeronautical company located underground in Kahla, in Thuringia, which resulted from the forced merger of the Gustloff Werke and Ago Flugzeugewerke arranged by Gauleiter Sauckel, one of Göring's creatures, who, in order to ingratiate himself even

more with his powerful protector, had thought it wise to give the new firm that barbaric name made up of the first letters of *Reich Marshal Hermann Göring*. If the Allies had given it the time to get fully under way, the new company by itself would undoubtedly have put several thousand jet planes in action. Most would have been the Heinkel HE-162 *Volksjäger*, the ill-starred "People's Fighter," which by means of a massive "air conscription" of very young pilots was planned to sweep every enemy plane from the skies of Germany. General Galland wrote apropos of this plane: "Incredible schedules were fixed, astronomical production figures were planned. Göring himself became a victim of the national frenzy with which the [People's Fighter] had infested almost everyone connected with air defense." In the decisive meeting that took place at Rastenburg on September 23, 1944, Göring cried, "Hundreds! Thousands . . . Until the enemy has been chased back beyond the borders of Germany!" Galland continues: "On December 6, 1944, the HE-162 flew for the first time. A few days later—far too soon—it was displayed to a large circle of interested experts at Vienna-Schwechat. . . . The aircraft started to disintegrate in the air. . . . In March 1945 the planes of the first series were ready. Until the end of the war 200 were produced." All this uselessly delayed still further the production of the ME-262 fighter, opening thereby a new and mortal gap in the already depleted German defenses. Some years before—on November 17, 1942, to be exact—Colonel General Ernst Udet, the director of aircraft construction, had committed suicide after a long controversy with Göring, Hitler, and the Oberkommando on the duties of the Luftwaffe. "Fighters, fighters and more fighters. This is what we absolutely must have. Thousands of fighters!" he had publicly declared just before he killed himself. By echoing that fatal refrain, Göring implicitly criticized his whole policy during the war years, but by then it was too late to do anything about it.

26. See Combined Intelligence Objectives Sub-committee, *Institutes of the Bevollmächtigter für Hochfrequenz-Forschung* (Report No. XXXI-37, London, H.M.S.O., 1945), p. 214.

27. Fields developed by the electrical charges that accumulate on aircraft surfaces and that are the product partly of the process of motive combustion and partly of aerodynamic friction (the triboelectric effect), or that are induced by the strong electrical charges present in the clouds. These latter, indeed, interfered with the perfecting of the *Kuhglocke* fuse seriously enough to cause the project to be interrupted at the beginning of 1945 and a special cycle of ancillary researches on atmospheric electricity to be undertaken.

28. In March 1945, while experimenting with this device mounted on the only model of the ME-262 jet fighter modified to take an oblique-firing Spitfire in the fuselage (the ME-262-D), Second Lieutenant Fritz Kelb shot down seven American four-engined bombers in a single action over Saxony. The Spitfire had been aimed upward and inclined about twenty degrees forward, and its fire power totaled twelve SG-500 rockets of 50 mm.

29. In the spring of 1946 the noted aviation journal *Flugwehr und Technik,* discussing the development of the German night fighter arm during the Second World War, wrote apropos of vertical fire: "[In addition to "tactical radar"] another decisive innovation in the equipping of the night fighters was the installation of oblique armament. Two 20-mm cannons were set in the fuselage behind the pilot's cabin in a more or less vertical position, so that when flying under the target the pilot could get the plane in his vertical sights (a reflex type) and fire upon the largest surface that the bomber presented. If he succeeded in getting under the plane without being observed, he had to worry only about not getting hit by metal fragments blasted off by the explosion of the projectiles. Under the same conditions, lateral attack proved almost impossible because the machine guns in the back and belly turrets of the big bombers could be trained on the attacker with a favorable angle of fire. The vertical weapons were first tried in actual flight in spring 1944, with a pair of rapid-fire cannons mounted on the ME-110 twin-engined heavy night fighters in addition to their normal armament. The test pilot of one of these planes

deserted, landed at the military airport of Dübendorf, near
Zurich, on April 9, 1944, and was interned by the Swiss. Fearing that the Allies might get their hands on its still secret
devices (the modified 'Lichtenstein' Fu-G-220 radar and two
30-mm vertical cannons), Hitler ordered Oberführer S.S. Otto
Skorzeny to organize a raid against the Swiss airport and
destroy the plane. In order to forestall the German operation,
which could have had serious consequences for Switzerland
as well as for Germany herself, the Swiss themselves destroyed
the plane in accordance with a secret agreement between
Gruppenführer S.S. Schellenberg and Brigadier General
Masson, the head of the Swiss secret service. As a *quid pro quo*,
the agreement stipulated the sale to the Swiss air force of
twelve ME-109 fighters."

30. See British Intelligence Objectives Sub-committee, *Weapons Section of the L.F.A., Volkenrode* (Final Report No. 61,
London, H.M.S.O., 1946).

31. It seems that the new fighter was also called the *Vergeltung* by the technicians who were preparing it. However,
this second designation is strongly disputed, since at the same
time the B.M.W. factories were constructing a huge antiaircraft rocket with the same name (Revenge).

32. See J. Nobecourt, *op. cit.*: "The final readying of the secret
weapons coincided with the period of counteroffensive plans
[on the Western Front], and Hitler hoped, not without reason,
that quickly getting secret production under way would give
him the means once again to reverse the outcome of the conflict. A few months would have been enough. They could have
been gained by retaking Antwerp and dividing the Anglo-
American front and by launching a new battle of France to
seize the Channel coast—precisely the objectives that were
assigned to the Ardennes counteroffensive. In fact, in autumn
1944 the means whereby the reversal of the situation could be
effected was already being prepared in German arsenals. The
U-XXI submarines, capable of remaining underwater for a
long time at great depths and with a speed of sixteen knots,

were already in the slips of the shipyards the year before. And the U-XXIII was much smaller, more treacherous and more maneuverable. In addition, the ME-262 jet fighters and various types of antiaircraft and artillery rockets were already a reality. All these weapons would soon be ready for a series of unexpected and concentrated military operations highly dangerous to the Allies. One hundred and twenty U-XXI and sixty-one U-XXIII submarines were about to be launched shortly before the armistice and the British found several miles of railway cars at Bremen filled with various bits and pieces (manufactured in factories in Silesia) for the assembly of still other submarines. They had, however, arrived a year too late, or perhaps only three months too late, to be used in large formations in the Atlantic and in the Channel that would have seriously compromised Allied supply lines in the crucial winter of 1944–1945."

33. See Combined Intelligence Objectives Sub-committee, *Underground Factories in Central Germany* (Report No. XXXII-17, London, H.M.S.O.), pp. 95–109. A secondary but nevertheless significant example of the astonishing demands made on German industry in the prosecution of the war, despite the catastrophic worsening of the military situation, is offered by the fact that only forty-eight days before the surrender a general meeting on air weaponry was called for March 20 at Bad Eilsen. This was the last of a long series of such meetings, and the technical authorities of the Luftwaffe and the chief designers of Focke-Wulf, Arado, Dornier, Gothaer-Waggonfabrik, Junkers, Horten, and Blohm-Voss were all present. The plans of these firms for the urgent building of a heavy supersonic fighter were examined and discussed at the meeting. This was to be an all-weather night fighter of twelve tons, designed to take the latest types of jet engines and the new seven-barreled machine guns, which had been devised in order to reduce to a fraction of a second the maximum time of "ballistic contact" necessary for an effective enemy hit.

34. In 1949 the American occupation troops emptied the munitions dumps. The year before, an unprecedented—was it

spontaneous?—invasion of tree-killing hymenoptera had literally cut the local forest to the ground, thus revealing all the constructions the Germans had prepared. The Americans did not, however, demolish the U-airfields, since that would have required a quantity of explosive equal to a nuclear explosion. Indeed, the U.S. Air Force command declared at the time that if the Nazis had begun the work only a few months before, the course of the European war would have immediately come to a halt and "in all probability the first atomic bomb would have exploded on the airfields around Landsberg instead of on Hiroshima." In fact, no type of demolition bomb known at the time—not even the monster British "Earthquake Bomb" of 22,000 pounds—would have been able to blast apart that massive concrete armor.

35. This was, perhaps, a secondary application of the results furnished by the research originally conducted at Sigmaringen on radioactive isotopes of the chemical element 85, and it would seem that the grenades were a later development of the Zippermeyer system in so far as it was attempted to mix—with safety for the workers—ordinary molecular explosives, both solid and gaseous, with substances that were highly radioactive over a short period, in order to create, by long-range artillery fire, impassable barrages in front of the principal Allied objectives.

36. In fact, the British secret service had masterfully caused the Nazi attempts to produce "radioactive gases" for the V-6 reprisal weapon to fail completely.

37. After a private exploratory thrust as far as Vienna just before the Soviet attack, Skorzeny reached the new headquarters for his special troops in the environs of Radstadt, in the Salzburg Alps. Inspecting the area, he noted that the local preparations for the famous Redoubt were proceeding sluggishly and, in the circumstances, would require a few more months at the most optimistic guess. Delicate and expensive machinery had been stored for some time in caves and other makeshift hiding places while waiting for their final positions to be made ready. The arsenals dug out of the mountains were empty, the

storerooms still without equipment. From a quick evaluation it was learned that the essential fuel reserves in the gigantic empty or partly empty buried fuel tanks did not total more than a thousand barrels. To have insisted on carrying out Hitler's plans for a defense to the last man would have been pure insanity. Ten days later, the Americans established their headquarters at Kitzbühel.

38. *Cf.* Hoettl, *op. cit.*: "After Field Marshal Model capitulated in the Ruhr basin, the Americans closely interrogated the officers of the captured General Staff in front of a large wall map of the presumed Alpine Redoubt, noting with astonishment that some of the prisoners were unaware of the existence of such a defensive plan and that some even refused to take it seriously." This is, nevertheless, a very weak argument, for it was common knowledge that the German armies in the Ruhr —or rather, as Hitler loved to call it, the Ruhr Redoubt—had orders to prevent or at least slow up as much as possible the Anglo-American penetration of German territory, by fighting, if necessary, to the last man. Therefore there were no pre-established plans for a strategic withdrawal of these units, at least not until the very end, when there was absolutely no possibility of effecting it.

39. And yet on April 10 Hitler had clearly shown his inclination to move to the south of the country, sending the bulk of his household personnel to Berchtesgaden to get his villa, the Berghof, which had been transformed into a fortified mountain refuge, in functioning order. This unexpected decision did not pass unnoticed by British secret agents. The Berghof had already been bombed in sporadic attacks, but on April 26 a heavy R.A.F. raid destroyed it completely. Besides, it must be presumed that Hitler was well aware that preparations for continued resistance in the alpine zone had not got beyond the embryonic stage, since he was, after all, one of the principal people responsible for the extremely indecisive prosecution of the plan. His attitude was, perhaps, influenced by his bitter disappointment in the failure of "his" counteroffensive in the Ardennes and his absurd hope that the Allies would squabble

and have a falling-out. In addition, with the surrender of the army groups in Italy (April 27, 1945) the heart and main source of troops for the Redoubt had practically disappeared. The transfer of various high commands to the Tyrol (Kesselring settled in at Alm on April 20 and General Jodl went to the nearby village of Niedersill with the remnants of the O.K.W.) was only a contingent formality for treating with the Anglo-Americans from a territory that was still nominally German and free. Kesselring sums up his recollections of those anxious days in his memoirs in the following passage: "Facing our fifty-five divisions, whose effectives were reduced to brigade or regiment strength, and ill-equipped and worse armed, were at least eighty-five powerful full-strength divisions abundantly supplied with everything they needed, not to mention that the Luftwaffe had been virtually nonexistent for several months. And the Alpine Redoubt? A great deal has been written about it, but in general it is all nonsense. Even the most essential thing for making it a reality was lacking: mountain troops. In such conditions how would it have been possible to resist the enemy's enormous pressure for any length of time? At the most, it was an attempt to gain time in order to avoid the worst, in other words that the bulk of the Wehrmacht on the Eastern Front should fall prisoner to the Russians. This objective was only partly achieved, but it did keep about half a million German soldiers out of Siberia. The sole military action in the area of the defunct Redoubt (and it was defunct before it was born) was in Villach on May 6, where a few regiments of the XXIV S.S. Alpine Division, the *Karstjäger*, tried to slow up the advance of the Eighth Army into Austrian territory after the surrender of Army Group South in Italy."

40. See H. R. Trevor-Roper, *The Last Days of Hitler* (London, 1945), p. 232.

CHAPTER 6

The Advent of
"Suction Aircraft"

Symptomatically, when the war ended the Foo Fighters disappeared from the skies of a conquered and dismembered Germany. And no one was interested in investigating the "mystery" any longer, for the occupying powers had quite different duties to assign to their air force technicians.

During the second half of 1945 the Russians, Americans, and French quickly set to work dismantling and sending home as part of their share of war reparations the best German scientific equipment—especially their very modern wind tunnels, which could already produce speeds well above that of sound.

The British, too, sent back aeronautical equipment to be installed in the experimental center they were building at Bedford and in the complementary research centers in Australia and

Canada that were occasionally mentioned in the British press with a certain air of mystery and with predictions of "a brilliant future" for them.

Nevertheless, at times the British preferred to have studies of immediate practical interest that had been interrupted by the sudden ending of the war in Germany completed by German technicians themselves (under strict military supervision, as in Darmstadt and Goettingen, for example) and then dismantle the plants and transfer the research staff to England to carry out the industrial application of the projects.[1]

In order to continue research on secret weapons, especially on those they had captured and retained exclusively without their allies' having hard data on them, teams of specialists belonging to the Ministry of Aircraft Production (M.A.P.) ranged up and down western Germany and Austria, filling in the picture of the state of development the Germans had reached in supersonic aircraft and guided missiles. In addition, they saw to it that inventions and documents of the highest interest that had already been sequestered and safely set aside by the T men—who followed on the heels of attacking troops and acted on detailed information supplied by the virtually omnipresent secret agent—were sent back home to England. This traffic had to be carried on with a certain amount of secrecy, to avoid regrettable conflicts over rights and authorities with other occupying powers of the Reich.

Let it be said at once that from this point of view the British were especially favored by the division of Germany into zones of military occupation. In fact, their zone extended from the Dutch frontier to Prussia and centered on the great port of Hamburg. In Austria it included a large part of the eastern alpine massif and therefore enjoyed direct access to the port of Trieste.

The importance of holding well-equipped and efficient ports in the wreckage of the immediate postwar period led the Americans to carve the enclave of Bremen out of the British Zone and to ask the Belgian authorities for the use of the port of Antwerp. They used these ports for repatriating troops being demobilized, supplying those that were remaining to occupy Germany, and sending home a number of V-2 rocket

bombs—found intact in the underground factories in Saxony—
together with thousands of cases containing tons of important
documents taken from the files of industrial firms and military
commands.

The American press never played up these operations, which
in themselves were not very interesting to the general public.
The British press was absolutely mum on them, for the Transport Service was discreetly controlled by a special section of
Intelligence, which distributed material and documents to
Britain, Canada, and Australia, according to the instructions it
received, by falsifying the declarations of the contents of the
cases that were shipped.

CONCERNING SECRET SERVICES
AND OTHER MATTERS

Since the beginning of spring 1944 the British Intelligence
Objectives Sub-committee (B.I.O.S.) had been compiling lists
of experts to be included in the various investigatory teams, so
that every sector of enemy technology would be covered.

One of these teams included professors Ben Lockspeiser and
W. J. Richards, Dr. S. H. Hollingdale, and Captain A. D. Green.
It was concerned with "Pioneering inventions, missiles and
rocket and turbine aircraft."

T. A. Taylor and M. A. Wheeler—also from the Ministry of
Aircraft Production—formed part of another team that was
chiefly searching for thermorefractive materials for gas turbines.

One team, described as being "of a high scientific level,"
remained in the Rhine Palatinate in the French Zone for a
long time. It was believed that Dr. Ernst Westermann, former
director of the F.D.R.P. institutes of Speyer and Saarbrucken,
was in the area and could furnish information on the activity
of the Fireballs.

In general, the experts on the various teams (there were also
mixed Anglo-American and Anglo-Canadian teams) were able
to put their finger unhesitatingly on the objectives to be
"explored." Considering that the state of war had been ended

for only a short time, how was it possible to obtain such accurate information in spite of the rigid barriers set up by the Nazis?

On the Allied side, the undisputed master in the European sector was the British secret service, flanked by the French Deuxième Bureau, which, however, was already in clear decline in 1939, in both its cadres and its activity, because of political interference. Before the war, the Soviet secret service had mainly functioned as a political police force. And the American O.S.S., formed in 1942, had as its principal assignment the countries of the Far East threatened by or involved in Japanese expansionism. No wonder then that the British succeeded in getting the lion's share in the secret division of German scientific booty, beating their allied adversaries in speed and accuracy.

Through various secret sources (aerial photographic reconnaissance, Jewish refugee scientists, favors from neutrals, espionage checks on German deliveries of gasoline to government institutes and military centers, and so on) British intelligence had been aware ever since the end of 1941 that the Germans were working on large flying bombs and on processes to release atomic energy. Knowledge that the Nazis were pressing the Vichy Government to have French industry supply certain synthetic resins particularly resistant to heat and acids, were increasing the production of liquefied gases in France, and were designing ultralight pumps gave further cause for concern.

The British secret service then got the bright idea that it would be possible to find out which German institutes and industries were engaged in avant-garde research and to keep track of them indirectly by selling advanced products to the Germans. At the opportune moment, large formations of bombers could keep those same products—now transformed into deadly weapons—from being used against the Allies. . . .

A dummy corporation called Omnium Société Française des Produits Synthétiques enabled the British to weave a tight network of specialized informers throughout German-occupied Europe. Very soon information began to flow into the London offices of the Intelligence Service, where a large map of

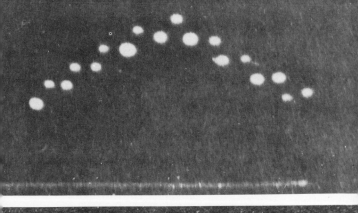

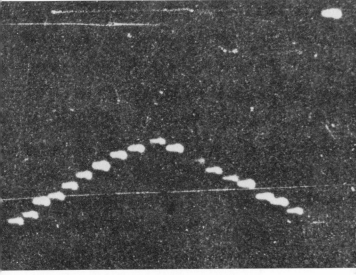

August 30, 1951. The "Lubbock Lights" were photographed at Lubbock, Texas. The U.S. Air Force investigated, concluding that there was "no reason to believe that any of the aerial phenomena commonly described as 'flying saucers' are caused by a foreign power or constitute a clear and present danger to the U.S. or its citizens."

July 16, 1952. This photo was taken by a Coast Guard seaman at the Salem, Massachusetts, Air Station. Rays of light seemed to extend in front of and behind the round objects, which the Air Force announced were "natural phenomena."

November 30, 1954. In Taormina, Sicily, four young men gaze at unidentified flying objects, which remained stationary for several minutes. The U.S. Air Force announced it would investigate these and other objects sighted all over Europe.

(Above) October 16, 1957. An unidentified flying object hovered for fifteen minutes near Holomon Air Development Center, Alamogordo, New Mexico. It was photographed by a government employee. The Aerial Phenomena Research Organization offered no conventional explanation for the object.

(Right) August 3, 1965. TV newsman took this shot of a UFO seventeen miles south of the Texas-Oklahoma border, at 2:00 A.M. Central Standard Time. The night was clear, and there were reports of other sightings in the same area.

(Above) August 3, 1965. In Santa Ana, California a highway investigator who did not believe in flying saucers photographed an object that he estimated was thirty feet in diameter and eight feet thick. It was visible for about fifteen seconds.

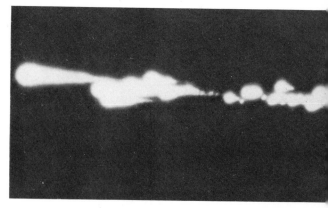

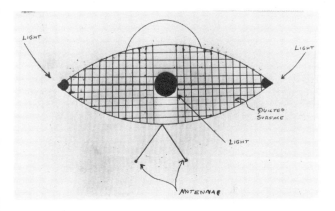

(Above) March 24, 1966. A county sheriff's department drawing illustrates what was observed by farmers and deputies near Ann Arbor, Michigan. Seen zooming, standing still, and landing, it had colored lights in the center and at the edges. *(Below)* April 25, 1966. A Syracuse, New York, *Herald Journal* photographer took the picture of fiery fragments breaking away from a fireball, which flashed across the Northeast.

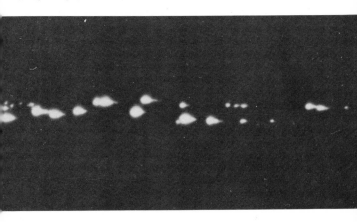

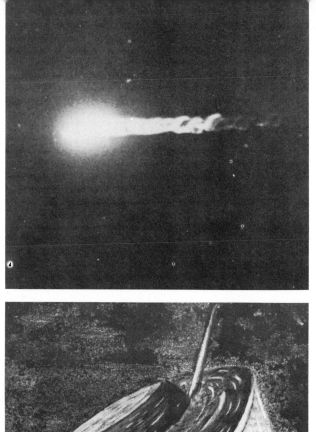

(Left top) April 25, 1966. Fourteen-year-old Dana De-George of Utica, New York (near Syracuse) got this shot of the flaming object at about 8:20 P.M. Thousands of citizens corroborated his viewing of the UFO. *(Left bottom)* April 1966. Dale Spaur was a deputy sheriff when he and four other lawmen saw the object sketched here in the sky. His life was radically altered by the experience and his memories of it are still disturbing.

(Below) January 16, 1967. This hamburger-shaped object was photographed by two brothers just northeast of Detroit. Dr. J. Allen Hynek, chairman of the astronomy department at Northwestern University and an Air Force consultant, stated that it appeared authentic and tended to support similar sightings.

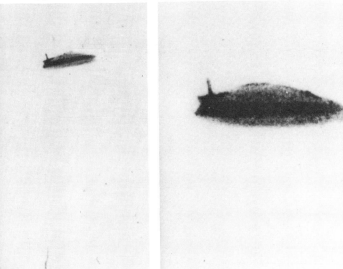

(Above) March 12, 1967. In Las Cruces, New Mexico, a university student took this picture while he was photographing land formations for a geology class. He said the object made no noise and disappeared as he changed plates in his camera.

(Right) March 6, 1967. Knox County, Illinois, Deputy Sheriff Frank Courson made this sketch when he saw an unidentified flying object coming from the southeast. He watched two other objects on March 8, 1967.

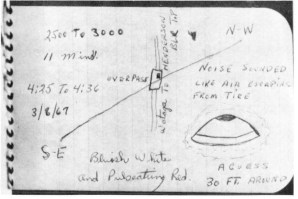

2500 To 3000
11 mind.

4:25 To 4:36
3/8/67

OVERPASS

N-W

NOISE SOUNDED
LIKE AIR ESCAPING
FROM TIRE

S-E   Bluish White
and Pulseating Red.

A GUESS
30 FT. AROUND

(Left) September 5, 1968. Passersby point at a brilliant object spotted over Madrid, Spain. Spanish Air Force planes chased the object but turned back after reaching 50,000 feet. The National Air Ministry said the object attained 90,000 feet.

(Below) March 1968. This picture was taken at a U.S. Missile Range in White Sands, New Mexico, by a newsman for the *Columbus Dispatch*. He reported that the device was at least fifteen feet in diameter and was used in a space testing program during the Mars tests.

December 6, 1968. After various reports of flying objects over remote Peruvian villages were received, a photographer and writer for *La Prensa,* of Lima, Peru, took these pictures of three flying objects near Puno, in southern Peru.

October 18, 1973. Governor John Gilligan of Ohio, and 150 other citizens called law enforcement officers after seeing four strange lights in the sky. The pictures were taken by the *Columbus Evening Dispatch*

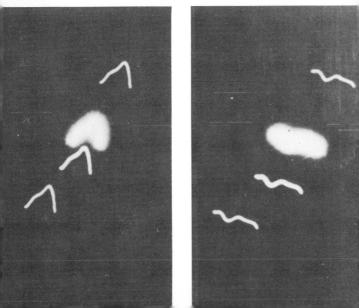

October 19, 1973. A Polaroid photograph of an unidentified flying object seen by architect Hugo Luyo Vega,
thirty-four miles east of Lima, Peru, in a secluded valley
near the Rimac river.

"special objectives" was gradually being filled in. One by one, these objectives were to receive the attentions of R.A.F. bombers, the Commandos, the T Men, and, when the guns fell silent, the teams from M.A.P. and other technically oriented ministries.[2]

One invaluable contribution to the completion of that map was finally furnished when certain S.S. files' were captured.

At the beginning of May 1945 Himmler had moved his general headquarters to Flensburg, near the Danish frontier, once again offering secretly and unsuccessfully to surrender all the German forces on the Western Front in order to be in a better position to oppose the Russian advance in the east. When he saw there was no hope that his crimes would be condoned, and well aware that he was a "war criminal," Himmler fled. By pure accident he fell into the hands of the British. While this diabolic personage was dying from the vial of poison he had bit into, the officials of his disbanded entourage were telling Intelligence Service agents the location of various hiding places in Germany where the most important or most compromising documents were secreted. And so the hunt was on for both the criminals of the Gestapo and the most jealously guarded secrets of German technology.

CHAIN RESIGNATIONS

In the meantime a radical political change was taking place in England as a popular reaction to the burdens of the long war. The elections brought the Labour Party to power. Consequently a small but perfectly legal and democratic political revolution produced by opposing political and economic ideas was added to the technological revolution that had already begun as a result of the sudden advent of jet propulsion and, even more important, nuclear energy.

Resignations, replacements, and changes quickly altered the physiognomy of government circles in the United Kingdom, even in the aircraft sector.

In July 1945 Professor E. M. Frazer left the M.A.P., where he had been a director attached to Lord McGowan's staff, which was entrusted with the development of civil aviation. In December W. S. Farren left as director of the Royal Aircraft Establishment, a position he had held since 1941, and joined the Blackburn Aircraft Company. His place was taken by Professor W. G. A. Perring, who had been a member of a team that specialized in the investigation of strategic missiles. And Air Commodore Frank Whittle, among many others, resigned as a result of disagreements over the new government's policy on developing jet aircraft engines, which he had been the first to create and build in England.

The M.A.P. itself was an emergency creation of the Second World War and the precursor of the German *Jägerstab*. It officially ceased to exist after March 31, 1946, and its functions passed to the Ministry of Supply, a far larger ministry, which then had to supervise the planning of new planes, their production, and even the contracting of aeronautical research. The minister in charge remained John Wilmot, who had been in the Ministry of Aircraft Production and also on the Tube Alloys directorate, the original British organization for atom bomb studies.

The person who most benefited from the power shift was without doubt Sir Ben Lockspeiser. Professor Lockspeiser, M.A., M.I., Mech. E., F.R.Ae. S., was a member of one of the best-qualified teams assigned to investigate the German aeronautical industry in 1943; he then became supervisor of scientific research. In 1945 he became Director-General of Scientific Research (Air) and chief scientist in the new ministry.

AIRCRAFT WITH NO TOMORROW

Under the auspices of John Wilmot, the chiefs of the various divisions of the Ministry of Supply held a series of lectures on July 18, 1946, in the Adelphi Theater in London. It was a semiofficial report to the nation on the theme of scientific research in war and peace. After recounting the contribution the British scientific effort had made to the winning of the war, the conferees set forth the programs for the immediate future in the fields of aviation, ballistic missiles, radio technology, and nuclear energy.

In his introductory talk, Sir John Lennard-Jones, director of the office for the coordination of scientific research, declared that the various fields of research—especially that of aeronautics—were already covered by more than seventeen functioning experimental centers created by or under contract to the Ministry of Supply and that others would later be added.

Finally some encouraging news, most of the conferees thought, ill concealing their inner satisfaction. Nevertheless, there were reasons for apprehension and discontent. The Empire was creaking in an alarming manner after the Pyrrhic victory over Germany. Britain's international prestige had dropped considerably. The United States was "overflowing" everywhere except in the countries being crushed by the equally growing menace of Soviet expansionism. Beyond that, the problems of demobilization, the conversion of war industries to peacetime production, the nationalization of heavy industry—all these in themselves were enough to paint a gray picture of postwar Britain. And as if this were not enough, the American invasion in the field of civil air transport threatened to suffocate once and for all the erstwhile thriving British competition.

This last threat arose out of a special situation. In 1939 the designing of civil aircraft had been suddenly and totally interrupted in England in order to dedicate all the resources of the country to military aviation. In addition, the needs of the "Battle of Britain" demanded that preference be given to single- and twin-engined planes (fighters). This prevailing type of construction had, generally speaking, been maintained subsequently, even after America came into the war. The United States assumed the task of developing mainly bombing planes, multiengined craft that have, as is evident, a number of similarities to civil airliners in transcontinental use.

It took seven or eight years of full-time work to design, construct, and put on the runway a multiengined transport plane. So in order to fill as best it could the gap that had begun widening in 1939, the British aircraft industry created a "provisional" or "emergency" category of transport planes after the war, using the major components from surplus four-engined bombers.

Some pretty good transatlantic planes were patched together

this way (the Avro Tudor and the Avro York), but in payload, speed, and efficiency they could not compare with their American competitors designed expressly for the purpose. What the British needed in order to make up the handicap and avoid rapid paralysis in the delicate sector of international air transport were designs that were fully up to date. It was well known that America was aiming directly at producing giant planes. Great Britain, which was then producing the best aircraft engines in the world, believed that she could do as well as the United States or perhaps even better.

Reacting quickly, the British laid down the Bristol 167 Brabazon I. The plane had eight paired Bristol Centaurus engines producing a total of 20,000 HP, driving three-bladed contrarotating propellers; the wing span was 230 feet; fully loaded the plane weighed 130 tons and carried 100 passengers at a cruising speed of 250 mph. The conservative press called it "our 285,000-pound giant of the airways" in a tone of pride not unmixed with apprehension. Would it be a commercial success or a costly bit of prestige condemned to early eclipse?

"The days when England had to get its planes from America are now over. Indeed, let us hope that, as before, the flow of business will be the other way," Sir Roy Dobson, president of the British Association of Aircraft Manufacturers, is said to have declared euphorically to the press.

Aviation experts began lively debates on cost per flight mile, special runways that would be needed by the giant planes, and the limited number of international airfields capable of handling this sort of machine. Some considered it a triumph of technology, others merely a dangerous adventure.

Opinions were divided, but meanwhile construction continued. In the end it swallowed up twelve million pounds (part of which was spent on fixed investments: hangars, assembly bridges, a reinforced runway), and two million pounds were later spent for the prototype of the Brabazon II, a more powerful model with the first Bristol Proteus turboprops (eight turbine engines producing a total of 25,000 HP, with a cruising speed of 340 mph and a range of about 5,000 miles).

At the beginning of 1950, when it was realized that this type of airplane could be an enormous failure from the point of view of commercial return, it was too late to try to get back any of the allocated funds. And there was little consolation in the almost contemporaneous failure of the gigantic Hughes M.4 Hercules flying boat, a similar project in transoceanic transport developed in California that also proved to be "without a tomorrow."[3]

The mistaken decision to build air giants (the two Brabazon models and the Saunders-Roe SR-45 Princess hydroplane) cost the English taxpayer a good deal, but it did not keep the British from embarking on other "essential" projects.

The directors of the M.A.P. had in fact cold-bloodedly shut off funds from duplicate projects, projects that gave little hope of success, and those that could be replaced with more promising, less costly or more modern projects.

In the list of victims destined to be cut off from government funds there was, to the incredulous surprise of the experts, the supersonic Miles M-52, being prepared by the Miles Aircraft Company of Reading, which had designed it in answer to a secret competition for a thousand-mile-an-hour plane that the Air Ministry had opened in 1943.[4]

And so in February 1946, a few months after the first test flight, the contract with the Miles firm was unilaterally canceled by the government, although the detail designs were 90 percent complete, the assembly jigs ready, and even partial assembly of the plane begun.

The M.A.P. took the responsibility for this serious decision on behalf of the R.A.F., giving as its reason that it would be very uneconomical to continue the original line of approach to matters of supersonic speed with the M-52 project.

Referring to this surprising change in program, Sir Ben Lockspeiser told the London press that the problems of supersonic flight would be solved through the use of rocket-propelled planes.[5]

THE SUPERSONIC ROCKET-PROPELLED VICKERS E-24/43

After going into the matter thoroughly, the aviation editor of the London *Daily Herald* summed up the whole question on September 6, 1946:

"Work on a 1000 mph aeroplane, which has already cost the Ministry of Supply £200,000 and is three-quarters finished, has been abandoned. It has been decided that no experimental aircraft will be flown by a human pilot until it is known precisely what happens at 750 mph, the speed of sound.

" 'We just have not the heart to send any test pilot out into the scientific unknown of supersonic speeds,' says Sir Ben Lockspeiser, Chief of the Ministry of Supply aeronautical scientists. . . . The official explanation given by the Ministry of Supply for the cancellation of the contract is: 'Other avenues of research are being explored.'

"These 'other avenues' include a spectacular radio-controlled craft which will probably be flown this year. It is expected to give Britain the first practical secrets of supersonic flight."

Wind-tunnel experiments proved to be unreliable when the wind velocity approached that of sound (1087 feet per second at sea level) because the test chamber then became crisscrossed by bands of shock waves that changed the conditions of the wind current of the model being experimented on. As a consequence, Vickers-Armstrong-Supermarine—builders of the famous Spitfire—had decided in 1943 to prepare flying models equipped with rocket engines. The higher-ups in the M.A.P. suggested that they use the M-52 configuration in one-third scale. Cessation of work on the plane coincided with the start of this new cycle of research.[6]

The Vickers rockets were attached to the belly of a De Havilland *Mosquito* light bomber, which released them at 35,000 feet at a speed of 400 mph. At the moment of release an automatic pilot kept the model in a glide for fifteen seconds until it reached 30,000 feet. At this point the rocket cut in and in eighteen seconds accelerated the model to the speed of sound and in seventy seconds brought it up to its theoretical maximum of 875 mph. After this, the fuel having been used up, the speed dropped rapidly and the automatic pilot put the model into a steep dive into the sea. During the short time that the model was traveling at supersonic speeds, a radio apparatus transmitted data on the aerodynamic behavior of the contours of the model and the functioning of its propulsive system to a ground station.

The tests took place in the vicinity of the Scilly Islands, off the coast of Cornwall, along a fifteen-mile flight path, and the rockets were tracked by radar into the open Atlantic. Although the tests were scheduled to start at the end of 1946, it was not until March 1947 that the R.A.F. received the first models of the Vickers rockets. They weigh 800 pounds fully loaded, so they were fairly large but not spectacularly so.

In early November the first rocket was tested, with mediocre results. It had been damaged in transit to Cornwall and was unable to do any better than 600 mph.

There followed a series of failures for various causes, and it was not until January 1949 that one of the models (the fifth in the series) finally operated perfectly, reaching Mach 1.36, equivalent to 1,035 mph. There was no further information because the testing cycle was over.

No public announcement was made—which was very consistent of the Director-General. In April 1947 Sir Ben Lockspeiser had brusquely told journalists who were besieging him for news: "This new plane is not a weapon but a flying laboratory of interest only to a few scientists. The dates of the tests will be kept as secret as possible because this kind of research does not thrive on publicity."

"SUCTION"

In the meantime the Miles company, which had put all its hopes in the M-52 project, was wrecked in the stormy waters of postwar British aviation. In 1948 Handley-Page took over whatever survived the bankruptcy, founding a new firm, Handley-Page Reading, Ltd., while the directors of the old Miles company formed the small company of F. G. Miles, Ltd., for the construction of light training and private planes.

Thus the first British company to conduct in-flight experiments on the secrets of suction of the boundary layer—a milestone in the development of flying saucers—disappeared from the scene. Willy-nilly, the company had been led into the study of these secrets while its main line of work suffered.

Here we must introduce a brief aside on what the boundary

layer is and how it is controlled. This explanation must of necessity be oversimplified and overconcise. Oily substances flow slowly because they are highly viscous. Air also is viscous, but to a degree four or five thousand times less than oil. Viscosity is manifested as a sort of friction in the molecules that hinders the free running of the fluid flow, generating imperceptible moving stratifications of decreasing speeds as the flow moves in from the free atmosphere and approaches the walls of the swept body. Everyone is familiar with, for example, the variations in the speed of water flowing through a canal. Only the central portion flows swiftly. At the edges, the water is almost stationary.

The layers of air that are influenced in varying degrees by the walls of the body moving through it are known as the boundary layer. An airplane, therefore, drags along with it a sort of mantle of air that is continuously renewed after being uselessly accelerated up to the speed of the flight (and then left behind), to the detriment of the propulsive power of the plane.

No matter what the speed of the aircraft, at normal altitudes the thickness of the boundary layer at the leading edge of the body is always less than one millimeter and the strata of air that make it up lie evenly on one another (the laminar boundary layer). Then, at a certain distance from the leading edge, depending on the extent of streamlining, its conformation changes and it becomes turbulent. At this point the thickness of the boundary layer increases sharply because the strata of air mingle violently to form a turbulent wake at the rear; this wake is similar to the one we can actually see following a ship because of the greater density of the medium it is traveling through.

Starting from the point at which it thickens (called the transition point), the natural microscopic eddying increases beyond its proper value and gives rise to a growing, excessive dissipation of energy. In other words, the aerodynamic resistance of the body increases.

It seems clear, therefore, even to a layman in aeronautics that the objective should be to move the point of transition as far to the rear of the moving body as possible in order to minimize the expenditure of motive energy required to propel the body through the air. This is especially true in high-speed flight, since the power required increases at about the cube of the speed.

The physical concept of the "boundary layer" was first delineated by Professor Ludwig Prandtl at Göttingen in 1904. Nevertheless, for many years—until about 1937, when both in Germany and in England aerodynamics specialists began full-sized experiments with specially equipped or planned planes —research on controlling the boundary layer was conducted without any coordination between the technologists and the industrialists in the area of practical applications.[7]

In addition, the research had a single, relatively modest aim, for it was limited to the boundary layer of conventional wing surfaces. In other words, the experimenters were trying to eliminate the "sacs of dead air" along the top wing surface that at low speeds (normally, at take-off and landing) cause dangerous crises in the lift of the wings.

This could and can be obtained in two different ways. With the method of "blowing" the boundary layer, the dead air is pushed aside by a tiny stream of compressed air continuously forced through slots so placed as to affect the point of transition. With "suction" the dead air is sucked into the wing itself, through tiny holes or slots, and then expelled by a pump located within the fuselage.

Blowing and suction are the techniques that have been investigated most; they are also the simplest and oldest techniques for controlling the boundary layer.

SUCTION WINGS

The experiments of the Miles Company in controlling the boundary layer began in 1936 with wind tunnel tests conducted on the wing section from one of their planes called the Whitney Straight. Encouraging results induced the experimenters to work on full-size models. Consequently, in 1937, with the assistance of the Air Ministry, which had got wind of similar German work, Miles modified a twin-engined M-8

Peregrine monoplane for the Royal Aeronautical Establishment (R.A.E.).[8]

The original plane was a light civilian transport carrying six passengers and with provision for two pilots seated side by side. After the internal structure was gutted, most of the top surface of the wing was recovered with perforated aluminum sheeting. Seven continuous very broad and shallow longitudinal canals, running almost the entire length of the half-wing, conducted the air that had been sucked in from the surface to the fuselage where a 10-HP Ford automobile engine ran the pump that sucked in the boundary layer.

The Miles rig was more or less the same as that of the contemporary German experimental plane, the Junkers AF-1 *Absauge Flugzeug*, designed expressly for the Aerodynamische Versuchsanstalt (A.V.A.) of Göttingen.

The data that the German experiment yielded are now well known from their publication by the American National Advisory Committee for Aeronautics (N.A.C.A.), but information about the British results has been kept restricted. Apparently all we know is that flight tests indicated that aerodynamic resistance was lowered by 22 percent.

The Miles firm did not really carry its researches on the possibilities of this very important principle all the way. After having worked out this brilliant stroke, for various reasons—the inherent difficulties in the pumping mechanism, the advent of wing flaps, the drying up of government funds—it returned to traditional designs. In this area, however, better equipped and more powerful companies competitively barred its road and finally drove it into bankruptcy.

On the other hand, the German researches prospered. In 1937 at the A.V.A. in Göttingen professors Betz and Ackeret and the engineers Stüper, Schrenk, Holstein, Schwier, and Wöchner, with the aid of a host of other experts, conducted a test flight of the AF-1, a light high-wing monoplane equipped with a 200-HP engine. It had only one slot for sucking in the dead air. Opposite the hinges of the movable wing surfaces, the slot ran along the entire length of the wing span. Inside the fuselage, directly under the point where the wings were attached to the fuselage, an auxiliary 20-HP engine ran a propeller fan to suck in that part of the boundary layer that could improve lift.

Generally speaking, the flight experiments confirmed what had already been noted—that the lift of "sucked wings" increases in proportion to the quantity of air sucked in up to a lift factor of 4. The maximum value of the lift factor for a normal airfoil often does not exceed 0.5. After that the mass of air that must be moved grows more rapidly than the lift, making it impractical to reach factors above 6. In any case, even with the factor limited to 4, the lift of the original airfoil was increased by eight times!

An improved version, the AF-2, was powered with a 270-HP engine and equipped with a 45-HP fan run off the same engine. At full throttle the fan could suck in 250 cubic feet of air per second. This made it possible in 1940–1942 to achieve, efficiency being equal, a lift factor of 5, an exceptionally high figure for a low-powered single-engine plane.

Rapid calculations by the A.V.A. technical experts revealed that for a multiengined plane of thirty tons with a wing area of 1000 square feet and a lift factor of 4, approximately 2100 cubic feet of air per second would have to be sucked in on landing. In those days, when most people considered the modern air-eating turbojet a utopian vision, this was truly an impressive figure.[9] Indeed, there was speculation to the effect that a huge 250-300-HP fan would have to be carried on the plane to suck in the dead air.

Complementary researches on thin airfoils, which were becoming more and more common with increasing speeds, especially in military planes, immediately made clear the practical difficulties of installing suction plants inside them. The slots on the top surface, the air collectors, and the channeling from wing to pump would in fact have had to share what little free space there was on the inside of the wing with the various complicated internal installations (retractible undercarriage, fuel tanks, weapons, ammunition, position lights, pipes, wires, and various trusses) that are generally situated even in the thinnest "razor-edge" wings of today's supersonic fighters.[10]

The AF models were very slow planes, however, and it was

decided to use them to study the behavior of suction during take-off and landing, operations that are performed at relatively low speeds by all planes. Those who backed the building of such planes were mostly trying to obtain high coefficients of lift, and in fact their hopes were not disappointed.

Nevertheless, it was known for some time that control of the boundary layer can also exercise a helpful influence on the penetration drag of the wings and indeed on all surfaces, fuselage included. This was to be translated into an increase in speed.[11]

A.V.A. DEVELOPMENTS AND PROJECTS

In the test flights with the AF planes another finding emerged: the necessity to preserve the volumetric efficiency of the intake pump for flight speeds that were slightly above the minimum speed.

Suppose, the German technicians said, we increased the force of the suction slightly—reducing it to the proper amount at low speeds—couldn't we design a plane with a very small wing area that would offer little resistance and therefore be capable of very high speeds? Or perhaps add a hundred miles an hour or so to conventional planes?

Both at Göttingen and at the L.F.A.'s wind tunnel in Volkenrode, research on suction became definitely oriented toward high-speed flight.

For some time supercharging by means of a centrifugal compressor driven by the engine itself had been common practice with piston engines. By using the compressor as a suction pump, the Messerschmitt ME-109G modified fighter flew a number of experimental flights. The flights demonstrated, however, the difficulties in reconciling the different volumetric capacities required by the two devices, and this dissuaded the technicians from extending the principle to the production series.

In the meantime, it was experimentally established that suction through an opening placed to the rear of a transsonic shock wave could slow down the sharp increase in aerodynamic resistance by approximately Mach 0.1, so that a plane designed to fly 900 kph would be able, the power installed being equal, to reach the fateful goal of 1000 kph. To attain this result a single-seater fighter would have to suck in from 565 to 812 cubic feet of air per second—a capacity that was of the same order as that sucked in by the first internal combustion turbines.[12]

In 1944 professors Prandtl and Busemann sketched out preliminary plans for a high-speed fighter—which never got beyond the design stage—in which the boundary layer was sucked in along the wing span and discharged against the sides of the fuselage through a narrow, half-moon-shaped orifice in such a way as to "blow" the tail boundary layer of the stabilizer area.

Gradually the Aerodynamische Versuchsanstalt technical experts of the L.F.A. reached different but interesting conclusions.

The first was that *it was not advantageous to transform ordinary aircraft into planes with a controlled boundary layer* because the suction principle was deprived of its best attributes and the difficulties of construction did not compensate for the limited advantages. (If this were not the case, we would not have today those special types of UFO commonly called "flying discs.")[13]

In addition, it was demonstrated that inasmuch as they were planning a special turbine-powered project, it would have been advantageous *to combine the two mechanisms into a single whole by feeding the turbine with air taken from the wing orifices* instead of by means of the usual forward-ram air intakes.

The outcome of the research is not officially known. This does not, of course, mean that there were no results! Whichever ally got it in his war booty may perfectly well be keeping it a secret today for some sound reason. It seems, in fact, that by reworking the old experiments on "potential frictionless current," the German technical experts may in the final days have succeeded experimentally in reducing aerodynamic friction on appropriately shaped bodies to very low values. And since it was known from results supplied by the Italian supersonic wind tunnel at Guidonia that while wave resistance to high

Mach numbers varies roughly in proportion to speed, frictional resistance increases almost as the square, certain rumors making the rounds at the end of 1944 about the imminent appearance of some new types of highly efficient and very fast planes, "moving through the air like a sponge through water and completely different from anything ever seen before," began to be listened to seriously.[14]

In addition, something less vague had already leaked out in France just before the German collapse in Normandy. There was talk of the feverish preparation of strange fighters powered by special turbines, without any wing or tail surfaces whatsoever and even without the usual air intakes, so that in scientific circles in Strasbourg it was thought to be a kind of new piloted rocket being prepared to take off from some well-hidden fastness in the Black Forest to send the Allied bombers scurrying off.

Similar rumors circulating among the higher-ups of the Luftwaffen-Motor Lager of Gallarate, in Italy, had it, however, that they were not rockets and that the planes would at first be radio controlled.

Does one have to be an experienced technical expert to recognize in all this certain details common to the sudden appearance of the *Kugelblitz* fighter as well as to the sightings of flying saucers in successive years?

STATIC INTAKE JETS

In the immediate postwar period Professor M. Sedille examined the question from a scientific point of view and at the first Congress of French Aviation gave a talk that was rich with original observations.[15]

In sum, Sedille declared that it would be advantageous to *expel the air that had been sucked in after having charged it with a speed equal and opposite to that of the flight of the plane, increasing thereby the propulsive force, for in this way the expenditure of energy required for flight would be reduced to one third.*

"Naturally, the necessary substitution of ram air intakes

with static intakes would make the advantage nonabsolute," he went on, "because supplementary mechanical compression of the air in exchange for the spontaneous one supplied by ram intake would be required in jet planes. *Besides, it would be very difficult with planes of conventional shape to extend suction to the entire external surface of the plane.* However, the method could make the use of jet propulsion worthwhile even at very low speeds, by replacing, that is, present very costly forms of 'jet lift.'"

Other theoretical calculations relative to the basic case of the flat sheet lowered the amount of energy required for propulsion to one-seventh. Now the game was indeed worth the candle!

But French plane designers paid no attention to Sedille's proposals. They continued developing conventional planes, and two years later, in 1948, in the *Comptes Rendus de l'Académie des Sciences* of Paris, Professor Maurice Roy "demonstrated," likewise mathematically, how illusory the proposal was.[16]

The negative conclusions of Professor Roy, a genuine aeronautical luminary, were based on the well-taken premise that if the aerodynamic resistance of the other parts of the plane not subject to the suction process (fuselage, rudder, cockpit) were to be balanced, such great quantities of air would be required that it would have to be taken from the free air well beyond the boundary layer of the wing. That was and would remain costly and difficult. For example, the wings of a modern single-seater fighter produce no more than 35 to 40 percent of the total resistance developed by the entire plane, and they are so thin that they do not permit moving large quantities of air with an internal velocity advantageously reduced with respect to that of the movement of the plane.

Would it now be necessary to give up the idea of "macrosuction," *i.e., suction extended to all the surfaces brushed by the wind of the flight?*

The answer is *no, certainly not, provided that everything that is not a "wing" or a surface with equivalent functions is eliminated by hiding or fusing it with the wing in the manner of "flying-wing" planes.*

We note that, except for the transparent dorsal bubble, flying saucers do not expose any non-wing element to the "apparent wind" in their high-speed flight.

A COMBINATION

At the time of the last prewar researches on control of the boundary layer, which were very promising in view of the reduction of the internal space required, a combination of suction and blowing appeared. It was also tested with modest success at the Italian aeronautical experimental center in Guidonia, where full-scale experiments had begun when the Italian surrender on September 8, 1943, interrupted all remaining research work.

In Germany, during the war, only the Arado and Dornier firms made experimental bombers (the AR-232/A and the DO-24) with short take-off and landing runs and with high lateral stability obtained by means of the "combined" system. The boundary layer was sucked in through continuous slots near the hinges of the ailerons (the A.V.A. method) and the air was then blown onto the ailerons by a small electric pump located in the wing.

After the war the American firm of Grumman reduced the landing runs of F-9 and F-4 planes on aircraft carriers by 50 percent by using the combined system. Cessna built a large number of light touring planes by applying the same principle in a more simplified form.[17] One of these, a two-seater engaged in taking aerial photographs in the vicinity of Pasadena, California, on January 3, 1956, encountered three circular planes having a diameter of about fifty feet, giving off a shiny orange glow from their undersides.

Dropping down to the altitude of the Cessna (about 4000 feet), within thirty seconds they flew around it in a wide circle, maintaining a distance of three or four miles. From a quick calculation, they were flying at an average of not less than 1800 mph. After widening the circle, one of the UFOs encountered a long, thin cloud layer as it was flying away and cut it almost exactly in two, producing a very clean break.

"It left a hole as if it had sucked up the cloud!" the pilots said. In fact, for a few moments the wake of the ship became visibly vaporous.

Could anyone deny that intense aerial suction was employed in the flight of the mysterious aircraft?

Two types of aircraft met that day, both using the same principle. Rudimentary in the Cessna, highly advanced in the UFO. The caterpillar and the butterfly . . .

NOTES

1. See Sir Roy Fedden, "Inquest on Chaos," *Flight* (London, November 29, 1945) pp. 575–578.

2. For example, the planned missions agreed on between the B.I.O.S. and the M.A.P. envisaged at the beginning of 1945 visiting some fifty-two German aeronautical research and production centers. In practice, it was possible to "explore" only thirty-three of them because the postwar distribution of areas of military administration excluded the British from certain areas of interest to them.

3. Somewhat bigger than the Brabazon, the Hercules had eight Pratt and Whitney Wasp Major engines for a total of 28,400 HP, a 300-foot wing span, weighed 226 tons fully loaded, and was to carry 700 passengers. The plane was conceived in 1942 as air transport for thirty- to sixty-ton tanks, heavy artillery, or entire troop formations. When the expenses for the original project exceeded $18 million, the American government canceled the contract. The builder—the capricious Howard Hughes, a very wealthy flyer and movie producer— then decided to continue the project at his own expense. By 1947 the Hercules had absorbed a total of $25 million. The newspapers reported as follows: "In American aviation circles the final word on the largest airplane in the world is anxiously awaited. There are two groups: one thinks that the M-4 will never get off the water or at the best after a hop of a cou-

ple of yards will sink forever; the other thinks that the plane is opening a new era in the field of transcontinental air transport." They were both mistaken. After an awkward test flight about a hundred feet above the water, the "birchwood giant," as skeptics sarcastically called it, was abandoned as too difficult and too expensive to fly. For some time it lay on the wharf between Los Angeles and Long Beach, before being scratched off the list of American flying matériel.

4. The government designation was E-24/43. The supersonic Miles M-52 was supposed to reach 1000 mph at about 35,000 feet. The engine was a gas turbine with a large after-burner, designed and built by Power Jets Ltd. Twenty-four feet long and with a maximum diameter of three and a half feet, this special jet engine took up virtually the entire fuselage. The trapezoidal wing (with a span of 26 feet and only 107 square feet of surface) was not swept back, a configuration that used to be considered indispensable for very fast planes. In order to keep the maneuverability of the plane within a reasonable margin at low speeds, it had been designed with a wing aspect ratio close to that of normal wings (while the M.A.P. specifications called for a wing aspect ratio approaching the figure one). This further contributed to the Ministry of Supply's decision to give preference in the area of winged aircraft to the delta wings that the A. V. Roe company of Manchester had meanwhile designed. The wing tips were diagonally truncated so as to reduce the marginal wave resistance (according to the Busemann scheme) and the symmetrical biconvex airfoil was exceedingly thin and had thin leading and trailing edges. The tail surfaces were designed to be entirely movable and worked by servo-assists with powerful servo-motors because of the aerodynamic loads on them, which were in the neighborhood of a hundred times the load on the tail of the heaviest plane in service at the time. The pressurized cabin could be ejected from the fuselage on command, to permit the pilot to get free of the plane even at supersonic speeds if necessary. Plastic explosive cartridges inserted in the tubular supports joining the cabin to the fuselage and electrically discharged were supposed to sever the frame, thus separating the cabin from

the body of the plane. A large parachute would automatically be released and brake the fall of the cabin to the point where the pilot could jump out of it and use his own personal 'chute.

5. This unexpected decision, however, had precedents. In January 1945 the aeronautical engineers S. P. Hutton and H. E. Gamble began a series of tests with solid models of the M-52 in the subsonic wind tunnel of the Royal Aeronautical Establishment. The final report, which was written in July but not printed until five years later, concluded its account of the aerodynamic research with an observation from calculated data that "at high Mach numbers the plane could be unstable." If not wholly negative, the verdict was clearly not very sanguine, and it marked the decline of the Miles approach, which ended with the firm's collapse just when certain German war designs (the supersonic D.F.S.-Siebel planes) seemed to promise superior operational qualities.

6. The devices constructed by the Vickers engineers were small rocket planes formed of a cylinder of steel sheet with removable caps at either end. They were eleven feet long, with a single cantilever wing having an eight-foot span. With its symmetrical biconvex airfoil as on the real plane, the wing was a solid wood construction composed of a number of plies of pressure-glued mahogany. The edges were reinforced with light alloy sheathing and had normal ailerons for maneuvering. The tail assembly was made of wood "improved" with birch, but only the leading edge of the rudder was reinforced with light alloy sheathing. The armoring also served as the radio antennae, the wing sheathing for the receiver, and the rudder sheathing for the transmitter. The interior of the cylinder contained the tanks for liquid C and liquid T and for compressed air; the automatic pilot; the radio receiver; the transmitter; the small rocket engine. The ailerons and the elevators had servo-controls operated by compressed air and commanded by the automatic pilot. (This system had already been successfully employed by the Germans on the V-1 flying bombs.) The rudder was fixed for straight-line flight. At the front were the Pitot tube for measuring speed and the balancing weights.

The switch for the electric installation was centrally located and easily accessible. The propulsion of the machine was obtained via diergolic (*i.e.*, two-liquid) propulsion: liquid C (34 liters of methyl alcohol with a 30-percent solution of hydrazine hydrate and 20 percent of water) and liquid T (54.5 liters of hydrogen peroxide with 20 percent water)—generally used in the German antiaircraft rockets. The combustion chamber was a light metal cylinder seventeen and a half inches long and four and three-quarters inches in diameter. In order to eliminate the necessity of cooling the walls, they were lined internally with a layer of carbon cement two inches thick, mixed with a special ceramic binder. The thickness of the cylinder was further increased at the rear end in such a way as to form the narrow section of the exhaust nozzle. When the construction was completed, the weight of the craft was about 500 pounds dry and about 800 pounds fully loaded. Parallel with the small series of rockets for the Royal Aeronautical Establishment (R.A.E.), Vickers also prepared different types of fuselages and wings for their own experiments toward achieving the best wing shapes and arrangements, according to eighteen different dispositions arrived at in the design stage. In addition, there were also "V" or "butterfly" wings (in technical parlance, frontal dihedral wings), to which the firm's experts attached a great deal of importance. It seems that it was also intended to equip the devices with a remote control of the type perfected for air-launched guided projectiles for precision fire against targets fifteen to eighteen miles away. This gave origin to a type of self-propelled projectile midway between planing bombs and flying bombs, but it had no practical results. In 1950 the Supersonic Division of the Flight Section of the Royal Aeronautical Establishment compiled in report A.R.C. No. 2,835 all the data furnished by the "flight trials of a rocket-propelled transsonic research model: the RAE Vickers Rocket Model," which remained a classified document until 1954.

7. During that long period of time the Göttingen "school" and the aeronautical faculty of the University of Cambridge stood

out above all. A systematic series of physical and mathematical investigations was carried out between 1919 and 1936 at Cambridge under the direction of Professor Melville Jones and with the assistance of Professor G. J. Taylor. The fresh ideas that were produced resulted in several patents. Some were by the noted German designer Lippisch, the Canadian engineer Stenstone, the British firm of Bristol (1936), and one by Air Commodore Whittle (1938) based on the adoption of a rudimentary gas turbine. There were still others but none of them ever became a reality. The main reason for their failure—apart from the aircraft industry's lack of interest—was that they used the residual energy in the exhaust gases of a piston engine (for blowing) or the slight vacuum developed during the intake stroke (for suction). But the few patents envisaging the use of turbines always ran into the ever present problem that there was absolutely no usable turbine orifice with long-wearing qualities and the ability to function with an acceptable degree of thermal efficiency. Another insurmountable barrier was the minimal advantages offered by limited application of the principle. The limitation still holds today within the range of conventional aircraft, for reasons that will shortly become clear.

8. See F. G. Miles, "Sucking Away the Boundary Layer: Results of some Full-Scale Flying Experiments," *Flight* (London, No. 1,570, January 26, 1939), pp. 82b–82d. For some time the Royal Aeronautical Establishment had a staff of specialized researchers in suction at its disposal. After the R.A.E. had completed and then filed the researches conducted with the Miles firm, it took up the wind tunnel studies again with reduced-size wing sections. In one of the most successful experiments —on a symmetrical airfoil derived from the National Advisory Committee for Aeronautics' development, NACA-0020, but with a single suction slot on the top surface that extended along 50 percent of the chord—a 60 percent reduction of aerodynamic resistance was achieved. (*Cf.* A.R.C., Report No. 1,913, published in 1943.) The long series of studies on "humped" airfoils—of which we shall have more to say—having failed in practice, together with the ever higher speeds reached by jets,

then focused the attention of government experts on the problems of swept and delta wings. A reawakening of interest in the problems of suction—based, however, on traditional concepts—has been shown in more recent times with the work of Dr. Lachmann of Handley-Page Ltd. In the spring of 1956 the left wing of a DH-113 night fighter was modified with the application of a perforated "glove" along the center line of the top surface. In flight, a local reduction of 82 percent in the surface-friction drag was obtained in this way and consequently *the drag of the wing was reduced to less than one-fifth.* Nevertheless, the energy gain rapidly fell off with the increase in speed, because of the dropping off of the degree of kinematic viscosity, once again confirming the axiom that the conformation of present-day aircraft does not lend itself to the full exploitation of the principle. For a concise examination of the most recent developments see S. Caldara, *"Le ricerche in Gran Bretagna sul controllo dello strato limite,"* Alata Internazionale (Milan, July 1967), pp. 31–32.

9. To give an example, the powerful Wright 18-BD "Cyclone" twin-radial of 2500 HP at take-off aspirates eight to nine pounds of air per second at full throttle, equivalent in round figures to not more than 100 to 125 cubic feet.

10. Now as then, between the powerful and violent suction of the jet engine and the removal of the boundary layer (especially if continued and extended) there is a series of not insignificant difficulties that are epitomized principally by the need to work with more rows of slots along the chord. These slots would have to be opened or closed as needed in order to make the suction zone coincide with the transition point; in other words, suction would have to take place where the actual separation of the fluid vein is observed—and this point, moreover, shifts with the angle of incidence. The slots would in addition have to be rather narrow—not exceeding $0.031''$— otherwise the volume of the sucked air would be excessive at the expense of the efficiency of the installation. The "velocity of suction" and the quantity of "dead air" sucked in would, however, have to increase in direct proportion to flight speed.

(That is, in the jargon of the technical experts, it is necessary to strengthen the aerodynamic effect of the "downcast shaft.") Unfortunately, as speed increases the wings become proportionately thinner and their slight internal volume does not lend itself well to the installations of the wide, straight, hermetically sealed channels necessary for the undisturbed, slow removal of the air that has been sucked in. To improve a plane's total coefficient of aerodynamic penetration, it would be necessary to extend the suction of the boundary layer to the entire upper surface of the wing and to the first third of the fuselage. (The rear portions, including the tail assembly, could be blown.) But even this solution entails cumbersome installations, all of them essential: cockpit, engine, main fuel tank, heavy arms and ammunition, radio, radar, a profusion of tubing and wires, from which it is clear that the "integral" solution is practically impossible with the present types of cross-shaped planes with wings and tail assemblies.

11. In 1932, for his researches on "sucked wings," the engineer Oskar Schrenk had constructed a model of a wing about nine and three-quarters inches thick, containing tiny fans operating on three-phase asynchronous motors, at first with a single slot on the upper surface and later with multiple slots. The second approach gave the German scientist the first confirmation of the fact that the movement of the air current along the wing for a determined value of suction was almost identical with the theoretical shape of the "potential frictionless flow." The same deductions were later extended by analogy to the moving bodies (three-dimensional) differing from the airfoils (two-dimensional).

12. The German turbojets of the Junkers-Jumo 004 series—mounted on the famous ME-262 fighters—when static sucked in about forty-four pounds of air per second. In 1946 German aerodynamic researches, especially the studies on combining turbojet propulsion with control of the boundary layer, were demonstrated to British experts by Professor R. Smelt during an interesting lecture at the Royal Aeronautical Society, in which part of the German illustrative material, which had been

restricted for reasons of military security, became public. (See *Flight,* London, October 17 and 24, 1946.)

13. This observation remains valid today, having been proved by the results of a recent American experiment. See A. Gattin, *"Un esperimento ancora troppo costoso: l'aereo con ala aspirate,"* Nuove Ali, Rome, XVIII (1966), No. 5/6, pp. 35-37. In the experimental Northrop X-21A—a complete transformation and adaptation of the Douglas WB-66D Destroyer, a light bomber—a double installation enclosed in two pods under the wings removes 60 percent of the boundary layer from the 1216 square feet of wing area by means of two low-pressure compressors, while the remaining part is sucked away by back-up high-pressure compressors (which also receive the mass of air sucked away by the low-pressure compressors) and carried to the internal combustion turbines which drive the compressors and whose exhaust contributes to the propulsion of the plane (which is principally taken care of by two J-79-13 turbojets located in the tail). This complicated process is matched by considerable complexity in the structure of the wing, which requires almost three miles of very fine slots in the wing with a width of from .003″ to .009″ (very difficult to make with current machinery) and about 800,000 holes ranging from a quarter to a sixteenth of an inch in diameter to move the air from the collection channels underneath the slots to the main piping bringing the air to the intakes. All this in order to guarantee—at a cruising speed of Mach 0.85 at 27,000 feet— a 60 percent increase in range or a 19 percent increase in gross take-off weight, which is about thirty-six tons. Interesting improvements, but not compelling. Indeed, despite the fact that the plane is in itself a mechanical jewel, not a single significant step has been taken to put the formula in actual production since April 18, 1963, when it was first flown.

14. *Cf.* B. Regenscheit, "Drag Reduction by Suction of the Boundary Layer Separated behind Shock Wave Formation at High Mach Numbers," *NACA Technical Memorandum No. 1168* (Washington, 1947), p. 13; and D. W. Horder, H. H. Pearcey, and G. E. Gaddy, "The Interaction Between Shock

Waves and Boundary Layers," Aeronautical Research Council Current Paper No. 180 (H.M.S.O., London, 1955), p. 50. See also NACA Technical Report No. 3223 (Washington, 1954). The importance of reducing aerodynamic friction is especially evident in prolonged supersonic flight and even more so in hypersonic flight. By lessening the overheating of the wall resulting from the kinetic effect, it would be possible to employ metal alloys lighter and less costly than stainless steel and titanium, thereby contributing as well to the most economical solution to the complex problem of supersonic commercial air transportation.

15. See Prof. M. Sedille, *"Propulsion par réaction en combinaison avec l'aspiration de la couche limite,"* Technique *et Science Aéronautique* (Paris, No. 4, 1946), pp. 229–302.

16. *Cf.* Prof. Maurice Roy, *"Sur la propulsion par regenération de la couche limite,"* Comptes Rendus de l'Académie des Sciences (Paris, November 8, 1949).

17. In the Cessna 170 monoplane there are in fact no mechanical pumps to remove the "dead air." The removal is effected by mixing ducts fed by a compressed hot air generator installed in the fuselage behind the pilot. The trailing edges of the outboard wing are "blown," while those of the inboard wing are "sucked." The principle is obviously original, but it is limited to only one-sixth of the wing surface and therefore does not lend itself to intense suction over the whole wing. However, it can give some idea of the complexity of the problems related to the "control of the boundary layer."

CHAPTER 7

A Time of
Spectacular Possibilities

It is certainly no exaggeration to say that the so-called UFO
question literally exploded in the United States in 1952.

Five years had passed since the first sightings, but no substantial change had taken place in the situation. Indeed, the
Air Force's continuous denials had ended by confusing even
those who were determined not to be hoodwinked.

In the concert of conflicting opinions there were those who
remembered when Captain Ruppelt took over the A.T.I.C.'s
commission of inquiry. In one of the press conferences that
accompanied the event, Ruppelt had hesitantly brought up the
hypothesis that the Russians might have discovered such completely new aerodynamic concepts as to make the fantastic
performance of the discs possible. But Ruppelt had so hedged
his statement with ifs and buts that the hypothesis was rendered almost unacceptable from the start. He overdid it, men-

oning the panic in Air Force circles toward the end of the summer of 1947 that arose precisely because of the growing suspicion that "someone" (the Russians were first choice) had found some new principle or method of aerial propulsion lying ready-made in Germany or had invented or accidentally discovered something radically new.

In actual fact, the "new" principle, as we have seen, was an old veteran of the mechanics of flight, nearly half a century old if we go back to its first elementary formulation. Moreover, in the past, American experts themselves had more than once underlined the alluring possibilities that control of the boundary layer offered to aviation.

In 1931, during some wind-tunnel experiments on various types of hyperlift wings, the engineer Millard J. Bamber obtained for the first time negative drag coefficients because the air flowing out of the top surface slot (in this case by "blowing") took such an active part in the aerodynamic process that it pushed the wing model against the wind.[1] In September 1936 J. B. Maloy summed up the various aspects of the question in the following five points:

1. Planes more efficient than those of today will soon be required and only control of the boundary layer can give them to us.

2. The power required is not prohibitive.

3. On the basis of experimental data thus far available the suction method is superior to blowing.

4. Control of the boundary layer in substratospheric transport planes and in military aircraft operating between 30,000 and 50,000 feet is rich with promise for the future.

5. Further experiments are required, however, to determine the distribution and the dimensions of the orifices for the suction and of the relative accessories.

Finally, how can anyone ignore or undervalue the conviction that the celebrated Theodor von Karman expressed in the spring of 1937, when at a conference of the Institute of Aeronautical Sciences in New York he placed control of the boundary layer first in the list of the aerotechnical conquests of the immediate future?[2]

In America these objectives were crushed under the heavy

yoke of the war, which demanded from industry mass production rather than pioneering research. When the war was over
the scales of aeronautical innovation (turbines, rockets, radar
and suction) leaned heavily in favor of the Old World, and
indeed, the situation threatened to grow worse. American political leaders were lulling themselves into a Nirvanic state—
although marred somewhat by the unexpected Russian awakening and the unfavorable turn of events in China—because
they mistakenly believed that they had started an Anglo-
American version of the famous thousand-year Pax Germanica
that the Führer euphorically promised the world as he contemplated his "secret weapons." But meantime a great mass of
scientific documents discovered in Germany, far in advance of
anything that was going on in the New World, were flowing
into Moscow and, above all, into London.

When America's leaders realized that although their aeronautical industry was indeed very strong it was likely to fall
behind if it did not take full advantage of the new ideas
developed in Europe during the final phase of the war, their
interest in revolutionary developments abruptly ceased to be
lukewarm. But by then, despite the zeal and insight of a few
far-seeing officers in the Air Force and Army, a considerable
portion of German scientific booty had already ended up in
other hands.

In England, for example, the Ministry of Aircraft Production
had hurriedly cornered and translated all the secret papers
concerning the most promising German experiments on the
boundary layer and the aerodynamics of supersonic flight at
high altitudes. Meanwhile, Russia had cornered the market on
missile experts and materials, which subsequently led to the
Sputniks.

THE AERODYNAMICS OF POROUS SURFACES

When the war ended and the British experts were able to
integrate their own experiments on the boundary layer with
the heavy contributions of German investigations, the watch-
word became: "New aircraft designs for new forms of propul-

sion!" Taking the *Feuerball* as the main model, they gave a perfectly symmetrical form to the "suction" aircraft, making it circular and wrapping the wing around the suction pump like a ring. Enlarged and flattened, the pump was transformed into a single rotor turbojet engine; thus it could also, indirectly, perform the functions of a jet engine.

Then the British got rid of every vestige of control surfaces, because since 1939 it had been established that the suction of the boundary layer could be used advantageously for maneuvering in place of the normal empennage and movable surfaces, or they could be integrated, making the movements of the craft quicker and more responsive. With the entire top surface of the aircraft made aeropermeable, or porous, they extended the suction to include the mass of air above the actual boundary layer with the aim of putting a large volume of air to work and thereby also improving the efficiency of the engine.[3]

The keystone of this new suction system was, finally, the replacement of the slotted or perforated skin panels used in the old experiments with a pitted covering in "porosint" and its derivatives. These are materials that possess among their numerous advantages (and some inevitable defects) that of being able to withstand continuous temperatures in the neighborhood of 500° Centigrade, despite the fact that there is a large proportion of aluminum in their composition.

An extensive series of experiments had, in fact, made it possible for the British to establish that the removal of the boundary layer by suction, especially when practiced on a large scale, was much more effective if it was done through a highly porous surface rather than through drilled and slotted panels.

Beginning in 1944 they developed a special branch of aerotechnical research that the researchers called "porous sheets aerodynamics."[4] Born in the hail of flying bombs and torpedo rockets, this branch of research seemed to reach its zenith in 1946, falling off—apparently—to the simple rank of an auxiliary technique for improving the lift of wings—rather sadly coming full circle. . . .

Officially, all these detailed experimental investigations came to no more than a few unpublicized test flights with models—

apparently certain mysterious television-guided flying models were experimented with in the winter of 1945–1946—and then to a complex series of wind-tunnel measurements on wings of various shapes and sizes.

After years of study and dedicated and costly research, there was not even one plane, not even an experimental one. Does that seem too little?

Too little indeed; and not believable. Especially since, as a number of qualified witnesses have unanimously declared, the top surface of the mysterious flying discs normally shows no visible air intake for propulsion, as could be seen on all jet planes built before then and in the twenty years since.[5]

SEMIOFFICIAL ADMISSIONS

In December 1946, during a conference on the future of British aeronautics, Sir Ben Lockspeiser declared that he was a partisan of the system of suction. Thanks to suction, "the plane would then slip through the air in the same way a piece of wet soap slips through the fingers . . . it is hoped eventually to obtain a wing drag of not more than about one-third of what is now common."[6]

Before that, during the thirty-fourth Wilbur Wright Memorial Lecture, held at the Royal Aeronautical Society in London on May 30, 1946, Professor E. F. Relf, one of the best British aerodynamics experts of the old generation, declared: "Recently a further system of regulating the boundary layer by means of suction through minute holes heavily distributed over the surface touched by the apparent wind, rather than through one or more slots as has been done until now, has been taken under study at the National Physical Laboratory. This idea, too, is not new. What is new is the production of the right porous material—sinterized in the form of spongy bronze—that possesses very small and very regular interconnected interstices.[7] Dr. Preston has studied this problem from the theoretical point of view and is convinced that it is very promising."

Promising from the point of view of aeronautic progress. But, according to the official story of this line of research, this progress was only an empty promise. So they say . . .

In introducing his heavily documented talk, which contained many significant disclosures, Relf stated that recent aerodynamic experiments on "suction" seemed rich in possibilities for the future. "I feel we are on the verge of discoveries and advances almost as spectacular as that flight of Orville Wright's, forty-three years ago.[8]

That is enough for the moment, for we will soon find this final concept—linked with certain truly portentous developments—fully confirmed.

Comparing the cautious but still rather euphoric tenor of these declarations with the equally compelling news quietly given to the British press at the same period concerning certain extraordinary ultra-high-speed aircraft being perfected at the government laboratories in Bedford, we will have to agree that a few simple wings and several large flying models cannot justify the loss of traditional British self-possession, notoriously sparing in superlatives and empty promises.

Something really exceptional was secretly boiling on the back burner of British aviation.

LUFTSCHWAMM

The development of the aerodynamics of porous materials is clearly creditable to the British experts who worked on the problem during the last two years of the war. But historically, it is equally clear, the original idea took form just before the outbreak of hostilities. It was, in fact, in 1937 that Perring and Dispose of the National Physical Laboratory tried unsuccessfully to repeat in full-scale size the old experiments of the German engineer Schrenk on "frictionless air flow," the concern and hope of all students of flight.

The same problem was successfully tackled by Professor Ackeret, who was in the dark as to the Englishmen's work and its failure, since they never published the complete results of their investigations.[9] His experiments, which were completed on the eve of the war, made clear from that time on that it would be necessary to create an "ideal surface" consisting of microscopic holes. But these aeropermeable surfaces would be very difficult to manufacture with conventional methods.

When the British experts learned of these conclusions (the last exchanges of technical information among the European countries before the curtain of military secrecy fell), they decided to look for some synthetic material. After all, the chemical industry had been using porous ceramic filters for about twelve years.

At the Applied Physics Laboratory of the National Physical Laboratory preliminary tests were made on the suction flow through a single orifice measuring .01 of an inch in diameter. With a long, almost imperceptible whistle the prescribed quantity of air repeatedly passed through the small orifice in the prescribed time without developing appreciable wave patterns. The principle worked!

This minor event was destined to give a new course to aeronautical progress, but no one foresaw it at the time. The event took place, it seems, in 1939; and from then on, the new aerodynamics began to take shape in both England and Germany.

The porous ceramic baffles were, however, soon replaced with materials that were stronger from a structural point of view but equally permeable.[10]

The British worked with a great variety of sheets: asbestos, phosphor bronze, glass textiles similar to Fiberglas, duralumin and various alloys.[11] During 1943–1944 the Germans also initiated a long series of researches on the sinterization of light alloys based on aluminum and magnesium and on both solid and porous aluminum bronze.[12] In Göttingen and Volkenrode the experts in the new techniques of flight gave these sintered porous materials the felicitous name of *Luftschwamm* (aerosponge) and proposed to revolutionize the laws of resistance to the forward motion of airplanes.

We still do not know whether they achieved any practical results. We do know the significant fact that in the autumn of 1945 Professor Thwaites of the Aerodynamics Division of the National Physical Laboratory brought together in an internal technical report—A.R.C. No. 9672: *Notes on German Theoretical Work on Porous Suction*—all the notes taken from the examination of German researches on porous materials (for which a special team of investigators had been formed), comparing them with what had been done up to then in England and with what the British intended to do in the near future.[13]

Needless to say, the report still bears the label "top secret." Nevertheless, a very small part of that information, unfortunately restricted entirely to the physical and mathematical fields of research on wing surfaces, came to the knowledge of the Americans. Professor Dryden of the National Advisory Committee for Aeronautics mentioned it publicly at the sixth International Congress of Applied Mechanics, which took place in Paris in September 1946.

In the first German experiments the velocity of the flow from suction was very low (not more than 2 percent of the velocity of the apparent wind) and the quantity of sucked air was therefore modest. But later on, by using more powerful pumps and improved porous sheets, they began to experiment with the dynamic pressure gradients developed at higher flight speeds, and 497.10 mph was now considered an "optimum" for the cruising speed of suction flight at altitudes between 20,000 and 40,000 feet.[14]

THE RELF LECTURE

The history of British postwar researches on suction is rather complicated—quite understandably, given the concatenation of circumstances.

The dissolution, or, better, the metamorphosis, of the M.A.P. into the Ministry of Supply coincided with Sir Melville Jones's resignation as secretary of the Aeronautical Research Council, the largest British government body concerned with the planning and development of aeronautical research.

In giving the news of his resignation—said to be for reasons of health—the technical publications referred briefly to the fact that in the last three years he had exercised "a great influence on the direction of government research, having successfully reorganized the old Committee and made it a council that was more in tune with the new times." In addition, he had laid down the plans for equipping the new experimental center at Bedford and for setting up the aeronautical college at Cranfield—a sort of scientific academy for the use of the R.A.F. and industry. A forty-two-year-old professor of applied mathematics at the University of Manchester, Sydney Goldstein, took Sir

Melville Jones's place. Goldstein was indefatigable in his research on "Frictionless Flow" at the National Physical Laboratory.[15]

The stature and work of this new personage would have been confined to the small world of specialists in the field if Professor Relf had not briefly explained the work of the Teddington staff in his Wilbur Wright Lecture, which was covered by reporters from all the major newspapers. Relf had been superintendent of the aerodynamic division of the National Physical Laboratories in Teddington until December 31, 1945.

Professor Relf began his interesting report by saying that although during the war they were particularly interested in bringing research on problems that were useful to the immediate war aims to completion, "the war years have produced some new ideas and discoveries that bid fair to open up revolutionary lines of progress in aeronautics. Some of these new ideas are still veiled in secrecy, but the veil has now been lifted. . . .

"I think it is fair to say that although aerodynamic research has always been full of interest, and even excitement, there never has been a time in which so many spectacular possibilities have been displayed before our eyes."

Ten years before, in 1936, during the proceedings of the James Forrest Conference, Relf had called the attention of experts to the usefulness of extending control of the boundary layer over as much of the surface of the aircraft as possible, since the evidence indicated that aerodynamic resistance could under the best of circumstances be reduced to about 10 percent of the current value—though this would not, of course, be easy to achieve.[16]

Like the experts listening to him, he surely could not have imagined at the time that the day would come when substantial progress in that direction would be made right there in England.

"HUMPED" AIRFOILS

During the war, but before the Anglo-American military agreement on reciprocal exchange of scientific information went into effect, rumors were circulating in American aeronautical circles about certain strange wing shapes with pointed trailing edges; and the Americans wondered what in the world was the purpose of them.

These new aeronautical shapes resulted principally from theoretical investigations worked out mathematically by Professor Goldstein, who had succeeded in defining "by points" the form of a two-dimensional body (an airfoil) developing a given distribution of the fluid velocity and hence of lift.[17]

On the basis of the theoretical premises, experts in the aerodynamics section of the National Physical Laboratory at first studied and designed elliptical airfoils with a tapering trailing edge and subsequently a new series or "family" of exceedingly strange, thick airfoils, generally having a roundish or lobate leading edge and a concave-convex trailing edge that came to a point and that had one or more suction slots where the concave-convex profile began. This family derived from an idea of Dr. A. A. Griffith. In 1942, it occurred to him to extend the Goldstein theory to the field of suction, by following the principle of "adapting the airfoil shape to the process of suction." In other words, Dr. Griffith tried to create true "suction airfoils," which in laboratory jargon were called "humped" airfoils because of their thick, curved upper surfaces that seemed like meaningless deformations to the layman.

Dr. Griffith experimented with several such profiles, differing in thickness, shape, or the position of the tail hollow, at the compressed-air tunnel of the National Physical Laboratory. He found that a "humped wing" easily developed lift coefficients on the order of 2.5 and that lift was about quintupled in comparison with the best wings of the period. The enthusiasm raised by these early results was, however, destined to be short-lived, for the aerodynamic resistance of the "humped wings" considerably exceeded the theoretical estimates. Furthermore, the studies conducted by the National Physical Laboratory experts to bring the grade of efficiency of those otherwise highly advantageous airfoils to at least an acceptable level came to nothing. In addition to Griffith, Richards, Lighthill, and Glauert also had a crack at the difficult problem. They designed a number of new airfoils of different shapes and thicknesses but did not get at the root of the trouble.[18]

To explain the long series of failures, it was finally concluded that turbulence in the wind tunnel altered the results of the phenomenon, which was really more favorable than the test results suggested since it had, after all, been promised by a theory that, also from the mathematical point of view, was flawless.

Since it had proved impossible to establish the actual level of efficiency of the humped airfoils through wind-tunnel tests, it was suggested at the Commonwealth conference on aeronautical research held in London in June 1946 that it might be a good idea to try them in flight tests on full-sized models by adapting an existing plane for the purpose.[19]

The Division of Aeronautical Research of the Australian Council for Scientific and Industrial Research undertook the job. Working in close collaboration with the National Physical Laboratory, they modified a large De Havilland G-2 troop transport glider. The humped wing was built with three slots along the back; a centrifugal fan powered by a Ford V-8 engine in the fuselage sucked the boundary layer through the slots and the hollow rectangular spar (the A.V.A. system). This air was then exhausted out the rear of the plane, developing sufficient thrust by reaction to maintain the craft in line of flight but not enough to enable it to take off by itself.

At the beginning of October 1948 the glider was shipped to the Royal Australian Air Force airdrome in Laverton, Victoria, where the tests took place, the glider being towed to its test altitude by a Dakota.

After the glider's first flights, Professor Coombes declared with obvious disappointment that all the mechanical problems had been clarified but that the usefulness of the new sucked airfoils still remained "to be proved"—a simple euphemism to mask a complete failure.

OTHER PLANES WITH "NO TOMORROW"

In October 1948—when the UFOs already had a good sixteen months of aerial incursions to their credit (it was the other branch of research on suction that had for some time surpassed

the stage of technical and operational maturity of the formula)
—the "humped" wings that had been so theoretically brilliant
but practically inefficient joined the supersonic M-52 plane in
the government files of abandoned projects, along with sketches
for subsonic "flying wing" transports with "humped" wings and
two laminar "flying wings." The two latter had actually been
built and flown, to a great public display of optimism, one in
1942 and the other in November 1947.

These were prototypes of an all-wing glider (AW-52-G Bat)
and two examples of a twin-engined all-wing jet (AW-52
Boomerang), made by the Armstrong Whitworth Aircraft
company.[20]

On November 13, 1947, one of the powered AWs successfully
completed its first flight at the R.A.F. experimental station at
Boscombe Down, with chief test pilot A. G. Franklin at the
controls. About ten months of frequent test flights followed,
then the Ministry authorized its presentation to the public. By
tradition, this took place at Farnborough during the annual
review of British aircraft production, September 7 to 9, 1948.

Roaring and shrieking, the plane performed its evolutions
for a considerable time, demonstrating unusual maneuverability
for a machine of its type, a clear indication of easy control,
quick response to the controls, and excellent stability. Nevertheless, this was its farewell flight.

One of the planes crashed into the earth a short time later
and the pilot saved himself by using the ejection seat. Little
by little news about the remaining AW-52 became scarcer and
scarcer, even in aeronautical circles. Then it stopped completely, and even though there was talk of the future preparation of "flying wings" of ninety tons for transatlantic transport,
the model had no successors.

This could have been foreseen for a number of reasons, not
the least of which was the failure of the "humped" airfoils, but
above all for the following reasons, here summarized from the
manufacturer's technical report:

a) because of difficulties in manufacturing and repairing the
airframes. In fact, the technical report states that the first impression the wing gives is the extreme smoothness of the
surface and the general care in construction. In order to insure

the laminar flow, the airfoil has been made with a tolerance of one one-thousandth of an inch, and for this reason special protection of the alclad sheathing has been prescribed and a protective cloth covering is furnished for transportation. This covering is left in place on the sheathing while the work is going on and is only partially removed for the riveting operation.

All this in order to maintain the extreme smoothness of the wing sheathing!

Anyone who has worked in military aeronautics knows that precautions of this sort are all right so long as the plane is in an experimental center, but when it goes to airfields for actual use, the situation changes markedly. Dozens of airmen and specialists come in daily contact with the machine and it is utterly utopian (especially in wartime) to try to get them to "always" wear chamois gloves and slippers when working on the plane, never to let a single drop of the 1400 gallons of fuel and oil fall on the wing, to scrupulously dust off every speck of dust or damp from that enormous flying mirror (1300 square feet of surface!), and so on.

b) because of the anticipated increase in the angle of the sweep back of the wings. The report says that the extremities of the wing are tapered with a camber at the leading edge of approximately thirty-five degrees. Later planes will have even more of a backsweep so that the wing will resemble the Greek letter delta.

In fact, the later products of the Hawker Siddeley Group were not only triangular in form but were actually called Aero-Delta (the Avro 698 and the Avro 707-B, both with triangular wings), and in addition seemed to be generally similar in appearance to certain mysterious "flying triangles" that a twin-engined U.S. Air Force plane unsuccessfully pursued over Carson Sink in 1952.

c) because a new line of development—agreed upon with the Ministry of Supply—showed even greater promise. Indeed, here are the conclusions of the company's internal report: Recently it was decided to abolish the air-intakes of gas turbine powered planes by taking the air for the jet engine from the surface of the wing. It is expected that the loss of power as a result of the missing self-supercharging effect of ramming will have no importance insofar as the total performance of the plane is concerned.

And so Professor Sedille also had his precursors!

BRITISH HOPES OF REVIVAL

The Hawker Siddeley Group, which later advertised itself as the "Pioneer and World Leader in Aviation," held its ninth stockholders' meeting in London on July 12, 1945.

It was the first postwar meeting and the euphoria generated by the recent victory over Germany (the victory over Japan then rightly seemed only a matter of months) led the speakers to relax very slightly the extreme secrecy that surrounded the new projects of the powerful industrial complex. Even then it was already very large, for in addition to the two branches of A. V. Roe (of Manchester and Avro-Canada of Toronto) and Armstrong Whitworth of Bagington-Coventry, other firms with long aerotechnical experience and originality of ideas were associated with it: namely, Gloster, which for some time was working on the Meteors, the first turbine airplanes; Hawker, the builder of the famous Hurricane fighters; Armstrong Siddeley Motors; Aluminium Ltd.; and a number of minor subcontractors (the system of subcontracting is an excellent method for successfully hiding certain projects that must at all costs be kept secret). This group alone accounted for 30 percent of British aircraft production.

The press and representatives for several ministries were present at the Hawker Siddeley Group's luncheon party. The secretary of the company, Mr. Sopwith, showed scale models of several types of airplanes in project stages in the research departments of the Group. These were "flying-wing" types with various power plants. Some had piston engines (from one to six engines) and propellers; others were powered with the first British turbojets, only one of which took concrete form as a prototype (the AW-52).

Making it perfectly clear that only a part of the new ideas

in gestation at Hawker Siddeley had been shown, Mr. Sopwith let himself go in his final toast with enthusiastic visions of the future. Although the idea that present conventional types of planes must be abandoned was still being debated, he said, it was nevertheless quite clear that within the relatively short space of two or three years the forms of aircraft now in existence, and likewise their engines, would be completely outdated!

Starting with 1945, a couple of years would bring us to the summer of 1947—the summer in which one of the strangest affairs of the twentieth century began.

Despite the polite probing of journalists, Mr. Sopwith declined to expand on his remarks and perhaps he was even afraid that he had said too much. In fact, for the remainder of the reception, which was now nearly over, he clammed up, as they say, whenever he was in the presence of journalists.

The Hawker Siddeley Group already employed tens of thousands of persons. Many of the numerous people on the executive level knew what was secretly being developed. It was, therefore, a foregone conclusion that someone would be indiscreet and that in the end something would leak out.

Reporters are constantly on the lookout everywhere, ready to go to any lengths to pick up any news that promises to cause a sensation. Thus when the first news leaks occurred—leaks that the publicists and ufologists cited to convince themselves that the UFOs were of terrestrial manufacture—they appeared in the London press. "*All British hopes for a revival of the aviation industry,*" one of these said, "*are based on several types of turbojet engines that, according to authoritative sources, are in a stage of development already so far advanced that we can expect them to be in use by mid-1947. These planes will have fantastic speeds at altitudes over 50,000 feet.*"[21]

A few months before—on November 7, 1945, to be exact—the English flyer H. J. Wilson had reached a speed of 595 mph over Herne Bay in the twin jet Gloster Meteor IV.

On September 7, 1946, over Littlehampton, E. M. Donaldson bettered Wilson's speed by a bare ten miles an hour. Then it took almost eight years before the English flyer Michael Lithgow wrested the speed record (though not for long) from the Americans with a flight of 737 mph.

RECORDS AND SILENCE

Such being the case—and in view of the well-known English technical competence—how can an increase of 142 miles per hour, spread out over eight years, be calmly passed off as "fantastic speeds"? And how explain the references to altitudes of "over 50,000 feet," where these mysterious planes would achieve their maximum speeds? At such altitudes the first turbojets lost power, and thereby speed, because of the thinness of the air.

Clearly the British were neither lying nor indulging in uncharacteristic bragging. The new types of flying machines presaged such promising developments that they induced the authorities to swallow the bitter pill of the lost speed record silently in order to keep their secret intact.

The importance of that brief communication easily slipped by laymen, and the press as well. So easily that not even specialists in aeronautical matters paid the least attention to it then or later. Conversely, it should be noted that it was precisely "mid-1947," that is, on June 24, that the American businessman Kenneth Arnold saw the first glinting, nimble flying saucers going through their evolutions among the peaks of the Cascades while he was piloting his private plane over the state of Washington.

Strangely enough, those titillating leaks went more or less unobserved even in England—perhaps because of political or economic preoccupations, or simply because of the preoccupations of daily life, not the least of which was the bothersome food rationing that was continued in the name of austerity despite the Churchillian defeat of Germany. Or perhaps part of the press kept silent for political reasons. (The Conservatives were greatly embittered by the unexpected election victory of the Labour Party.)

Whatever the reasons, perhaps the same ones caused the declarations—double-distilled, in any case—of the aeronautical experts of the Ministry of Supply in its "Report to the Nation" the following July to be received with only the faintest echo. A few inches in the papers (no more than half a column, for paper was still severely rationed) and a few hasty comments in the technical journals. Nevertheless, once again there was a little leak—completely involuntary, of course!

Supporting his view that the most vital problem in aeronautics that required study was not overheating caused by aerodynamic friction in supersonic flight but human resistance to sharp accelerations, Sir Ben Lockspeiser in fact declared at one point that experiments with an airplane capable of reaching 4500 mph were being conducted for the Ministry of Supply. Now this was a truly "fantastic" speed, and one that by a strange coincidence was the stratospheric speed reported for one of the UFOs followed on the radar screen in Washington in July 1952.

THE MISUNDERSTANDING
ABOUT THE ATHODYDS

The editorial comment of the authoritative journal *The Aeroplane,* the only magazine that mentioned the matter, was couched in an obviously scandalized tone. Indeed, the experiments were simply called "a dangerous thing."[22] "This is much greater speed than we are accustomed to from official enterprises," said the editorial. "In any case, the athodyd has still to be developed as a practical power proposition at rates of progress still within our comprehension."[23]

The mistaken conclusion that a ramjet plane was concerned had been induced both because during the conference Sir Ben Lockspeiser had praised this simple propulsive device and because a model of an *athodyd aircraft,* with the pilot lying prone, had been officially exhibited at the Farnborough Aeronautical Exhibition, which took place from June 27 to 29.[24] On another occasion a photographer had caught Lockspeiser in a curious meditative mood, holding the scale model of a ramjet fighter that reminded him of his recent visit to Germany. It had been a fruitful trip. No one could have dreamed that enemy technology was so far in advance also in the field of ramjets.

At the experimental station of the Walter Werke in Wik, the

technicians of the T Unit had saved four perfectly operational models from the destruction ordered by their builders, together with various interesting bits of information about a prototype built in the Walter plant in Beerberg in Silesia and subsequently lost in the war.[25]

Farther south the T Unit had found other experimental machines of the same sort at Bad Eilsen, in the huge Bavarian plant of Focke Wulf, where Professor Pabst had, in addition to several ramjet fighters, designed the strange subsonic helicopter powered by rotary ramjets that went under the name *Triebflügel Flugzeug* and was capable of a speed of 500 mph. Later, many ill-informed publicists incorrectly concluded that this was the father of flying discs of possible terrestrial manufacture.[26]

Still farther south, in Ainring in the Bavarian alps, the T Unit men found the giant D.F.S. engines, which had already been flight tested by Professor Sänger; and then in Austria they found the strange propulsive tubes operating on "coal slag" built by the Viennese Luftfahrtsforschung.[27]

The best jet planes of the time, the British record-holding turbine-engined Gloster Meteors, barely reached a speed of 620 mph. The German rocket engines seized as war booty did not appear, at least for the moment, to provide much more speed. Even the highly touted ramjets failed in the stratosphere. No new direction in air technology then known justified the enormous progress announced by the Ministry of Supply.

By a curious coincidence, the press did not ask for either confirmation or details (which perhaps would not have been granted), but the supporters of high-speed flight immediately found that England had equally determined opponents—in the opposition party.

The papers of the period reported that Lord Mottistone's speech in the House of Lords during the second debate on the Civil Aviation Bill raised a number of conflicting views when he excitedly asked for the floor in order to criticize "our lust for speed," directed toward developing ever faster airplanes whose pilots would be "condemned to a terrible ordeal!"[28] The shelving of the supersonic M-52 had already been decided and acted on since February, but Lord Mottistone's oratorical volley came just at the right time to make the impelling necessity of the action still more acceptable.

As for the athodyds, in succeeding years some experimental planes powered with ramjets did fly in the United States and France. But none flew in England.[29]

THE COMMONWEALTH CONFERENCES

A third source of leaks—somewhat delayed, but very valuable and immediately plugged—appeared in the circle of the Aeronautical Research Council itself, which in June 1946, at the behest of the Ministry of Supply, called a Commonwealth Conference on Aeronautical Research. Held in London, the meeting brought together a hundred experts connected with both governmental and private institutes of air technology in Great Britain, Canada, Australia, New Zealand, and South Africa.

Organized by the retiring secretary, Sir Melville Jones, this was the third such conference to take place after the limited conference between Great Britain and Canada in the summer of 1941 that spelled out the close collaboration between their two industries (especially concerning war production and "certain proposals for scientific investigations to be conducted in the Dominion") and the big Commonwealth meeting in the autumn of 1944, which was mainly directed toward the future of aeronautical research. Part of the work of the third assembly was communicated to the press. Secret sessions were conducted behind closed doors. Nevertheless, a crack did open.

The official comment released at the end of the conference by the Ministry of Supply and the Aeronautical Research Council was vague and cloudy, but not without importance. It established, for example, this solid point: "The best progress in research can be expected only from investigation of a few specific designs combined with a study of the fundamental physical problems which arise in the course of development and construction. We have also commended this for serious consideration."[30]

Not that anyone would have dared doubt it—but what was this serious consideration?

This we heard through a B.B.C. broadcast in August 1946, a bumper year for leaks that were to the advantage of the press and the history of ufology: "The little village of Thurleigh in Bedfordshire will soon become the largest aeronautical research center in the world. The new experimental station that will be constructed there will cost twenty million pounds and its scientific program will include the development of three different categories of aircraft:

"1) low-speed machines, that is, those slower than 450 mph and that can, therefore, still advantageously use propellers.

"2) machines that will have a speed of 1000 mph.

"3) *machines that it is hoped will be able to reach at least 1500 mph. According to some experts, these planes have already been built and tested and it is probable that in the near future they will be flying over Great Britain. If necessary, such planes could fly nonstop around the world many times, because they need fuel only for take-off and landing. Great Britain has already astonished the world with its excellent turbojet engines, but this new development of British scientists is the greatest step that aeronautics has taken since man began to fly.*"[31]

THE ORIGIN OF THE NATIONAL
AERONAUTICAL ESTABLISHMENT

The intention to create a large experimental center on very modern principles in order to put Great Britain in the vanguard of aviation took concrete form in 1943, when the Ministry of Aircraft Production commissioned the Aeronautical Research Council to draft an estimate of the equipment considered essential for carrying out research in what would presumably be the aeronautical future in the first five years of peace.

In the Aeronautical Research Committee's internal report No. 7500, the experts of the committee (it was not yet elevated to the rank of council; that came in 1945, with the war's end) suggested that the experimental establishments be centralized in the Bedford area, specifically in the village of Thurleigh, which would have to be sacrificed to make room for the large hangars and cement runways for the new airplanes. Parallel to this scheme, and carefully worked out down to the least detail, were various suggestions for the development of engine research, with particular reference to gas turbines. Later these suggestions became the basis for the conversion of Power Jets Ltd. into the N.G.T.E. governmental center.

The new center at Bedford was supposed to absorb part of the existing facilities in Farnborough, the old and praiseworthy Royal Aeronautical Establishment, especially the equipment concerning research on supersonic flight. Immediately after the war, the plan was modified to include German plants seized as war booty, some of which, however, were later silently put on ships for other destinations—Canada and Australia.

In August 1946 the Ministry of Supply released to the press the first details about the new center, which appeared to be modeled on the once justly celebrated Italian "aeronautical city" of Guidonia. Since the original village was completely swallowed up by the new constructions, the center officially received the name of the nearby city of Bedford and the organization itself was named the National Aeronautical Establishment. Five thousand people, including 1400 scientists and technical specialists, were envisaged as working there.[32]

In July 1948 official news about the National Aeronautical Establishment appeared for the second time. It reported that "despite the present economic difficulties" preparations for the center were proceeding apace.

The first of the eight supersonic wind tunnels that had been planned—the one that measured three by three feet and could develop a continuous flow at 1500 mph—did not go into operation until 1950. Work on the last five—developing an intermittent flow of 2600 mph—did not start until the beginning of 1954.

Nevertheless, despite the notable amounts of energy and money expended, no truly "revolutionary" airplane was ever seen to taxi down the runways of the National Aeronautical Establishment. Originally—that is, when the East Bloc threat was still in a purely formal state—these runways had been constructed to fill the skies with the three fundamental types

of airplanes which were to put the seal on British air supremacy. Let us examine these categories a bit more closely.

The first type obviously doesn't interest us. The second type,
erroneously including the supersonic M-52, which was to have
reached a top speed of 1000 mph but unhappily reached only
the files of the Ministry of Supply, appears instead to have
been assigned to certain aircraft destined to develop their top
speeds in the relatively dense air of altitudes just below or just
within the stratospheric range: cigar-shaped aircraft with tiny
wings and jet-lift, airplanes with triangular wings of a special
sort described as "gothic," and "convertible" airplanes with re-
tractable wings hinged at the fuselage—planes for which 1000
mph was not the goal but the starting point and whose subsequent rare appearances also figure in the case-histories of
the UFOs.

The third type, which according to London press circles included the Ministry of Supply's ramjet plane—the wild discrepancy between the publicized performance (4500 mph the
first time and only 1500 mph later) was taken to indicate that
a healthy realism had prevailed—indicated that an extraordinary type of airplane existed. It was not only capable of
surpassing, and perhaps by a considerable margin, the still
unreachable speed of Mach 2, but was propelled by an astonishing kind of engine that burned fuel only during take-offs
and landings. In the stratosphere it would not have used any
fuel at all.

THE THIRD CATEGORY

More than twenty years have passed since the B.B.C. broadcast that communiqué thick with astounding promises and
supported by Sir Ben Lockspeiser's most thoughtful declarations. But we have still officially to see the prodigious planes
that the B.B.C. heralded back in 1946.

"Officially" is the operative word, because "practically" it
is now twenty years that these aircraft have been appearing,
disappearing, reappearing and disappearing again, generally in
well-defined periods, astonishingly fast, almost everywhere,
never overtaken, and never identified. They are the delight and

desperation of ufologists and newspapers, who can search as much as they like to find anything that even remotely resembles the B.B.C. broadcast either in the American press of the time or among the "rumors" about secret Soviet production (almost always inflated beyond all belief) or that would justify equally well the mysterious apparitions of the following years.

Even within British aeronautical circles the news was received and commented on with a certain detached skepticism because of the phrase "flying without using fuel," which smacked too much of the Utopia of visionaries dedicated to discovering perpetual motion. There is no motive impulse without the expenditure of energy, they said, and to produce it something has to be consumed. All too true.

But when Sir Ben Lockspeiser, or someone speaking for him, stated that *those planes would not have burned fuel, he did not implicitly rule out the use of a propellant easily found along the flight path, proportionately accelerated and expelled.*

In fact, anyone who took the trouble to query those in the circle of the Ministry of Supply with the proper circumspection would have received an evasive but sufficiently explicit answer: namely, that the planes in question would have used *"the inexhaustible natural energies present in the atmosphere at very high altitudes."*

All right! Whether or not this explanation was true, the matter then became more credible. In the light of that long-ago revelation, the very long hovering of the intensely bright UFO that flew very slowly over the Spanish province of Albacete from 7:00 A.M. to 12:00 noon on June 26, 1953, also becomes credible. The object was at a superstratospheric altitude—between fifty and sixty miles up. Any other known type of jet-lift aircraft after at most a half-hour of continuous hovering in the favorably dense space of the lower atmosphere would have plummeted like a stone.

Detailed analysis of the B.B.C. broadcast brings out another very important fact. According to some experts, those mysterious aircraft had "already been tested," and it was probable that they would be flying over Great Britain "in the near future."

Once again blowing hot and cold: did that mean, then, that

these craft not only existed but that they had passed the study stage in wind tunnels and by means of models and were already flying like real airplanes?

Where had they been prepared, since the Bedford center did not get under way, and then only partially, until 1950?

For a number of years the Royal Aeronautical Establishment of Farnborough had been in operation on British soil. This center had a number of high-altitude supersonic wind tunnels, developing wind speeds ranging from 970 to 3580 mph. These were small plants adapted immediately after the war from the old equipment for research on piston engines. This center had contributed in great measure to the beginning studies on questions concerning suction and porous bronzes.

Nevertheless, how can we reconcile the possibility that the aircraft in the third category were built in the British Isles with the fact that the new machines would soon "be flying over Great Britain"? Evidently the first test flights and the preparations for them were carried out elsewhere, after the book had been closed on the German chapter and not yet opened on the British one.

Information obtained from Ministry of Supply circles at the time located the "elsewhere" a bit more precisely: *"overseas."* Even more confidential information was even more specific: *"in the new Canadian factories."*

A year later the flying saucers—the genuine New Aeronautics of the postwar period—took off on their prodigious flight from the remote western regions of the faithful Dominion, catching by complete surprise the forgetful public, the press, and even aeronautical experts who had been hardened by excessive skepticism. Barely a year later!

With time, people's memory of the original news leaks became so vague that it was possible to "produce" tiny macrocephalic Martians; delicate blond Venusians; the beautiful Aura Rahnes, the saucer pilot from the planet Clarion; the Uranians; the Ethereans; and the whole vast range of creatures that today are known throughout the world under the general appellation of "Our Brothers from Space," who bear messages of salvation for Humanity.

From Top Secret to farce.

NOTES

1. See M. J. Bamber, *Wind Tunnel Tests on Airfoil Boundary Layer Control Using a Backward-Opening Slot* (N.A.C.A., Report No. 385, Washington, 1931), p. 38. Working with a wing section having a "blown" top surface—arranged at varying incidences from minus 6° to plus 30° and with an artificial wind of 40 mph—at the incident of minus 6° Bamber obtained negative drag coefficients. ($-C_r$ max. $= -0.12$) deriving from the interaction between the reduction of the profile drag and the thrust produced by the reaction of the air blowing through the slot on the top surface. Bamber concluded his report by pointing out that in order to make a functioning "jet-wing" (that is, of the type invented three years before by Katzmayr and lumping together into a single whole the lift and propulsive functions in place of the propeller), and in order to obtain thereby, thanks to the permanent development of negative C_r, horizontal flight and climb, it was necessary for the "negative drag" to exceed the sum of the passive drag of the wing and of the other parts of the plane (fuselage, controls, landing gear, and windshield). Even in this case the only solution worth trying would have been the adoption of an appropriate "flying-wing" formula.

2. It might be a good idea to recall that in 1947 Professor L. G. Whitehead of the Royal Aeronautical Establishment declared decisively that the proposed move away from the common airfoil to suction airfoils would be perhaps a still greater change than that which led from the conformation of the slow biplane to that of the fast monoplane. Despite the interesting studies of Professor Busemann and of the Italian A. Ferri, aeronautical technology would never have been able to achieve what it did in supersonic speeds with the glorious old prewar biplane.

3. Apropos of this it should be noted that occasional observers have independently affirmed that if the back of the flying discs—when they are hovering in mid-air or maneuvering at very low altitudes—was struck by a glancing ray of sunlight it gave off a strange shimmering light. Ufologists delude them-

selves when they seek to explain the phenomenon by anti-gravity or, worse yet, anti-matter. It is the reflection in the sunlight of the convective movement generated by the energetic suction of the air layers next to the top surface of the aircraft. But the best proof of intense local air suction is offered to us by a little-known episode that occurred on October 20, 1954, when the UFOs seemed to spread over a good part of the inhabited world. Leaving his house very early in the morning in a distant suburb of Teheran, the Persian businessman Ghasim Faili saw a mysterious circular "thing" in an empty lot near his house giving off a reflection from the moonlight. When he approached the machine close enough to see that a human being was moving around inside it, "with a head like an elephant because of the strange headgear" (evidently a pilot equipped for breathing in the stratosphere), and placed his hand on the edge of the object, his curiosity soon gave way to fear. "Allah help me!" exclaimed the unfortunate witness, remarking that with a "sort of strong suction" the strange device seemed to pull him toward it (more than one careless mechanic has lost his life or been seriously injured when he went too close to the intake of a turbojet being ground tested). As Faili shouted for help, the disc hummed dully and an instant later took off vertically, giving off "a strong, hot blast."

4. The bibliography on the subject amounts to about fifty works. The following Aeronautical Research Council Reports and Memoranda are basic and of particular historical interest since they were the first chronologically: G. J. Taylor, *The Aerodynamics of Porous Sheets* (A.R.C., R.&M. No. 2237, London, H.M.S.O., 1944), p. 14; G. J. Taylor, *Air Resistance of a Flat Plate of Very Porous Material* (A.R.C., R.&M. No. 2236, London, H.M.S.O., 1944), p. 4; Simmons and Cowdrey, *Measurements of the Aerodynamic Forces Acting on Porous Screen* (A.R.C., R.&M. No. 2276, London, H.M.S.O., 1949), p. 20; J. H. Preston, *The Boundary Layer Flow over a Permeable Surface through which Suction Is Applied* (A.R.C., R.&M. No. 2244, London, H.M.S.O., 1946), p. 29; B. Thwaites, *On the Flow Past a Flat Plate with Uniform Suction* (A.R.C., R. & M. No. 2481, London, H.M.S.O., 1952), p. 11.

Other complementary works will be cited in successive notes.

For a more extensive bibliography see R. C. Pankhurst, *N.P.L. Aerofoil Catalogue and Bibliography* (A.R.C. Current Paper No. 81, London, H.M.S.O., 1952), p. 20.

5. While the functioning of an internal jet or rocket—that is, independently of the contribution of the atmosphere—would be practically irreconcilable with the various speeds of flight and the astonishing ranges reported of the circular-shaped UFOs.

6. *Cf.* Sir Ben Lockspeiser, "Progress in Aeronautics," *Nature* (London, No. 157, 1946), pp. 787–792.

7. Sinterizing is a metallurgic procedure that, starting from specially prepared metallic powders, makes it possible to manufacture economically pieces of relatively complicated shapes to close degrees of tolerance under cold, dry pressure. The pieces thus formed are then placed in controlled atmosphere ovens, where a temperature close to that of fusion reestablishes the molecular cohesion by restoring the mechanical characteristics of the original metal. In the prewar period, industrial production of sinterized parts had been practically developed along four basic lines:

1) sinterization of hard metals (tungsten, cobalt, molybdenum, vanadium, etc.) for the manufacture of machine tools and all those mechanisms that must operate at very high Rockwell numbers or that require a high degree of surface hardness.

2) sinterization of bronze or iron for the manufacture of parts with exceedingly complicated shapes that would be too costly to produce by machining. (This process follows the system of stamped plastics.)

3) porous sinterization of bronze, iron, and aluminum for the manufacture of bushings, guide shoes, thrust bearings, etc., that absorb appropriate lubricants and consequently possess the characteristic of self-lubrication for a long period of time.

4) sinterization of bronze—or, more rarely, of other metals —with a controlled porosity to serve as air, water, oil, and gasoline filters, or as filters for other fluids generally. (Around

1935 the Krupp locomotives were equipped with condensers with porous baffles. Four years later, at Farnborough, British technicians using the same type of material perfected the Dunlop T.K.S. deicing wing.)

In the postwar period the technology of sinterization developed three new productive systems:

5) sinterization of plasto-metallic materials in order to impregnate metals with plastic substances for lubricant seals or waterproof parts.

6) sinterization of cero-metallics, obtained by mixing metal and mineral powders (porcelain clay [kaolin], alumina, feldspar, etc.) in order to produce material with a slow specific weight and a high mechanical and thermal resistance. (For example, experimental vanes for turbine engines.)

7) sinterization of metals with the infiltration of a different metal or of metallic carbides, in which the parent metal (aluminum, iron, copper, steel, bronze, etc.), possesses intercrystalline inclusions of copper or aluminum or of vanadium or titanium carbides, or nickel-chromium alloy or cupronikel for the manufacture of matte-finished parts that are resistant to very high temperatures or are self-cooling. (In the United States the Thompson Products Corporation mass-produced until a short time ago vanes for aircraft turbines employing iron powder impregnated with molten copper in final molding.)

8) porous sinterization of special and ordinary steels for filtering and measuring very hot liquids.

As far as the specific subject of the UFOs is concerned, British production of light bronzes and aluminum is significant. They have been manufactured for some time with the "ground" metals at Coventry by Powderloys Ltd., according to exact technical specifications worked out by the huge Anglo-Canadian industrial complex Aluminium Ltd. and by the Fulmer Research Institute of Stoke Poges in Buckinghamshire. The latter was founded by Colonel Wallace Charles Devereux, who carried out important ministerial functions in the Ministry of Supply from 1941 to the end of the war.

Therefore, even the porous bronze briefly mentioned by Professor Relf was not, in an absolute sense, anything really new.

8. See Ernest F. Relf, "Recent Aerodynamic Developments," *Journal of the Royal Aeronautical Society* (London, May/June 1946), pp. 421–449.

9. Professor Ackeret succeeded in the intention, thanks to the proper distancing of the suction slots.

10. In fact, it was Doctor Roff, of the chemical laboratory attached to the Department for Scientific and Industrial Research, who suggested that Dr. Preston, of the aerodynamic laboratory, replace the fragile ceramic with a porous bronze (at first called sintered bronze, then Porous Phosphor Bronze, and finally, in happy simplification, porosint). A type with controlled porosity obtained by the techniques of powder metallurgy was chosen. The first experimental samples—sheets measuring six by twelve inches with thicknesses running from one-sixteenth to one-eighth of an inch and pores measuring from 2.5 to 100 microns in diameter—immediately proved to have a satisfactory distribution of porosity relative to the aims of the study. In addition, the original porosint could be easily welded or brazed. Unfortunately, it had the defects of being somewhat heavier than the ordinary sheets used for the skin and of having lower mechanical resistance. And this was not all. At the beginning of 1945, when Dr. Preston and his associates had finished the technical tests and went on to the windtunnel experiments, it was discovered that because of the tortuous construction of the air cells, this "labyrinthine structure" retained rain water, slowing down the anticipated rate of suction. Then small screens of phosphor bronze were woven with a density of 240 wires per square inch and then copper plated, but the results were disappointing because the process was so rudimentary. After the laboratory equipment had been improved and the intensity of the galvanic current increased, they first tried electroplating with granular cuprite and then tried nickel plating. In a later research stage they prepared porous grills of large dimensions and an effort was made to strengthen them by applying vitreous sheeting to the edges. Another partial disappointment: the wind-tunnel tests demonstrated that there were considerable local variations in the degree of

permeability of the material. From the technological point of view, however, the system of the reticulated sheet with granular cupronickel plating fulfilled all hopes, the mechanical properties of the material proving to be nearly equal to those of a thin sheet of solid metal. Following this, other improvements were gradually adopted in the experimental cycle of production of porus materials. Reticulates running from 120 to 240 interstices per square inch in plated bronze produced by cold lamination and resulting in flat, smooth surfaces proved to be an unprecedented success. Using the same procedure, excellent sheets with "variable porosity along one side" were finally produced.

11. The typical request for maximum porosity remaining constant—parallel with the most advanced experiments on porosint—the experts of the National Physical Laboratory immediately investigated other materials that, with a similar degree of aerodynamic permeability, offered or gave promise of offering greater mechanical resistance. In the Aeronautical Research Council reports relative to the postwar experiments on airfoils, in fact, can be found vague references to possible substitute materials such as sheets of synthetic resin with asbestos (durestos), which, however, proved excessively hydroscopic; vinyl resins of the expansion (or spongy) type with a metal reticulate incorporated in the resinous mass; cerometallic sheets in which the metal was principally alumina; and bronze reticulate sheets used as a support for layers of nylon fabric or glass fabric similar to Fiberglas and Fiberfraz. In addition, there were even vaguer references to exceedingly light sinterized and plated products of aluminum and duralumin. It may perhaps astonish the reader that a weak metal-like aluminum was included among the metals to be used in a porous state, but sinterization gives metals special mechanical characteristics by raising their tensile strength and resistance to corrosion through a very wide range of temperature from $-50°$ C. to $500°$ C.

12. The principal suppliers of the experimental materials were the Plansee Werke of Reute, in the Tyrol, and the Vereinigte

Leichmetall Werke of Linden, a suburb of the city of Hannover, which specialized in the field of powder metallurgy. Concerning the German sinterization industry, see R. A. Hetzig, *Powder Metallurgy in Germany During the Period 1939–1945* (British Intelligence Objectives Sub-committee "Overall Report" No. 20, London, H.M.S.O., 1949), p. 27.

13. Two years later Thwaites himself, in collaboration with Prof. H. B. Irving, established in another internal report (No. 10,720, *Research Summary of Boundary Layer Control Problems*) all the developments that had been planned for the work that was carried out at the National Psysical Laboratory in that sector as well.

14. At such altitudes the air is already sufficiently rarefied and its index of kinetic velocity so high that the minuscule superficial roughness of the *Luftschwamm* would not have had in practice any appreciable negative influence on the functioning of suction. Concerning the directives for the German research see H. Schlichting, *The Boundary Layer of the Flat Plate Under Conditions of Suction and Air Injection* (R.T.P. translation No. 1753 of the British Ministry of Aircraft Production, London, 1945; taken from *Luftfahrtforschung,* Bd. 19, Lfg. 5 to 9, October 20, 1942, pp. 293–301). Even today the current opinion among the best qualified air technologists is that a good airplane with sucked wings should not exceed 500 mph under penalty of losing its efficiency because compressibility drag comes into play. This consideration—quite valid, for it has been proved by a long series of wind-tunnel tests—naturally concerns *airplanes of the conventional type,* in which only the wings are subject to a *limited* reduction process according to the usual means of removing the "dead air" from the top surface depression.

15. His basic and most important work, *Una teoria per il calcolo di profili alari aventi piccolo spessore,* was published in a number of installments by the Aeronautical Research Council between May 1942 and March 1945 in internal Reports and Memoranda Nos. 5804–6156–6225 (with the collaboration of

E. J. Richards) and Nos. 8548–8549–8877 (with the collaboration of H. I. Preston).

16. According to his statement, in addition to airfoils as strictly understood, aerodynamic bodies with an extended laminar boundary layer were also studied and tested at the National Physical Laboratory. The Aeronautical Research Council's bibliography is silent on this matter save for the experiments with porous cylinders.

17. See Prof. Sidney Goldstein, "Low Drag and Suction Airfoils," *Journal of the Aeronautical Sciences* (New York, April 1948), pp. 189–214; and Prof. M. J. Lighthill, *A New Method of Two-Dimensional Aerodynamic Design* (Aeronautical Research Council Reports and Memoranda No. 2112, London, H.M.S.O., 1945), p. 53.

18. Here, in chronological order, is a necessarily superficial and summary review of the British research into cusped (or "humped") airfoils. The germ of the idea is to be found in the Goldstein theory (worked out between 1939 and 1942) of the computation of the characteristics of any sort of airfoil through the evaluation, point by point, of the distribution of speed along the airfoil. Later (1940–1941) Dr. A. A. Griffith, while studying a system to meet the separation of the boundary layer in a convergent diffuser, extended the results of his investigations on bowed airfoils and designed the first example of a "humped" airfoil characterized by an unevenness of speed at the tail section. A theoretical contribution by Sir Geoffrey Taylor (1943) made it possible for professors Richards (in 1944), Lighthill (in 1945), Glauert (in 1945), and Gregory (in 1946) to perfect the principle later on, thereby giving rise to other bowed airfoils variously thickened or shaped in the rear portion. These airfoils were subjected to a long period of wind-tunnel testing and proved to have exceedingly high lift coefficients but low efficiency, with often uncertain results because of disturbances caused by the defective functioning of the aspiration slots (acting at times like organ pipes), and therefore with a trailing edge movement of the boundary layer

different from that anticipated in the case of the integrally laminar flow. The principal types of cusped airfoils show clearly the many solutions that were tried. Two types were designed by Dr. Griffith, one by Professor Richards, four by Professor Lighthill. One (called Glass II) is the work of Professor Glauert (his had a suction slot with an internal chamber or collector to move the dead air from the wing surface to the suction pump).

19. During his lecture on low-resistance suction airfoils at the Institute of Aeronautical Sciences in New York on December 17, 1947, Professor Goldstein said that the model of a complete airplane with a symmetrical airfoil having a pointed trailing edge and with a thickness of 16 percent had, among other types, been experimented on in the Royal Aeronautical Establishment's wind tunnel. He gave no further details. He was referring, however, to the adaptation of new contours along the lines of the twin-jet Gloster Meteor fighter, holder of the world speed record. But this also led nowhere. (*Cf.* D. A. Clarke, *Wind Tunnel Tests on a Griffith Meteor Model (Without Suction)*, (Aeronautical Research Council "Current Paper" No. 37, London, H.M.S.O., 1951), p. 9.

20. The Bat experimental glider was a one-third-scale model of the twin-jet Boomerang and was constructed in order to study the aerodynamic behavior of the new formula in actual flight. In flight trim the twin-jet weighed 33,000 pounds and was powered by two Rolls Royce Nene turbojets partially faired into the wing. The wings (with a span of ninety feet and a maximum chord of thirty-six feet) had a "laminar profile," as the director of scientific research of the Ministry of Supply had expressly requested, and in addition boundary layer control was limited to the trailing edge of the wing tips, in order to improve the stability of the plane at low speeds. In 1944, when tests with the glider had brought to light the advantage of using such reduced suction, Rolls Royce prepared a special version (Mark III) of the Derwent turbojet, with 2300 pounds of static thrust, which was then shelved in favor of the more modern Nene. (*Cf.* "*L'Armstrong Whitworth AW-52 senza*

oda con due reattori," *Rivista Aeronautica* (Rome, September 1947), pp. 553–560; and *"L'aeroplano tutt'ala AW-52 azionato da turbina a gas a getto,"* *Rivista Aeronautica* (Rome, December 1947), pp. 781–784.

21. See *"Dalla stampa: Speranze inglesi,"* *L'Ala* (Florence, March 1946), p. 6.

22. See *"A Dangerous Thing,"* in the column *"Matters of Moment,"* *The Aeroplane* (London, August 9, 1946).

23. The ramjet (statoreacteur, athodyd) is the simplest of the "exojets," or aeronautical jet power plants that make use of the air as a propulsive mass, scooping it up by forward motion. The ramjet has no primary rotating elements (compressor or turbine) and the air is compressed spontaneously through the effect of the special divergent conformation of the long forward air scoop (the diffuser). The fuel is injected where the conduit is largest and the flow has the lowest internal velocity and hence the maximum pressure. In the next cylindrical portion (the interheater) the mixture burns under constant pressure and the increase of temperature causes the burned air to expand through the short, converging tail tube (the propelling nozzle) with a speed greater than on entry, thus generating the reaction thrust. Unfortunately, for obvious reasons (*i.e.*, the tube is open at both ends) the ramjet does not function when stationary but begins to give an appreciable thrust and to become efficient only at a speed of 1000 feet per second, and, equal to the speed reached, its thrust coefficient diminishes with the increasing rarefication of the air owing to the lessened velocity pressure in the cycle. For a long time it was held that it would have to be limited to supersonic speeds (not above 2500 mph), but for several years hypersonic ramjets (for speeds of 7500 mph) have been under study in America and they give promise of functioning regularly along the densest borders of the high stratosphere.

24. The curious, marked thickening of the wings and tail assembly was notable and in apparent contrast with the supersonic attributes given to the model. (This is explained

by the fact that it was planned to use "elliptical" contours, which were not yet considered inefficient, on this project.) The wing recesses were to hold the large quantity of fuel that would be used by the plane, which would be propelled to a high altitude and the upper limit of subsonic speed by a pair of auxiliary external rockets. The idea never got beyond the static model and—supposing also that this has nothing to do with the M-52—perhaps it is this type of aircraft that is referred to in the Aeronautical Research Council's internal report No. 7481 (*Research on a Model of Supersonic Aircraft*), written by Dr. Warren in 1944 and still "not available."

25. See Combined Intelligence Objectives Sub-committee, *Walter Werke, Kiel* (Report No. XXVIII-53, London, H.M.S.O., 1945), p. 15.

26. See Combined Intelligence Objectives Sub-committee, *Focke Wulf Designing Offices and General Management, Bad Eilsen* (Report No. XXVI-6, London, H.M.S.O., 1945), pp. 63–66. During 1944 the following major dimensions and maximum performance figures were established for this helicopter project (it was also called a "helicogyre"): climbing speed (vertical) 110 mph; ceiling 60,000 feet; gross weight 12,345 pounds; length 30 feet; rotor diameter 35 feet; powered by three ramjets located at the tips of the three-bladed rotor turning in neutral over the center of gravity of the fuselage. No torque reaction. Control afforded through a cross-shaped tail assembly. Ground parking in vertical position. Armament (presumed): four Mauser 20-mm cannons.

27. See Combined Intelligence Objectives Sub-committee, *Deutsche Forschungsanstalt für Segelflug, Ainring* (Report No. XXXII-66, London, H.M.S.O., 1945), especially the section "Experiments on Coal Firing for an Athodyd," pp. 122–126; *Cf.* also G. B. Millikan, *Survey of German Ramjet Development* (C.I.O.S. Report No. XXX-81, London, H.M.S.O., July 1945), p. 23.

28 See "High Speed Flying and the Pilots: Lord Mottistone's Speech," *The Times* (London, July 19, 1946), p. 3.

29. The experiments with the Bristol Thor and the Napier NRJ-1 ramjets occurred, in fact, several years later, and these engines were not used on any airplane expressly designed for them.

30. See Aeronautical Research Council, *Review for the Years 1939–1948* (London, H.M.S.O., 1950), p. 29.

31. See *"Inghilterra: Nuovo centro di ricerche aeronautiche," Notiziario di Aviazione* (Rome, Ministry of Aeronautics, September 16, 1946), p. 19.

32. *Cf.* "The National Aeronautical Establishment," *The Aero-Plane* (London, August 30, 1946), pp. 243–245; and "Supersonic Research," *Aeronautics* (London, Vol. XV, No. 3, October 1946), p. 71.

CHAPTER 8

Nothing to
Give in Exchange

In March 1946, while describing to the House of Commons the "great future" in view for the British aircraft industry thanks to new projects that were in gestation, Wing Commander John Strachey, Undersecretary in the Air Ministry, declared that the government was also considering "several pilotless aircraft possibilities" that were particularly promising and reassuring for Britain's defense.

At that time the British had only two missiles, neither of which seemed to justify the undersecretary's expressions of faith.

The first was the Fairey Stooge radio-controlled antiaircraft rocket, only a few of which had been built.[1] And it was, in fact, a rocket and not a plane. As for the other, the Vickers rocket that was still on paper, Sir Ben Lockspeiser himself had clearly stated that it was not a weapon but a flying laboratory. Transforming it into a flying bomb would in any case have taken time, and it seems that despite the quite different view held by Vickers it did not even figure in the plans of the Ministry of Supply once it was demonstrated that the German Henschel flying bombs had a limited success, for they were all subject to British radio jamming.

The prevalent opinion in London press circles was that the R.A.F. had secretly developed a "new weapon" that had been found virtually completed in one of the many underground factories in southern Germany.

Strachey's declaration gave strong support to the undoubtedly praiseworthy (if sincere) desire of the higher-ups in the Ministry of Supply to avoid, as they constantly proclaimed, risking anyone's life. Theoretically, this desire lasted until 1949, when the problems of supersonic aerodynamics had been sufficiently clarified (and besides, the Americans and the Russians were developing supersonic planes for military use) for the Supply Ministry to give a go-ahead on the first two British experimental piloted fighters capable of reaching the speed of Mach 2. These were the Fairey Delta-2 and the English Electric P-1-A.

The dropping of the Miles M-52 project had, in fact, been justified on the grounds that "we have not the heart to ask pilots to fly the high-speed models, so we shall make them radio controlled" (Sir Ben Lockspeiser's exact words).

The respect of the British for individual safety is well known, but despite that the pious expressions of the Ministry must have been very relative, what with conventional planes' continually approaching closer and closer to the "sound barrier" (which could be placed in the neighborhood of 745 mph) and trying to penetrate into the then still largely unexplored field of supersonic speeds, sometimes with fatal results. In fact, the echoes of ministerial regret for the death of Geoffrey De Havilland had hardly died down. De Havilland had been killed when the prototype of the tailless De Havilland DH-108 Swallow which he was testing over Suffolk exploded in the air. And the aim of that ambitious flight was indeed the breaking of the sound barrier. The undertaking was a private one, but the Ministry of Supply had been informed about it and the Ministry neither prevented it nor threw any obstacles in its path. (Here is a disturbing but pointed question: if the flight had succeeded, how could the torpedoing of the M-52 have been justified?)

The second part of the declaration seemed, as a result, more consonant with the actual state of affairs—*i.e.*, the part dealing with the study of new systems of supersonic flight—especially when compared with what was stated apropos of the research program that would be continued at Bedford.

In general, it is still widely believed today that the "spectacular radio-controlled aircraft" that Sir Ben Lockspeiser announced at the time was the Vickers 24/43 winged rocket. It is clear, however, that that device was not in fact radio-controlled in the true sense of the term, but made use of short-wave radio solely for simple corrections of the flight path and for transmitting flight data to the ground.

Instead, rather numerous formations of circular-shaped objects of only fifteen or twenty feet were more than once observed flying over American states along the Canadian border in July 1947. Considering the rather small dimensions of those machines (as compared with those sighted later), wouldn't one logically conclude that they were radio-controlled from some guide-aircraft flying some distance off or at higher altitudes?

Two years before, the British had got their hands on a "device that could be controlled at considerable distance by another aircraft" while they were digging among the technological secrets that had been moved into the Alpine Redoubt. This device had a television apparatus, developed by Telefunken in their large factory at Bad Liebenstein, that worked to perfection. The British never made clear exactly what kind of device was involved, stating only that it was a "remotely controlled pilotless aircraft;" hence we must assume that it was something quite different from the many types of rockets which had been described in the press with a profusion of details.

In addition, a number of examples of television apparatuses

King Size
or Deluxe 100's.

Micronite filter.
Mild, smooth taste.
America's quality cigarette.
Kent.

Try the crisp, clean taste of Kent Menthol.

The only Menthol with the famous Micronite filter.

Warning: The Surgeon General Has Determined That Cigarette Smoking Is Dangerous to Your Health

built for the Henschel HS-293-D flying bombs fell into British hands. One of these was later exhibited at the German Electrical-Apparatus Exhibition at Earl's Court in London in March 1946. The others were sent to various centers concerned with military applications of television, the Telecommunication Research Establishment and the Royal Radar Establishment at Great Malvern being the most important such centers. Here world-famous physicists specializing in the properties of electricity, such as Sir Watson-Watt and Sir Henry Tizzard, delved into their innermost mechanisms in order to adapt them to the needs of British research.

QUESTIONS WITHOUT ANSWERS

That there was a close relationship between the "pilotless aircraft" of Undersecretary Strachey and the "planes that use no fuel" of the Ministry of Supply can be deduced from previously published news stories in the British press, which had been informed—perhaps secretly—by the same highly placed sources interested in adding a bit of luster to the nation's aeronautical prestige. One of these stories, which had appeared in January 1946, said briefly:

"Apropos of radio-controlled airplanes, we learn that high-speed experiments have been made with planes piloted by radio and equipped with television transmitters. As is well-known, it sometimes happens that an airplane that has begun a maneuver at speeds above 560 mph no longer answers to the controls—which often means the loss of a pilot. With the above-mentioned planes, however, experiments can be carried out without this danger."

We know that the first Vickers rockets flew in November 1947. The devices reported in the news story, however, had already begun their operational phase at the end of 1945. Unlike the Vickers rockets, they had a television apparatus aboard. They were, then, "pilotable" in the full sense of the word. What did they look like? Where did the experiments take place? What were the results of those experiments? What kind of propulsive method did they employ? Who built them?

Why was their testing kept secret? Why were there no detailed press releases? And why were there no further leaks about it? Here we have a series of questions that remained without answers, mute but eloquent evidence of the extreme importance of those experiments.

It should not astonish us, however. The chronicle of British aviation over the past twenty years has a number of "mysteries" of the same caliber. For example, in March 1952—just before the "Big Flap" that shook the circles around the A.T.I.C. and the U.S. Air Force—Her Majesty's Stationery Office printed Report No. 2612 for the Aeronautical Research Council. It was taken from confidential internal report No. 10294 and was clearly and thoroughly censored. In the report, Professor Thwaites of the National Physical Laboratory briefly illustrated the results of several of his physical-mathematical investigations on elliptical airfoils capable of developing a high degree of lift independent of the incidence of the entire wing structure. The subject was interesting, but it was nothing new.[2] What was new was the sibylline reference to bizarre suction airfoils called constant-velocity airfoils, one with an elegant two-pointed meniscus shape and the other with a curious if not monstrous-looking mushroom shape.[3]

The report mentioned them incidentally, saying only that unlike the elliptical airfoils, the lift developed by the constant velocity types "is not independent of the incidence and the possibility of applying them to airplanes can be considered only after the limits of their stability are exactly determined. It is possible that these profiles are unstable at zero incidence and it is certainly difficult to imagine what the behavior of the aerodynamic flow for the other incidences would be. In addition, the fact that they can operate at a unit value of the coefficient of lift might require a special flight technique and a particular type of plane." Unfortunately, the board of directors of the Aeronautical Research Council classified the information on these two last points, which were the kernel of the whole question.

Nevertheless, the technical press in 1947 published a concise description of a number of daring British innovations concerning wing structure and high-speed flight. At one point it wrote:

"Concern with obtaining absolute stability in all cases in accordance with the principle that it is an intrinsic quality of the aircraft, not to be acquired at the cost of some static or aerodynamic balance, has led to the development of a new wing formula called the Boomerang both because of its shape and its behavior. A project for a commercial plane called the Spuffing Boomerang Airliner with an independent, gyroscopic cabin has begun."[4]

PLANES WITH GYROSCOPIC STABILIZATION

Perhaps completely accidentally, the press had erroneously combined and blended two different bits of news from the same source—the Hawker Siddeley Group—but referring to two different aircraft projects.

The first, the AW-52 Boomerang flying wing—with its wing tips perceptibly swept back and reminding one of the weapon of the Australian aborigines—carried two powerful turbojets, whence the name Spuffing Airliner. But the pilot's cabin was completely normal.[5]

The other should have caused the most die-hard skeptics in the Air Technical Intelligence Centre to ask themselves (at least in 1952) this basic question: Over five years have passed since these leaks were published in the papers. Which of Britain's numerous aircraft that have flown from then to now has an independent, gyroscopically stabilized cabin?

None, officially; and that even includes types now in the project stage, would have been the inevitable answer.

The ingenious solution—which escaped the technological doubts that Professor Thwaites had voiced years before and was absolutely new in the field of aircraft construction—allowed it to be clearly understood that the cabin was ringed with a rotating organ of large dimensions (as in the Italo-German turbo-projectiles and the Fireballs), involving the need for autonomous and automatic stabilization. This was required in order to offset, among other things, the motion of tangential pull on the craft (the fixed plane) by the propulsive rotor (the turbine). On the flying saucers this rotor rapidly rotates within the not at all metaphoric saucer, or inverted funnel, which surrounds the central cupola and which obviously must be kept stationary in the direction of flight. (Otherwise the continual rotation on its own axis would not only upset the flight path but would put the nervous systems of the poor pilots to a severe test.)

In 1945 the National Physical Laboratory's division of applied physics had reexamined a system of direct gyroscopic stabilization. It was modeled on the same system that at the beginning of the century had made the "miracle" of the Monorail train possible (a curious vehicle that has never come into widespread use; it was kept balanced on a single rail thanks to the gyrostatic inertia developed by a small but heavy and rapidly spinning flywheel). In addition, the laboratory put to profitable use in its own studies the experience accumulated by the scientists of the Kreiselgeräte G.m.b.H. of Berlin Britz, a dissolved company that had specialized in the study and construction of mechanisms employing gyroscopic phenomena. In 1943 the Kreiselgeräte had succeeded in reducing the oscillations of a violently disturbed moving body to not more than one-tenth of a degree.

During the next decade—it is an established fact and one that has not been demonstrated elsewhere to the same degree —the British made considerable use of the gyroscopic apparatuses for the most diverse military and technical applications.[6]

Evidently the officers in the A.T.I.C. did not know or did not want to draw the conclusions that one recurrent phrase in the sighting reports would have broadly supported: ". . . seen from below the UFO seemed to spin rapidly on its own axis, except for the central part, which appeared to be stationary. . . ."

THE GREAT AIR TECHNOLOGY
"MIGRATION" OF 1946

Among the fragmentary news stories that reported the transfer by the Canadian government of the Turbo-Research Ltd. plants to the Hawker Siddeley Group there were several that referred to the imminence of other radical changes in the local aircraft industry, which because of war production needs had grown quite large, especially in the eastern part of the country, over the preceding five years.

Plans were laid for a sort of gigantic "migration" to the western area of the Dominion, with the formation of research, testing and production centers—centering on the urban area of Vancouver—for new types of planes and engines that would be "Canadian designed and Canadian built" and for the local production of "special fuels." The whole thing was to be accomplished in record time.

The greatest impulse toward this development, which was rapidly brought to a conclusion, came in the spring of 1946, when Professor B. S. Shenstone—described by the technical journals as a "Canadian scientist with a brilliant scientific background" and an expert in, among other things, problems dealing with the control of the boundary layer—was named general manager and technical assistant to vice-president W. N. Deisher of Avro-Canada. Previously he had been an assistant director in the Ministry of Aircraft Production's office in charge of the development of projects relating to postwar air transport.[7]

But we had an authoritative indication of what was developing in Canada in the fall of 1945, when a brilliant aeronautical future was openly being predicted in England for its overseas dominion. For example, *The Aeroplane* wrote: "The recent purchase [July 1] of the Victory Aircraft,Ltd., plant at Malton, Ontario, which is at present engaged in the production of the Lincoln bomber, by the Hawker-Siddeley Co., might mean that Canada will become the British Empire's aircraft production centre within the next ten years."[8]

At the beginning of 1946 the British group also took over the plants of Turbo-Research of Leavside and put them under the administration of its Gas Turbine Division in Malton. Turbo-Research was a government body created in 1944 on the model of the British Power Jets for the study of local problems of jet propulsion. It had an experimental station in Winnipeg.

Foreign aeronautical circles were considerably surprised

by all this activity. True, the aeronautical industry was in a state of economic crisis. But the crisis certainly could not be overcome by selling a factory that promised to be highly productive and an experimental center that still had something new to contribute to jet propulsion, which, it should not be forgotten, was then taking its first steps.

It was thought that if the Canadian government had decided that it was a good idea to get rid of the factory and experimental center, perhaps that meant that Canada intended to concentrate its money and energies in some other direction.

When the UFOs appeared over Canada, the country's first crisis in the aviation industry had been laboriously overcome.

THE BASIS FOR SUCCESS

"Today Canada is to be counted among the greatest aeronautical powers in the world," N. S. Currey wrote in 1950. "But this abrupt leap forward from insignificant beginnings must not be attributed solely to its production of certain excellent types of planes but rather to the far-sightedness of the Canadian parliament. Canada has made its mark in a spectacular manner above all in the field of jet propulsion."[9]

The idea that Canada is an advanced and highly qualified producer of really excellent, modern jet planes of both military and civilian types will appear new and strange to the reader unfamiliar with aeronautical matters. In general the public thinks of Canada as an endless, cold, inhospitable land, rich in lumber, fish and fur-bearing animals, recently opened to large-scale immigration from Europe in order to exploit its immense natural resources. In other words, many Europeans still think of Canada as "a few acres of snow," as Voltaire put it long ago. "A few acres"! Nearly four million square miles containing gold, iron, copper, lead, nickel, aluminum, asbestos, and uranium, and producing large quantities of wheat, meat, fish, furs, and lumber. But the French administrators of the eighteenth century could not know all that, and after a series of military reverses they abandoned Canada to the British in 1763.

Actually, even the present twenty million population, for the most part inhabiting the two coastal areas, on a land almost the size of a continent (it is nine-tenths the size of Europe) comprises a decidedly modest human nucleus when compared with the tens of millions who live in countries with a long aeronautical tradition, such as England, Italy, France, and Germany.

Describing Canada as "the Promised Land of Aviation," the British aeronautical writer J. H. Stevens noted in 1952 that "the principal aircraft companies (A. V. Roe, Canadair, De Havilland) that build aircraft of their own design number two in Toronto and one in Montreal. Other minor specialist firms that contribute to making those places the centres of national aeronautical production are located in both of these cities and in their surrounding areas. The British Fairey Aviation Company has a well-known factory near Halifax in Nova Scotia. Other islands of air technology are on the Niagara peninsula, in Fort William, Winnipeg and Vancouver. The largest builder is, however, A. V. Roe Canada, Ltd., or Avro-Canada, which derives from the 'shade workshop' of Victory Aircraft Ltd. and is a branch of the British Hawker Siddeley Group. Nevertheless, it has an independent board of directors, like the other divisions, over which Sir Frank Spriggs and Sir Roy Dobson exercise only a general policy control. Other industries cover the whole field of accessories, instruments and aircraft materials. Hundreds of firms produce various parts according to the designs and standards of aircraft construction. Finally, Canada produces steel and light alloys for all its own needs making use of its vast mineral deposits. There is also a 'pilot plant' for the production of titanium. Canada possesses complete scientific and experimental equipment in the National Research Council of Ottawa. Wind tunnels, laboratories that are equipped to examine materials and construct models make it possible to carry out any kind of experiment. Another sign of Canada's determination not to remain behind in aeronautical progress is the fact that there are two electronic computers in Toronto: one at Avro-Canada and the other at the university, which also has a hypersonic wind tunnel in Downsview. During the winter, industrial production remains unaffected, for the factories are all well-heated. Even the hangars are kept at a temperature of 70°, avoiding drafts in a way that seems miraculous. The working conditions, for example, are better than those in the average British factory, and it is common practice to work in shirtsleeves during the winter, both in the offices and in the shops. The cold, however, makes it necessary that all the planes be kept under roof."[10]

AVRO SAUCERS FOR THE FAR NORTH?

At the beginning of 1953, when no one was thinking about flying discs, they suddenly began to appear in the columns of Canadian newspapers.

On February 11, the *Toronto Star* announced in a banner headline that flying saucers should no longer be confined to the realm of fantasy, because they were actually being developed in one of Avro-Canada's hangars at the Malton airfield. Two columns of details and the news that the device was supposed to have a top speed of 1500 mph gave the clear impression that the writer had obtained his information from a very well-informed, if not completely candid, source that obviously worked somewhere in the powerful company.

Certain government experts who were immediately interviewed by reporters from the nearby capital sought to extricate themselves from the awkward situation by evasively declaring: "The Defense authorities are examining all ideas, even revolutionary ones, that have been suggested for the development of new types of supersonic aircraft, *also including flying discs*. This, however, is still in the beginning phase of research and it will be a number of months before we are able to reach anything positive and seven or more years before we come to actual production."

According to the *Star*, on February 16 C. D. Howe, minister of defense production, told the House of Commons that "the government was constantly studying 'new concepts and new designs' for fighters . . . adding weight to reports that Avro is even now working on a mock-up model of a 'flying saucer' capable of flying 1500 miles per hour and climbing straight up in the air."

On February 27 the company involved also joined the chorus of "surprising" revelations. The president of the firm, Crawford Gordon, Jr., wrote in its house organ: "Like all aircraft companies who want to stay in business, we are directing a substantial part of our efforts towards new ideas and advanced designs.

"One of our projects can be said to be quite revolutionary in concept and appearance. The prototype being built is so revolutionary that when it flies all other types of supersonic aircraft will become obsolescent. This is all that Avro-Canada are going to say about this project."

After this vague and inconclusive statement, there were almost two months of relative calm. It seemed that the story was about to starve to death from lack of further specifics and that it would go the way of other journalistic revelations. But this was not to be. On April 21, the *Toronto Star* published the following: "Field Marshal Montgomery . . . became one of a handful of people ever to see Avro's mock-up of a 'flying saucer,' reputed to be capable of flying 1500 miles an hour. A guide who accompanied Montgomery quoted him as describing it as 'fantastic.' . . . Security precautions surrounding this super-secret are so tight that two of Montgomery's escorts from Scotland Yard were barred from the forbidden, screened-off area of the Avro plant."

This news, which was much more authoritative since a noted military personage was involved, gave rise to the strangest deductions. Later, on April 22 and 23, even the austere London *Times* opened its columns to news from the distant Dominion concerning those flying saucers, which it had hitherto severely banned from its cautious news columns.

On April 24, the *Toronto Star* confirmed its February story, adding that some of Canada's most noted aeronautical engineers were secretly working on a mysterious flying disc made of metal, wood, and plastics, which would allegedly be the "weapon of the future." For some time, said the *Star*, there had been rumors that an aircraft of this type was being built in Malton, but no one had got definite confirmation on it.

According to Air Vice Marshal D. M. Smith, what Field Marshal Montgomery had seen was the preliminary study of construction plans for a *gyroscopic fighter that could take off vertically and fly at a speed of 1500 mph. A gas turbine would revolve around the pilot, who would be positioned at the center of the disc.*

A SYMPTOMATIC SILENCE

For some time the leaks continued along the same lines, although without adding anything new, favored by the fact that the organ of British military aviation, the *R.A.F. Review,* reprinted almost the whole of the original Canadian inquiry, thereby conferring, so to speak, a semiofficial status upon the news.[11]

As a precaution, however, the review felt obliged to state that "none of the opinions expressed in the article" had been confirmed by the Air Ministry. In fact, all during the period that the news was breaking, the Ministry carefully kept its lips sealed. The Canadian flying saucer (the one in the newspapers) did not concern the Ministry, since, luckily for it, the truth about the real flying saucers of the R.C.A.F. was not even touched.

At this point began the discussions that played directly into the hands of the authorities that were directly interested in keeping the secret.

At the beginning of June, the daily information bulletin of the Swiss review *Interavia* reported that on the basis of inquiries made by its Canadian correspondent, the A. V. Roe flying disc was probably not in fact an airplane in the shape of a disc but, more simply, a delta-winged jet fighter–interceptor, that is, it had the shape of a triangle. In other words, it was a further development of the well-known Avro 707 heavy fighter and the Avro 698 Vulcan bomber powered with four jet engines.

The correspondent of the review was mistaken (or had he been deliberately misled?), since the firm had for some time been working on at least a third example of a delta-winged plane: the supersonic CF-105 Arrow, a twin-jet all-weather fighter of thirty-five tons, the testing date of which had, however, been scheduled at the earliest for the end of 1955. Evidently this project had nothing to do with the discs, which were several years in advance of it and had a radically different shape. And the proof of it is that when the press had completely forgotten the subject, a new, very brief story that appeared in Toronto on November 1 unexpectedly brought the subject up again.

The story read: "A mock-up of the Canadian flying saucer, the highly secret aircraft in whose existence few believe, was yesterday shown to a group of twenty-five American experts, including military officers and scientists."[12]

Further news on the Avro pseudo-disc, which had in the meantime been officially baptized the Avro Omega, came on the following October 21, when the press declared that the aircraft had been under study for at least two years and that the cost of the prototype was reported to have been in the area of $200 million.

According to the papers, the Canadian government was planning to form entire squadrons of flying saucers for the defense of Alaska and the frozen reaches of the Far North. Their claimed low cost of manufacture and maintenance, their ability to intercept any high-speed plane in operation and to take off vertically, made them the ideal weapon for operations in wooded areas of Canada and in the subarctic and polar regions, for they were "completely independent of vulnerable runways or any fixed special equipment."

The press of the Western world naturally received the news with a great sense of relief, and it unreservedly proclaimed: "The flying discs are real!" But waiting for the production-line Omegas (not to mention the prototype) began to drag out. A number of months passed. The summer came, then autumn, and still the Omega did not fly. Other saucers did fly, however, those that had been well known for a number of years.

UFOS OVER ENGLAND

The story began as follows. Sergeant Harry Waller of the 256th Anti-aircraft Regiment was setting up a radar installation in the southeast section of London when, between 3:30 and 4:15 P.M. on November 3, 1953, he noticed a strong signal at the edge of the scanning screen. After the blip was centered, it was received solidly.

Through the eyepiece of a theodolite, the object appeared to be white—"an incandescent white"—perfectly circular, the size of a tennis ball, and just about directly over the installation. By comparing the data obtained from the radar and the theodolite, it was deduced that it must have been hovering between 60,000 and 65,000 feet.

In the report forwarded to the War Office, the observer stated that it could not have been a weather balloon because the type of signal received by the radar indicated the presence of a metallic object of gigantic size. The return signals had actually been three or four times larger than those produced by the largest plane known. In addition, after hovering motionless for about ten minutes, the strange object flew rapidly out of radar and eye range.

From an investigation that was launched immediately, it was learned that no research balloons measuring 200 feet in diameter (for that was the size of the body that had been received on radar) had been launched in Great Britain for three months. A meteor trail would not have yielded the sharp edges of the image on the radar screen and a rocket could not have remained motionless in mid-air for so long a period of time.

On the same day—indeed, during just about the same period of time—T. S. Johnson and C. H. Smythe, two pilots who were flying over Kent at 15,000 feet in a Vampire training fighter, caught sight of the shiny UFO, which was flying at very high speed at about 60,000 feet, and they mentioned it in their flight report to the authorities. In the report they stated that it seemed to be spinning on its vertical axis and giving off fiery jets around its circumference, while a vivid, bluish light emanated from the central portion.

The interest aroused by the mysterious apparition—which finally brought the UFO psychosis to phlegmatic Britain—and additional sightings of unknown flying objects that continued to be reported from various parts of the country (sightings that naturally would have to be discounted because of the saucer excitement that was spreading among the public) ended by upsetting a number of highly placed personages. They demanded reassurances.

On November 19 the *News Chronicle* reported the Air Ministry's announcement: "We are not prepared to comment on individual reports . . . Every report is investigated, but 95% are found to be due to natural phenomena. About the others, the experts can reach no conclusion."

In the House of Commons a group led by Labour M. P. Bellenger introduced a question demanding whether the War Office was able to state the exact nature of the object that had been picked up by radar.

The government spokesman asked for a week in which to make the reply. Strange things occurred during that week. The Air Ministry backed up its declaration. The spokesman of the Defense Ministry also warmly approved: it was a weather balloon. Nothing unusual! The War Office—which was responsible for the questionable statement—after conducting a "new" series of investigations did a complete turnabout and in its second statement candidly admitted that the sighting was to be attributed to "mechanical deficiencies," that is, to certain transitory anomalies in the operation of the radar apparatus when it picked up a balloon of normal size and characteristics. (Someone, easing his conscience even more, added: electrical.)

The spokesman for the Ministry of Defense quickly disposed of the matter to an unusually crowded House on November 24, and although the newspapers showed considerable skepticism, they printed the official declarations and dropped the matter. Evidently the time was not yet ripe for the "big news."

THE SECRET OF THE CANADIAN STORY

The scanty news that was coming out of Canada in the meantime gave more and more support to the initial skepticism of the few people who lacked faith in the Omega. There was talk of sending the whole project to the United States, which would receive the honor, not to mention obligation, of building it and other projects that were under study and might replace the original model, which had "proved rather inefficient." The name of a certain aeronautical engineer, J. C. M. Frost, who had been identified as the principal designer of the project, began to appear with greater and greater frequency.

Finally, in March 1954, the American press described both Frost's hopes and the project in complete detail. The start of this new story was rather unusual.

Concerned about the marked progress that Soviet scientists had shown in the fields of jet aircraft and guided missiles, the United States Air Force had allocated a large sum (the exact figure was a military secret) for building within three years a prototype of the flying saucer that had been so well publicized in the press.

According to rumors circulating among military experts, U.S.-Canadian joint defense authorities had agreed to build the craft. "This is a ship that will be able to take off vertically," declared those who enthusiastically believed that the Western hemisphere could be defended by flying discs, "to hover in mid-air and to move at a speed of about 1850 mph. That is, it would be capable of performing all the maneuvers that flying discs are said to be capable of. This astonishing craft is the brain child of the English aeronautical engineer John Frost, who worked for the large De Havilland factory in England during the war and who later went on to A. V. Roe, in Malton, Canada. The aircraft that will be built for the U.S. Air Force is not, however, the first of this type that Frost has designed. Two years ago he had designed and submitted to American experts an aircraft which was called the Flying Manta because of its behavior on take-off. It more or less resembled the present disc, but it could not take off vertically.[13] In addition, its top speed did not exceed 1430 mph. The Manta had interested the American General Staff, but in view of these operating deficiencies, it was decided not to build it."

Month after month of 1954 went by without further news from Canada, either official or semiofficial.[14] By now people were expecting to see the Frost discs, with a combined emblem of the United States star and the Canadian maple leaf painted on them, flying through the skies by the dozen. Instead, on December 3 the Canadian Defense Ministry suddenly and officially announced that the project was being abandoned because, although a number of sub-assemblies had been built and it was believed that the machine would fly, *it was agreed that it would have served no useful purpose.*

When he was interviewed by reporters, Minister of Defense Howe confirmed the decision, adding that perhaps four or five million dollars had been spent on the Frost disc, but that the project had been given up without being carried to its final development because that would have involved a total expense in the neighborhood of 100 million dollars on something that was highly speculative.

THE QUARLES STATEMENT

On October 25, 1955, Air Force Secretary Donald Quarles released a statement through the press office of the Department of Defense permitting the A.T.I.C. to divulge some of the conclusions it had reached after its investigation of the UFOs. Among other things, Quarles declared:

"We are now entering a period of aviation technology in which aircraft of unusual configuration and flight characteristics will begin to appear. . . . The Air Force will fly the first jet-powered vertical-rising airplane in a matter of days. *We have another project under contract with AVRO Ltd., of Canada, which could result in disc-shaped aircraft somewhat similar to the popular concept of a flying saucer. . . .* While some of these may take novel forms, such as the AVRO project, they are direct-line descendants of conventional aircraft and should not be regarded as supra-natural or mysterious. . . . Vertical-rising aircraft capable of transition to supersonic horizontal flight will be a new phenomenon in our skies, and under certain conditions could give the illusion of the so-called flying saucer. The Department of Defense will make every effort within the bounds of security to keep the public informed of these developments so they can be recognized for what they are. . . . *I think we must recognize that other countries also have the capability of developing vertical-rising aircraft, perhaps of unconventional shapes.* However, we are satisfied at this time that none of the sightings of so-called 'flying saucers' reported in this country were in fact aircraft of foreign origin."[15]

Whether it was deliberate or merely a slip (even the newspapers failed to catch it!), Quarles got his tenses all wrong. He was talking about aircraft of the near future, while the flying discs belonged to the past and not a very recent past at that.

According to news stories in the American papers, the new Avro project was the latest Frost project and was described as an aircraft resembling a plate turned upside down (finally!) with 180 adjustable nozzles distributed around its perimeter that would make vertical take-off possible and then, by changing the angles of the nozzles, enable the craft to move forward, sideways, or backwards.

Even leaving aside doubts about the seriousness of the project, it is at least astonishing that for the first time in the history of flight an aircraft (and a pioneering, supersonic plane at that) promised to take shape solely according to suggestions of the public at large!

In any case, the first reliable news came in February 1959. It was then called "a revolutionary type of vertical take-off plane based on the principle of the 'ring jet' that promises a 100 percent or more increase in lift at take-off through the 'ground effect' as compared with the 15 to 20 percent obtained by helicopters." In other words, an aeronautical adaptation of the physical principle behind the Vickers Hovercraft that was conceived in 1953 in order to exploit the so-called "air cushion" produced by a jet aimed at the ground: a curious machine of considerable utility that is in current use and is also being produced in the United States. Its field, however, is limited, for it cannot in practice fly any higher than six feet or any faster than 300 mph.

In fact, semiofficial statements later described it—without, however, adding any noteworthy details—as "a type of aircraft that combines the characteristics of air cushion machines and airplanes, the development of which is being jointly undertaken by the U.S. Army and U.S. Air Force and the Canadian government because the project promises to result in a machine that could revolutionize all the ordinary methods of aerial reconnaissance."

The American papers did not, of course, fail to feature this latest bit of news. For openers, Field Marshal Montgomery was involved again: it was said that he had been given a model of the new machine. A few weeks later another "well-informed" (but anonymous) source baldly declared that England had a considerable fleet of flying saucers at the ready in Canada and that Field Marshal Montgomery had been present at recent, highly secret maneuvers of these craft. "These machines," the cautious reporter wrote, "were built by A. V. Roe and then shipped to a special secret airfield in the center of the country."

In reality, Avro was going through a bad period.

THE END OF THE "AVRO-CAR"

After stating that the potential air threat to Canada had diminished because the Soviets had only a limited number of intercontinental bombers, the Canadian government used the statement as a pretext for canceling the contract for the CF-105 (the Arrow), a heavy bomber, and for its power plant, the Iroquois turbojet, thereby forcing Avro to lay off a large portion of its personnel.[16]

These decisions by the government and the company threw almost 10,000 people out of work, most of them specialists, for the Avro Saucer project—renamed the Avro-Car and financed by the United States (for the simple reason that, according to official sources, "there was as yet no comparable project in the United States")—could barely keep the technicians and skilled workers of the main plants fully occupied.

On April 14, 1959, General Frank Britton during a short press conference in Washington restated the facts, implying that the first test flight of the aircraft would soon be taking place and cautiously declaring that the new type of airplane was "perhaps" destined to revolutionize traditional aeronautical concepts but that there had been some difficulties in developing the idea.

Again a number of months passed without any news, but finally, in August 1960, the American authorities decided to allow reporters to see the prototype, which in the meantime had been changed from a single- to a two-seater. The difficulties had not disappeared. Even though masked by optimism for the occasion, the results were not very encouraging. Quite the contrary. The official report ended, in fact, with the obvious observation that "even for this type of V.T.O.L. plane (vertical take-off and landing) the principal problem is low speed stability. Tests with a full-scale model have been made at the large forty by eighty foot wind tunnel at the Ames Research Center, belonging to N.A.S.A., but they were not completely successful. It became clear, however, that the various problems inherent in a circular aircraft of this type are not insurmountable."[17]

While ufologists jumped with joy on learning of the serious shortcomings of these phony earth-made discs (shortcomings that, according to them, our Brothers from Space had brilliantly overcome several centuries, or perhaps even several millennia, ago), the first model of this type continued in its period of gestation for yet more months, occasionally rising clumsily above the cement runway at Malton. Finally, in December 1961 the United States Department of Defense decided to withdraw from participation in the development of the Avro-Car on the grounds that the formula had failed. It was another plane that definitely had "no tomorrow."

Here ends the *official* story of the Canadian flying saucers. An endless series of half-truths and manipulation of facts, perhaps agreed upon at the highest levels, in order to deliberately muddy the already dark waters of the whole affair.

In any case, the significant fact is established that the only country that has publicly stated that it was working on plans and actually building aircraft having some resemblance (at least externally) to the "notorious" flying discs has been Canada.

GRATIFIED AMBITIONS

The Canadian desire to do something big and new in the field of aviation was first manifested in 1942 when the government had a large military airfield, with room for expansion, built near Arnprior, about forty miles from Ottawa.

The aeronautical circles of the capital made no bones about their plans to transform the Arnprior Airport into a Canadian Farnborough (or, better, into a Canadian Royal Aeronautical Establishment) for the Canadian National Research Council. Requests for technical and financial assistance to carry out these plans were made to the British government at the time of the Commonwealth Conference of 1944.

A duplicate of the Royal Aeronautical Establishment? It would only be extra work and expense. The wooded mountains of southwest Canada offered much solider possibilities and guarantees for the erection of a large experimental center that could develop not only the types of aircraft that everyone was familiar with but also types of aircraft that *no one* should know about, at least until some indefinite time in the future.

With the help of the most close-mouthed civil servants in the Canadian Department of Mines and the Technical Surveys Mapping Branch, conditions in four selected zones in the southern part of the country were examined. This was a vast mountainous and almost deserted region (over seventy-five square miles) situated astride the boundary between British Columbia and Alberta, bordering the state of Washington on the south and reaching the Peace River District in the north.

The location was ideal: a few mountain roads and all of them easily controlled. Virtually nonexistent local traffic in the area round about. Not a single agglomeration of houses that could be called a city. An extensive string of islands and islets off the coastal zone. A thin network of railroads far to the north and to the south: the spur of the Canadian National Railway that links Prince George with Edmonton and the spur from Vancouver that runs along the United States border. One single large automobile artery—the Alaska Highway—

winding through the silent valleys and running almost due north.

The remote and wooded nature of the area would act—as it did indeed act—as a natural barrier to any indiscreet eye.

THE SHADE WORKSHOPS

The British were not new at undertakings of this sort. In the extensive area of the New Forest in Hampshire, the R.A.F. had secretly set up five airfields for the Bomber Command in 1942.[18]

The keystone of the British camouflaging of large secret factories was, however, the "shade workshops," which were developed in order to put the war industry in a place of safety by distributing it among the wooded regions of the country.

The public relations department of the British Railways printed a booklet in 1945 entitled *It Can Now Be Revealed* in order to publicize the railways' contribution to victory. Here we read:

"Whenever a new arms city has been born, the railway has usually been prenatal consultant, midwife and full-time foster-parent in turn.

"A certain big ordnance factory in South Wales provides an excellent example. This factory—its name must still remain a secret—was conceived when the first war clouds began to appear on the horizon, but its designers planned it on so vast a scale that thirty-five months were to pass before the digging, the building and the equipping were finished and a start made upon production. . . .

"The factory grew up on twin sites. On one of these sites the work of burrowing deep into the hillside to build a warren of underground magazines was begun. . . .

"The completed ordnance factory contained 1100 separate buildings, mostly of bricks . . . and concrete, occupying an area of four square miles. It is served internally by 58 miles of roads and 24 miles of railway. Its electric power is carried by 300 miles of cable . . . At peak production it was estimated that 37,000 men and women, working on three shifts, would be needed. . . . As with the workers, so with the raw materials upon which they work and with the products of their industry, representing two perfectly controlled flows of hundreds of tons daily."

With the exception of the persons concerned, the rest of the population of the United Kingdom worked or fought without remotely suspecting the existence of this and other similar emergency set-ups. (And today people say that it would be impossible to have UFOs operating out of secret bases!) Even the Luftwaffe had no inkling of this appetizing objective, but if by chance it had been lucky enough to hear of the place, through spy channels, it would have been very difficult to spot among the natural evergreens and those that had been transplanted there, the camouflage nets scattered about in profusion, and the "bird lures" erected in the vicinity.

On the other hand, the R.A.F. command did have a general notion about the existence of the L.F.A., the large experimental center dedicated to Hermann Göring, from repeated reports from the Intelligence Service. According to these reports, the center was engaged in highly important research and was located in Volkenrode, near Braunschweig.[19] Allied reconnaissance planes repeatedly crisscrossed the area looking for the mysterious center, but unsuccessfully. All that could be seen on the photographs were scattered farmhouses and extensive woods interlaced by highways and country roads. There was no indication of military structures.

In reality, the more than seventy buildings comprising the center seemed merely to be innocent farms or were so scattered in the depths of a thick pine forest and so well protected by this natural camouflage that although it covered a total area of nearly two and a half square miles it could not have been spotted even by a low-flying plane.

The town itself was repeatedly bombed by Anglo-American planes. Only two bombs ever fell on the L.F.A., and they were dropped by accident: an American four-engined bomber that had been hit by flak jettisoned its remaining bomb load to lighten the plane for the return flight.

To set up the UFO bases and keep them hidden from any prying eyes that might fly over them, technicians already had at their disposal a choice of tested systems: they could either put the bases underground (using old abandoned mines) or depend on the camouflage afforded by the natural vegetation.

It was decided to use prefabricated hangars because—since there was no fear of air attack—they could easily be built, shipped, and set up even in remote areas; in time, if it proved necessary, they could be put underground and covered with shrub so that they would be invisible from above.

The original nucleus of the buildings—the work of a special branch of the Hawker Siddeley Group that specialized in manufacturing prefabricated buildings—grew rapidly with the influx of German technicians and projects. And finally Soviet secret agents in Canada got indirect word of the matter.[20]

THE "OTTAWA SCANDAL"

Nevertheless, it must be assumed that these agents did not succeed in drawing a complete and exact picture of Canadian activity in the highly specialized branch of suction aircraft, spherical rockets, and other types of unconventional aircraft, for government authorities had immediately taken Draconian measures that virtually isolated from the outer world the entire area where the secret aircraft industry was being developed.[21]

The newspapers of the time mentioned atomic spying, but the affair was in reality a good deal more complicated than that.

Administrative and technical personnel of the Soviet Embassy and four Canadian civil servants were involved in the proved accusation of industrial and military spying that became known as the "Ottawa scandal."

On February 19, 1946, Defense Minister Howe declared curtly to the press: "The spy affair does not involve either atomic secrets or the smuggling of uranium. It's another matter entirely!"

According to the Exchange-Telegraph Press Service, the spies had come into possession of information on radar and on Canadian factories engaged in the production of war materials, "continuously obtaining information over a period of several months." To be exact, since August 1945.

On March 4, 1946, the Royal Canadian Commission of Enquiry made public its final report. We do not know whether it is complete or was censored. It gives a list of the individuals concerned and a list of Soviet requests for information concerning twenty-one different military, industrial, organizational, and scientific areas or matters. These included: radar, snorkels, V-2 torpedo rockets, floodlights, the locations of known and secret military factories and what they produced, the units and deployment of the armed forces, large troop movements, supply services, special air and field grenades, antisubmarine bombs, industrial and chemical techniques, samples of uranium, explosives, atomic centers, the correspondence and movement of diplomatic officials, highly placed persons who might be corrupted, projects under study at the Canadian National Research Council.

The official report ended with the following observation: "We can demonstrate completely only the activity of four of the agents employed in the service of the Soviet embassy. The evidence indicates that many other agents besides the four specifically mentioned were involved and *information more intrinsically important has been sent out of the country.* We are not in a position to report on it yet because further evidence has to be taken."

The sequel was never made known. Since secret matters were involved, the veil of secrecy fell over all.

And since military secrecy does not recognize friendships or alliances except in the hour of danger, even the United States was kept in the dark as to what was being done in, so to speak, its neighbor's backyard.

LET WHOEVER DOES IT WAIT FOR IT

In order to understand this curious inconsistency better we must go back to the end of 1945, when the Americans were walking tall because of their brilliant victory over Japan and their exclusive possession of the atom bomb. They had not yet experienced the anxieties and disappointments of the "cold war" and the small "hot" wars in colonial countries. American power spread over the whole world, and the world that was rising out of the ruins of war was hungry: hungry for flour for underfed masses and hungry for money for industries with empty bank accounts.

Even England needed economic and financial assistance, and it asked for help in the name of the recent victorious alliance. Help was given, but psychologically and practically England was made to feel obligated.

In January 1946, just as they were beginning to be open-handed about giving important information to the press, the British authorities had to come to a reckoning concerning the sudden but not completely unexpected American objections to the exchange of scientific information. This exchange had been agreed upon during the war and had made it possible for the Allies to meet and beat the Germans' formidable technological potential. Now America refused to bring the British government up to date on the atomic secrets being studied at the various centers in the United States with an excuse that must objectively be recognized as almost an insult to the United Kingdom.

The sensational development that suddenly spotlighted one of the "silent struggles" dividing the two biggest Western powers had begun on October 8, 1945. On that day President Truman declared that the secret industrial and mechanical processes that had led to the production of the atomic bomb would be communicated "to no other nation." He indirectly explained why this rule was also applied to England, stating that although England had spent $100 million to develop the atom bomb before turning the work over to the United States (that is, before 1943), America itself had subsequently spent $2 billion before the bomb was ready for use. Ergo: the bomb had become by fact and right an exclusively American property.

American obstructionism was then extended to the mining of uranium and to the processes for its peaceful, or industrial, exploitation. A news story published by the British press in January 1946 aroused the indignation of every good British and Dominion subject:

"The American authorities," the papers said, "have recently forbidden the communication of the results of researches on atomic energy to Great Britain because she has nothing to give America in exchange. British plans for the development of atomic energy are virtually at a standstill since the plant of an experimental station in Berkshire is hobbled by the lack of trained personnel. In addition, the lack of plutonium and uranium 235 that Great Britain has failed to obtain from America has delayed the start of experiments for which one and a half million pounds have been allocated."

Could touchy British pride take this hidden blackmail lying down? After all, it also involved powerful financial interests that were being seriously hurt.

The flow of official statements on aeronautical matters stopped almost abruptly. In addition, the secret negotiations being conducted with the highest American authorities who had been invited to take part in the development of new methods of flight that they could not comprehend, or underestimated, were interrupted. These negotiations had, however, come to a standstill when the Pentagon demanded to know exactly what the British had in mind and what advantages those particular projects would offer over and above those already being developed in the United States. This had occurred during the time when Secretary of Defense Forrestal was trying to impose his own style of Anglo-American collaboration, on the basis of an approach that he claimed would give equal voice to the two countries but that might later, in practice, perhaps be translated into a new Yankee hegemony extending to the field of new aircraft construction.

The British and Canadian authorities then decided to go it alone also in the field of nuclear energy, and they succeeded completely.[22]

As for the New Aviation then aborning, on June 24, 1947 (that is a real "date to remember"!), a formation of nine circular-shaped suction aircraft took off from a secret Canadian airfield and really let America's leaders know that England did have "something to give in exchange."

NOTES

1. Planned during the final phase of the Pacific War by the research and development division of Fairey Aviation Company

as a defense against the Japanese Kamikaze, the "Stooge" was a rocket bomb that resembled a torpedo seven and a half feet in length and a foot in diameter, with a rectangular-shaped wing having a span of nine feet and a conventional tail assembly with a rectangular surface. In its essential lines it followed the German V-1 flying bomb, except for the propulsive mechanism, which was a quadruple rocket using solid fuel and located in the after third of the body, and for the high-frequency control. It carried an explosive charge of 220 pounds, and its top speed was between 500 and 560 mph.

2. *Cf.* Prof. B. Thwaites, *On the Design of Aerofoils for Which the Lift Is Independent of the Incidence* (Aeronautical Research Council Reports and Memoranda No. 2612, London, H.M.S.O., 1947), p. 17. See also the same writer's Report No. 2611, *The Production of Lift Independent of Incidence: The Thwaites' Wing Flap* (London, 1947) and the report published in the *Journal of the Royal Aeronautical Society*, February 1948, the subject of which is "The Production of Wing Lift Independent of Incidence." This subject was not completely new, as can be deduced from the fact that as long ago as 1929 the German technician Oskar Schrenk had published a memorandum entitled "Researches on the Production of Lift without Recourse to the Angle of Incidence" in the *Zeitschrift für Mathematik und Physik*, issued by the University of Heidelberg.

3. Their appearance might well astonish even experts in aeronautical problems, who could look for information in the latest aeronautical texts without finding it. They belong to a secret experimental "family" of special suction airfoils called G.V.A., worked out by Professor Thwaites. Their application to flight was subordinated to the adoption of special norms. At the time the report was published, wild rumors were circulating among aeronautical circles in England stating that these profiles were designed for a "flying wing" project that would be circular in plan view and for the main section of "all body" (wingless) aircraft of mixed lift (aerodynamic-jet). The idea of a fuselage with lift must have been

suggested by examination of data the Germans had obtained on the aerodynamic behavior of the spindle-shaped inclined body of the V-2 rockets when they were tested in the supersonic wind tunnel at Kochel. These tests were carried out initially to study drift patterns and subsequently, in function of the relationship between lift and resistance, to lengthen the gliding range of the missiles. Later on, the idea, which in its basic form derived directly from the German studies, was also studied by the Americans with their Pluto project; but the Marquardt low-level supersonic unlimited-range vehicles—missiles with a nuclear ramjet without wings or with only vestigial wings—which were supposed to be ready to fly in 1963 really existed only on paper.

4. Cf. "*Nasce una nuova architettura delle cellule?*," *Alata* (Milan, February 1947), pp. 10–11.

5. Nevertheless, to avoid any misunderstanding, it should be noted that after the AW-52 "flying wing" was shelved, the appellation "boomerang" was given to another type of wing with a tapering plan that also more or less vaguely resembled the weapon of the Australian aborigines: the crescent-shaped swept-back wing (it was also called the "scimitar" and "half-moon" wing). The Germans had conducted studies on this shape in 1944 for their heavy jet bombers. The British subjected it to prolonged testing in the National Aeronautical Establishment's wind tunnel and mounted it on the Handley Page HP-88 (an experimental single-engined plane that crashed in 1951), the HP-80 (a heavy bomber with four jet engines), and the HP-97 (an unsuccessful transatlantic airliner powered by four jet engines).

6. For example, they had the subsonic "Jindivik" aerial target built by the Australian subsidiary of the Hawker Siddeley Group take off from a gyroscopically controlled bogey in order to prevent the target from running off the airstrip. The turrets of the fast Centurion Mark III tanks were stabilized by the Foucault top. They built a secret apparatus to stabilize fighter planes automatically during the time the radar-controlled firing

was in operation. They used electric gyrostabilizers to regulate their air-to-sea torpedoes. (They may have taken as a model the ingenious G-13-C electrical roll stabilizer designed for winged naval torpedoes that had been tested in the hydrodynamic tank of the experimental aeronautical center of Guidonia in 1942 and that had given results on the order of a tenth of a degree. The G-13-C never got beyond the test stages because of the turn the war took and also because of a persistent lack of interest by the so-called responsible authorities in Italy.) These examples are sufficient to indicate the degree of interest the British showed in stabilizing devices.

7. Professor Shenstone knew Germany quite well, having worked at Junkers in 1930 and maintained cordial relations with German scientists up to the outbreak of the war. Hence he had been included in an Anglo-Canadian team responsible for investigating German aerodynamic researches with particular reference to the problems of suction.

8. *Cf. Flight* (London, August 3, 1945).

9. See Norman S. Currey, *"L'Industrie aéronautique du Canada," Interavia* (Geneva, May 1950).

10. See James Hay Stevens, *"Il Canada, è la terra promessa dell'aviazione, nido ed arsenale dell'Occidente," Alata* (Milan, June 1952).

11. See "Man Made Flying Saucers," *The R.A.F. Review* (London, April 1953), pp. 11–12. When the magazine published the schematic profiles of the "Omega" (as it was called in the American press, perhaps because of its shape in plan view), it was seen that it was not, in fact, a device having the shape of a saucer turned upside down—as might have been expected after a number of close-range North American sightings—but a more or less horseshoe-shaped "flying wing." According to the British magazine, the craft had been designed as a test of the new formula and for the subsequent building

of fast supersonic interceptors. It was supposed to be relatively small, with a wingspread and overall length both of about thirty-six feet. Along the leading edge of the machine were about twenty air intake slots to supply the propulsor in the wing of the craft. At the sharply cut off tail there was a large, elliptical exhaust nozzle containing ten deflectors by which the craft changed direction (deflector vanes for control) by means of a flow of compressed air coming from the central turbo-compressor. (There were ten of them, but a couple would have done the job.) The burned gases were discharged from the numerous exhaust ducts, thereby propelling the craft. In the middle of the back was a narrow cabin for a single pilot, topped by a teardrop-shaped cupola in transparent plastic from which the pilot could enjoy perfect visibility over 360° at the level of the horizon. (However, he was completely blind as far as vision beneath the horizon was concerned.) Around the vertical axis of the aircraft and inside the wing a large turbine engine revolved, but no details about it were supplied. However, a short time later the magazine *The Aeroplane* made good the lacuna by publishing a schematic longitudinal section that was purely hypothetical and based on the adoption of a radial centripetal turbine that exhausted the gas that expanded in the collector. Nevertheless, granting for the sake of argument that the "Omega" actually did exist, wouldn't a centrifugal radial turbine be the most likely kind of power plant, since it was easily adaptable to the flat conformation of the plane and to its special propulsive arrangement? The plan indicated the collector of the air that was to be compressed, the combustion chambers of the turbine, the fan for the centrifugal compressor, and the duct for excess air. In the sketch the exhaust gases mixed with part of the fresh, rammed air from the front air intake were erroneously shown to flow in from the rear aperture. Although this justified the type of turbine that was suggested, it was clearly contrary to the original news from Canada. However, the rotation of the motor was supposed to give a gyroscopic stability to the interior of the craft, since a rotating gyroscope could maintain its position in space without change. (True, but what about the violent forward motions that would have obtained while the craft was in flight?)

12. During the last years of the war the most incredible tricks and stratagems to mislead the enemy and to wreak havoc among his troops were worked out at the Inter-Services Research Bureau, which had its headquarters in several rooms in the Victoria and Albert Museum. There explosive rubber snakes and orchids were thought up for the Burma front, explosive souvenir statuettes for Japanese-occupied Borneo; rubber tunas loaded with light arms and ammunition for the Maquis to be washed up along the French coast; coffins with radio transmitters for Norwegian partisans, and other such devices. It was in the obliging penumbra of this old Victorian building that the plans for "bird lures" were born: more than five hundred false objectives made to mislead the Luftwaffe: fuel deposits, railway yards, generating plants, workshops, and airfields built of wood and tarpaper, which drew a large number of bombs away from the real, camouflaged objectives in the vicinity. (It has been estimated that 5 percent of the bomb tonnage dropped on England hit only the "bird lures.") In the same building the idea of the "Starfish" took shape. The "Starfish" were fires lighted at night to simulate burning cities, and they drew off into the open countryside the fury of the German bombers. In the same building too, British countermeasures against the German radio finders guiding the raiders across the Channel were coordinated. (When a German pilot flying over England at night asked the central radio for his location, the British stations received the answers and retransmitted them in altered form, thus confusing the enemy pilot; flying over the outskirts of London, he would be led to believe that he had flown far off course and was over Manchester, about 200 miles north.) Therefore it should not astonish anyone that in 1942, on the suggestion of the Inter-Services Research Bureau, the British fast and furiously "built" a whole cruiser out of a laid-up tanker in Alexandria. The point of this was to mislead Italo-German reconnaissance and give the impression that the British had established naval equality in the eastern Mediterranean. During the war these expedients were generally called "psy-

chological weapons." In times of peace they successfully serve to distract the attention of third parties (the general public or the national press—journalists being the thorn in the side of generals and cabinet ministers—or even agents of foreign secret services, although they have exceedingly sensitive noses) from things the military have accomplished or are interested in. Was the wooden mock-up at Malton a genuine full-scale model of the new machine? Or was it rather an expedient thought up to mask one of the many postwar secrets? It seems that even Field Marshal Montgomery, at least at first, was allowed to see only the mock-up. Can this be possible? Certainly. In England one can be a high-ranking officer and still be subject to heavy restrictions if national security so demands. In corroboration of this little-known truth we cite a news story that appeared in British military publications shortly after the war. In March 1942 a secret airfield was set up at Tempsdorf in Bedfordshire for two "special" squadrons of night bombers. What was special and secret about these squadrons was their job of dropping supplies to the European resistance movements and of flying French, Dutch, Czech, Polish, and Norwegian agents into their respective areas. The pilots and crewmen at the airfield had absolutely no contact with the local residents and the secrecy about their activities was so strict that even if a high-ranking R.A.F. officer unfamiliar with the functions of the airfield asked them for information, they were required to give him false information. Besides this, not even the mechanics who worked on the planes had any idea of what they were actually being used for. Colonel Pickard, the commander of the formation, is the only person involved whose name is known, for the Air Ministry and the War Office have never given out the names of the pilots who took part in these missions. Were the first cautious statements and the later contradictory ones, as well as the whole matter of the Avro disc, merely part of a smoke-screen that was handled very expertly? If the British had any interest in confusing the issue (and they did!), they succeeded marvelously. Even today the truth about the UFOs seems to have fallen into a bottomless well, and the most daring conjectures and the most foolish nonsense are all one as far as most people are concerned.

13. For the "Stingray" a jet take-off was planned by inclining the craft at a seventy-degree angle on a special ramp. This was certainly not the ideal solution, but this curious type of take-off was necessitated by the installation of an exclusively pro-pulsive engine. (This was, in fact, a "flying wing" with a shape that tended toward the circular. It was a type of installation that would never have permitted the craft to hover in the air, one of the characteristics of real flying saucers. In addition, it would have been impossible to pilot such a plane, which ap-peared to lack elevators or any other kind of aerodynamic or gaseodynamic vanes capable of producing the basic climbing and diving maneuvers. The Frost project was completely ex-temporaneous—in the matter of new conceptions the British aircraft companies were already officially orienting them-selves toward the gradual application of jet lift—and basically was only a badly worked out imitation of an excellent product which, strange to say, owes its fame above all to the fact that it is still secret and thus unknown and uncopiable.

14. Or, to be exact, the Canadian press returned to the now forbidden subject only once more, but this time apropos of the other flying saucers, those called UFOs. The American ufologist Donald Keyhoe, in the first of his well-known editorial labors, states that from the beginning the Canadian authorities were openly skeptical about the flying saucers, but that in the spring of 1952, "after a long series of exceptional sightings, their attitude changed and a conference of highly placed persons was held in Ottawa. Four days later, the secret service of the R.C.A.F. publicly admitted that it had begun a serious investi-gation. At the same time the commission for Defense Research announced the creation of an office (modeled on the American Project Blue Book) that would conduct its inquiries in secret." (But why, then, even mention the fact?) In September 1954 the Canadian press reported that "after three full years of con-tinuous and absolutely useless sky watch, the government has decided to transfer the personnel of the office and of the rela-tive station to less speculative duties than those of hunting down the phantom saucers." In reality, during 1952 the discs flew over the region more than once. As soon as construction

on the observation station was begun, the saucers obstinately began to avoid that part of the sky: who knows through what underground channels the Martians got wind of the matter?! A successful bit of extraterrestrial spying? Ufologists find it easy to consider highly surreal opinions perfectly valid, but if we subject the whole affair to the cold light of reason, it seems to have the same amount of credibility as movie adventures of the James Bond type.

15. After debunking all 131 reports of sightings in North America during the first half of 1955, Mr. Quarles stated that the government had "some time ago initiated negotiations with the Canadian government and with Avro-Canada for the preparation of an experimental model of the Frost flying disc. This aircraft will then be mass produced and used for the common defense of the sub-arctic area of the continent." After they had rejected various projects that appeared too costly or inefficient, the choice of the American experts finally fell on Type Y. News release No. 1053-55 put out by the Office of Public Information to report the statement of the Air Force Secretary, informed the press that a photograph of the projected disc (or, more accurately, a photograph of an "artist's conception" of the disc) was available on request from the Pictorial Branch of the Department of Defense. This curious publicity photograph —which depicted the disc flying over American skyscrapers (see Figure 29, which is an enlargement of the disc detail)— revealed that project Y was something radically different from the Omega. The new Frost project had the classical external shape of a saucer turned upside down, like the real discs, but it depicted, to be blunt, an absurd propulsive system for a machine of that type.

16. Nevertheless, shortly afterwards the decision was revoked. The Arrow, a twin-jet fighter with a delta-wing formation, was originally designed to replace the CF-100 Canuck beginning in 1951. But because of a long series of modifications in both the developmental and the manufacturing stages, necessitated by the continued lack of jets of the proper power (the planned Iroquois turbojet being delayed in mounting), the prototype

did not fly until autumn 1957, when it was temporarily equipped with two Pratt and Whitney J-75 turbojets. It was estimated that the plane would go into assembly-line production in 1959. On the other hand, to get an unfortunately somewhat sketchy idea of the extraordinary potential of Avro-Canada, one need only recall that at the end of the first six months of 1955, the date of the last progress report that was made public, the jet engine division had already produced 1500 Orenda turbojets and over half a million turbine vanes, succeeding in producing toward the end about 100,000 vanes a month, each of which required sixty different mechanical operations, most entailing a high degree of precision.

17. In autumn 1959 a very out-of-focus photograph of the Frost disc (subsequently called the Avro Air-Cushion Aircraft and finally simply the Avro-Car) was making the rounds of the press. It was claimed that a "free-lance photographer" had taken the picture during a "surprise flight over the Avro factory at the moment the 'disc' was taken out of the hangar" for testing in "a tethered condition." It was necessary, however, to await the release of the official photograph, which did not come until August 1960, to be able to make any accurate deductions about the mysterious aircraft. On the top surface of the machine—whose thick rounded edge revealed that the designers intended to remain within the lower subsonic speed ranges (one of the U.S. Army's contract specifications)—the first thing noticed is the central air intake with its large, shrouded vertical fan driven by three Continental J-69 turbines housed within the lens-shaped body. The superpressure of the underside (the air cushion) was created and maintained (but only when close to the ground) by a jet of air coming from the fan and expelled through the Venturi tube ring nozzle around the edge of the disc. For horizontal flight, the jet flow from the ring was directed toward the rear, thus developing a component of forward motion and the ordinary aerodynamic lift produced by the flat belly of the aircraft moving at a slight positive inclination was added to the lift component. In 1960 the final objective of the project was to perfect an efficient and reliable method for swinging the ring

jet through a 90° arc in order to limit the thrust developed by the lift-jet to vertical movements of the aircraft (*i.e.*, to take-off and landing) and to use aerodynamic lift for horizontal flight. This would, in any case, have been the first step toward the realization of the future supersonic type (requested by the U.S. Air Force). The circular wings, by reason of their low aspect ratio, are, however, very unstable, being subject to tipping over suddenly. This basic and serious defect, which proved to be unremediable despite every effort, signed the death warrant of the project.

18. See "Forest Hid Five 'Dromes," *Eighth Army News* (Trieste, January 1, 1946), p. 1.

19. See "The L.F.A.: A German Research Station," *Aircraft Production* (London, November 1945); and especially Col. L. E. Simon, *German Scientific Establishments* (New York, Mapleton House, 1947), pp. 11–45.

20. The A. W. Hawksley factory of Hucclecote, which had been absorbed by the Hawker Siddeley Group for the production of rough-finished aeronautical parts and accessories, produced tens of thousands of prefabricated houses during the 1945–1947 period. These were made of a light alloy called "Airoh," and after home needs had been fully supplied, a good part went to Australia and Canada.

21. In the postwar period, before the United States' defensive radar network was extended to the Far North (that is, up until the end of 1952), Soviet long-range reconnaissance planes from Siberian and subarctic air bases often returned the visits that American reconnaissance planes based in Japan made over Manchuria and eastern Siberia, by flying over Alaska, the Yukon Territory, and the Mackenzie District, areas which proved within their range. If the secret reconnaissance has not been repeated and extended with the technological advances in flying, this is owing mostly to the installation of the triple radar chain extending across Canada that the American military authorities have set up as a first line of defense for the

United States and, beginning in 1958, also to the disconcerting availability (on payment) of all the aerial photographs made for the Ministry of Power and National Resources. According to news stories in the Ottawa papers in 1966, a good part of the photographs, which now cover virtually the whole of the nearly four million square miles of the country, reproduce military stations, barracks, bridges, ports, and airports. All restrictions on the sale of this precious material were in fact lifted in 1958, when it was concluded that the advent of spying by means of stratospheric photographic reconnaissance planes of the U-2 type rendered further precautions superfluous. Later on, various secret types of both American and Soviet strategic reconnaissance satellites equipped with high-resolution tele-photo lenses were added to the U-2s. Nevertheless, it remains true that an underground installation or one that is properly camouflaged with live vegetation easily escapes being identified from a distance photograph and that the maps relative to a specific zone can be quietly retouched beforehand in the photographic offices of the military censors. (Unless, in the meantime, the UFO bases have been moved elsewhere, having fulfilled their original mission.)

22. And American obstructionism naturally continued. On January 26, 1956, the scientific editor of the London *Daily Telegraph* revealed, in fact, a new disagreement between the British and Americans over the development of nuclear energy. "Pressure," he wrote, "is being brought to bear by the U.S. to discourage Britain from making thermonuclear weapons. This will almost certainly be one of the matters discussed when Sir A. Eden sees President Eisenhower. The American action is in line with her invariable policy since the end of the war of denying to all other countries any information or material that would aid in the design or manufacture of atomic weapons or other military developments such as nuclear-powered submarines. Under this policy, Britain and Canada, who collaborated with her in making the first atom bomb, have been treated in the same way as other countries. One reason for this is the fear in America that bad security might permit data gained by other Western countries to reach Russia. Another is belief in the

political expediency of keeping other Western countries dependent on America. America could deny Britain supplies of heavy water, which has double importance in the atomic field. It weighs about 1 percent more than ordinary water and occurs as about .02% of all natural water. Heavy water is an ideal working medium for some types of atomic reactors used in electric power production. It is also a starting point in the manufacture of lithium deuterise, a nuclear explosive used in hydrogen bombs. Britain, as reported in the *Daily Telegraph* on Monday and confirmed by the British Atomic Energy Authority last night, has abandoned the only project of its own for industrial-scale manufacture of heavy water. This was to have been in New Zealand, at Waireki. Steam from hot springs was to have been used for heavy water production and electric power generation. Partly because of a substantial increase in the cost of plant since the idea was first mooted, Waireki heavy water would have cost about £90,000 a ton, instead of an estimated £40,000. Britain has been paying between £65,000 and £75,000 a ton to Norway for supplies from the Norsk Hydro. In August the Americans offered to sell some of their own surplus supplies at £25,000 a ton. Admiral Strauss, head of the U.S. Atomic Energy Commission, said to me then in Geneva, 'Of course we shall want to know what it is going to be used for.' The condition that America has actually made is that recipient countries should satisfy her that none of it is being used for weapon manufacture. While Britain pursues her declared intention of manufacturing thermonuclear weapons, it would be difficult to give satisfactory proof that supplies from America were not being diverted to this purpose, or were not releasing supplies from other sources for that use. The trouble is that even if the Waireki project had been pursued it would have produced only some tens of tons of heavy water a year. For a single reactor producing 100 megawatts of electricity, enough for a city of 70,000 people, 400 tons might be needed. This means that if the Americans did not relax their conditions for Britain she might have to give up, for the time being, any plans for power reactors of this type until other sources could be expanded."

The American reply was not long in coming and generally confirmed the old precautionary measures. On November 2,

1957, the Democratic senator Clinton Anderson declared to the press that especially following the sensational Soviet missile achievement the most important internal American problem at the moment, susceptible to important international repercussions, was that of changing the federal laws on nuclear secrets in such a way as to share the data and scientific and technological discoveries in nuclear energy with the most qualified Western countries. He felt it necessary, however, to add immediately that Congress should examine the proposal to exchange with Great Britain the secrets inherent in atomic weapons and missiles with the greatest care in order to make sure that the English did not intend a "one-way" exchange. *In addition, unfortunately, they had little or nothing to offer in exchange for U.S. weapons* and the rest of the NATO countries had still less. Senator Anderson then stated that the secrets of the *Nautilus* atomic-powered submarine had been given to the English against their promise of turning over to the Americans information about their gas-cooled atomic reactor, but that after receiving the plans of the *Nautilus*, the English had not given the United States any details on their reactor. Naturally, it is very difficult in cases like this to separate right from wrong. But the facts speak for themselves.

CHAPTER 9

How to Do the Impossible

"In the light of logic and our experience of the methods generally employed by the Great Powers in the development of weapons, can we reasonably hypothesize that we are dealing with a secret weapon?" the journalist Franco Bandini rhetorically asked his readers at the time of the great "celestial invasion" of 1954. And he answered: "No! For, examining the technical side of the question, if we concede that the flying saucers have the performance attributed to them by the public, it is clear that they are not in an early stage of experimentation but something already perfected, gems of aeronautical science with astonishing characteristics. And all this has been achieved without the least scientific preliminaries, without preliminary studies or a movement in technology that might at least suggest that such result was in the offing?! Clearly, the secret weapon hypothesis arouses the greatest perplexity."

"Let us suppose," Bandini had written some years before, in 1950, "that some new and terrible weapon built by one of the two great powers, Russia or the United States, is really concealed under the generic name of flying saucers. Is this possible? The strongest evidence against this supposition is that the saucers apparently show no geographical preferences. One time they appear here, another time there, without, one would say, the least reason. Instead of showing a preference for desert areas, the seas, or the polar regions, as would be natural if it were a secret weapon, they dally like carefree tourists over cities, coast lines, the most crowded areas; they make low passes over industrial plants, and it almost appears that they are methodically exploring every corner of the earth. Let us add that they hover in the air for a quarter of an hour at a time (many reports speak of hours), making it easy for local photographers to shoot miles of film. What secret, then, could these extraordinary 'secret weapons' possibly hold?! If these devices belong to the United States, why do they also fly on the other side of the Iron Curtain, with all the risks and dangers of being shot down and comfortably and carefully examined? If they are Russian, why do they fly over American territory, running the same risks? And if they are experimental, how could they maintain the same forms over a number of years? And is it possible that in the meantime not even one of these saucers has ever crashed or been shot down or, in any case, examined in sufficient detail to yield positive information? Are these saucers, then, already 'perfect'? And if they are, how can the silence that the interested power has maintained be explained—not to mention the silence of the power that is the object of their perennial and gigantic threat?"

Let us examine these objections in detail, one by one. They appear—but only "appear"—to be very well founded, if one thinks along ordinary lines or is forced to for lack of sufficient evidence.

There is no law that says an air weapon, if possessed in sufficient quantity and already at the necessary stage of technical perfection, must remain forever in the plants where it has been secretly prepared. Indeed, sending squadrons of unidentifiable flying machines that are so fast they cannot be intercepted through the air space of a (potential) enemy in time of peace would be a tacit but eloquent show of strength! (If, on the other hand, Bandini's reasoning were correct, the Russians should have jealously hidden their guided missile systems in their Siberian arsenals. Instead, they installed a good number of them in Cuba, right on America's doorstep.)

Any device, whether a weapon or not, can remain secret indefinitely even if exposed to the gaze of the public, provided that no one can determine its provenance, the way it operates, its manufacturing details, its purpose, and so on. And truly one cannot gainsay that for over two decades a whole complex of prearranged and fortunate circumstances have conspired to erect and maintain an impenetrable wall of silence around the real solution to the "mystery of the UFOs."

The fact that the discs have never attacked planes in flight or on the ground (contrary assertions by some ufologists are all without foundation), never dropped bombs or done anything that might be interpreted as aggression has, therefore, led those who support the idea that the discs are of extraterrestrial origin to speak of the "feelings of benevolent observation" that the pilots of the mysterious space ships are supposed to have concerning us. The list of these people, some of whom are innocents and others complete charlatans, is very long, but all their books are riddled with unlikely details and clear fabrications.[1]

In fact, one can now calmly maintain that the UFOs do not fly over the areas in which they are sighted with any deliberate intention of exploring them; they are simply in transit, coming or going to far more distant places.

We can unhesitatingly agree that they are *secret*. "Weapon," however, is far too restrictive a term. Strictly speaking, anything indispensable to war is a weapon. Extremely useful instruments designed for peaceful use can, if necessary, be adapted to military use, thereby acquiring the attributes of a weapon. A knife, obviously, can cut, and it can kill. In the first case it is a tool; in the second, a weapon. In short, what you call it depends on what you do with it. The UFOs cannot, therefore, be called weapons. They could be weapons, and they would become weapons (very deadly ones) when and if necessary; but at the moment they most certainly are *not* weapons. And if one finds the term "unidentified flying objects" that is so beloved of the ufologists displeasing, one need only call them "special aircraft with a secret operating cycle."[2]

What about the charge that the behavior of the UFOs is incautious? This doesn't seem to be the case. When some conventional plane tries to approach a UFO too closely, the device invariably pulls away, climbs, and disappears. On the other hand, even if one takes a series of photographs of the object hovering motionless in the sky, often at a very high altitude or surrounded by clouds of gas or vapors, how much secret information does one acquire? None, clearly; for the camera lens registers exactly what has been seen by the eyes of observers—that is, merely the external form of the device—and this means nothing to anyone who does not have the highly specialized information known only to the designers and builders of the mysterious machines.

The assertion that the UFOs cross the Iron Curtain is not completely true, although this idea has been fairly widespread for some time, thanks to the efforts of ufologists. With the exception of rare flights over German and Austrian territories previously occupied by the Soviets (but geographically a part of continental Europe), the UFOs have never appeared at altitudes *at which they could be seen* over territories belonging to the U.S.S.R. in such numbers or with such frequency that they aroused mass hysteria even remotely comparable to that aroused in the United States in 1947 and 1952 or in Europe in 1954.

The discs are marvels of engineering, but absolute perfection is not, alas, of this world. Even if today they are, logically, more evolved and reliable than at the time they first appeared, like any man-made machine, they were born with latent imperfections. One need, in fact, only recall the pitiful end of the little "flying oyster" that crashed in Montana to bring things back to their proper proportions.

If the "formula" seems to be much better than one can hope for today in terms of aeronautical safety, that certainly is not the result of superhuman help but devolves from the intelligent fusion of certain revolutionary technical principles. For *there are no miracles in aeronautics but only a good dose of farsightedness, great daring, and a very large number of experimental studies, a great part of which are secret.*

FORTUNES AND MISFORTUNES
OF MILITARY SECRECY

"We know," Bandini continued in his careful examination, "that at times the flying saucers literally infest the skies. They go in pairs, in threes; some have seen them in the hundreds. This posits large-scale production of technologically very complicated objects, the existence of laboratories and experimental centers, special airfields, recently built factories, special bodies of trained crewmen and pilots, an enormous consumption of television and radio-control apparatuses, a complex of activities and an absorption of energies of enormous proportions. Information would inevitably have leaked out, with the usual accompaniment of spying, treason, and the like. Is it possible that such a big secret could have been maintained so long, so perfectly?"

Certainly—provided we leave out the word "perfectly," which does not apply to the case after what we have set forth in this book. More—we have illustrious and well-known precedents.

In 1943 the neutral press printed some strange news about an apocalyptic experimental American bomb that had destroyed every living thing on a small island during its first test. The facts as reported were not true, but the rumors were based on concrete data, or on the first rare leaks that were coming out concerning the frenzied preparation of the supersecret atomic center at Oak Ridge. The news, then, was in advance of the appearance of the new bomb. A kind of science fiction before the proper time.

Two years later vague references to unknown, large-scale phenomena ("a deafening roar and a towering column of smoke") that had been noted in the desert region of New Mexico appeared in some Texas and Arizona newspapers. Mass hallucination or a meteor, the military authorities declared brusquely. Then it was learned that precisely at 5:38 on July 16, 1945, under the code name Trinity, the first American atomic bomb had been detonated on the top of a high steel tower a dozen or so miles from the air base of Alamogordo. "We learned of the existence of the A bomb at the same time the Japanese did!" the surprised citizens of the United States exclaimed. And it was perfectly true![3]

Isn't it perhaps likewise true that all the inventions of the last war (the flying bombs, the rocket torpedoes, magnetic mines, radar, jet planes, even the atom bomb) were revealed only at the moment they were used in the field? The public —journalists and technicians included—always remained in the dark about what was going on, whether at home or elsewhere, even when the military authorities already knew something of the enormous and complex train of work in researching and preparing the new enemy inventions. Generally the exceptional inventions (those that interest both the government and the military) deceive or surprise even clear-sighted people who are trained and equipped to understand. At the time of the First World War (to cite an example from a less mechanical-minded epoch than the present), it was not until the war was over that people were convinced that Big Bertha was actually a Krupp cannon of very long range that was bombing Paris from a distance of about seventy-five miles, a range inconceivable up to then for any type of artillery.

Every war of importance and every stormy postwar (or prewar, if you like) period has its well-guarded secrets. A random example. The following interesting paragraph appeared in the newspapers on July 9, 1947: "Professor T. D. I. Leech of the University of Aukland, New Zealand, head of a group of scientists responsible for the construction of an ultrapowerful weapon that is very close to the atom bomb in importance, did not wish to comment on the appearance of the shining discs in the United States."

Here is half (or almost half) of a revealed secret. Here is a "leak" that was made voluntarily. Who can tell us about it?

And who knows when they will tell us? Perhaps tomorrow, perhaps in another twenty years. A British Top Secret is maintained with all the inflexibility of a Polynesian taboo.

The curious affair whose chief protagonist was Count Helmut von Zborowsky is the best demonstration of the magic power that military secrecy has in its relations with outsiders.

In 1943 Von Zborowsky, who worked in France after the war on the development of the tubular-winged plane called the "Beetle," was at the Bayerische Motoren Werke, directing research to perfect a hypergolic propellant for use in rocket engines. Long trains of tank cars carried mysterious liquids labeled *Tonka*, *Salbei*, and *Mell* to Camp R Zuehlsdorf and to certain decentralized hangars of the Allach plant.

One day a B.M.W. executive became suspicious about such strange supplies. Rockets using hundreds of tons of salvia and molasses? Was this a joke or was it a cover for black marketing? From the encyclopedia that he immediately consulted, the observant executive learned that the tonka-bean tree "belongs to the family of the South American papilionacee, which resembles our plum tree, and from whose fruit coumarin, a perfumed substance resembling vanilla, is extracted." Perturbed, he started a rapid inquiry to determine why large quantities of exotic plants were being used in the experiments on rocket engines—exceedingly costly plants to boot, and presumably in very short supply.

His request for clarification as to the use of these materials, Von Zborowsky later said, laughingly, was nevertheless phrased "discreetly and urbanely."

"For experiments," was the curt written reply.

After four weeks, the top executives of the factory asked the next logical question: "For what sort of experiments?"

"Secret experiments," came the reply from the secretariat of the R center. Such was the shadowy power evoked by that disturbing adjective that the B.M.W. administration never again dared to ask further explanations, and until the collapse of Nazi Germany, without batting an eyelash, it regularly paid the invoices for the large supplies of exotic beans (in reality a complex mixture of natural and synthetic hydrocarbons), sage leaves (nitric acid 98 percent) and molasses (methyl alcohol).

THE SUCCESSES OF AERIAL
RECONNAISSANCE

Following a proposal advanced by generals Becker and Dornberger and supported by Kesselring, then a Luftwaffe general, an experimental center for the study and testing of self-propelled long-range projectiles was set up in 1936 at Peenemünde, on the Baltic. The station was to be shared by the army and the air force.

That was where the Luftwaffe tested the winged flying bomb FZG-76 (later called the V-1). With the deliberate intention of going beyond the stratosphere and working in the field of supersonic speeds, the army completed at Peenemünde its development of the A-4 torpedo rocket (the famous V-2), which it had begun two years earlier at the old and by then inadequate center at Kummersdorf.

Despite the lack of interest and understanding that the highest Nazi authorities at first showed, a V-2 rocket launched over the sea on October 3, 1942, in its first test had a range of 120 miles. Nevertheless, it was agreed that further improvements were necessary to make the deadly torpedo practical. It did not have its baptism by fire until September 8, 1944.

During eight years of intense work no less than 65,000 modifications were made on the weapon, requiring a select group of specialists (one now famous name can represent all the others: Werner von Braun) and a work force composed of over 7000 technicians and workers skilled in widely disparate specialties. Despite the participation of so great a number of people, the many years' work—including the period during the war—was carried on rather smoothly under the label *Geheimnis* (top secret). And yet Germany was overrun with spies and informers of all nationalities, its position in the center of the continent making it an area easy of access. And if at the beginning of the war the British had a vague inkling of the existence of the studies for the rocket bomb, they owed it to an unknown informer who never revealed his identity and whose information was therefore suspect.

In October 1939 an anonymous letter reached the naval attaché of the British Embassy in Norway. Out of pure anti-Nazi sentiments and with no desire for recompense, the writer offered to reveal important German secrets. If the British accepted, all they would have to do was to alter the conventional introductory remarks in the B.B.C.'s nightly German-language news bulletin according to a prearranged formula and on a specific date. The Intelligence Service gave the instructions to the B.B.C., and right on time the unknown informer replied by radio on a previously arranged wave length. He reported that the Germans were working on a rocket bomb, two different types of radar, turbine aircraft engines, and other weapons whose details were gradually supplied by radio and immediately recorded by the competent British authorities.

Most of the secrets concerned the aircraft industry, and it was Professor R. V. Jones, the former director of the Scientific Research Department of the Air Ministry, who revealed the whole story (known in Intelligence Service circles as the Oslo Report) on February 20, 1947, simply because the threat from those weapons had disappeared with the end of the war.

Nevertheless, it was not until the night of August 17–18, 1943, that the British decided to subject the experimental station to heavy bombing, and they did so only after having noted, in a certain sense *de visu*, the seriousness of the prospective threat—apparently via certain troubling reports from agents operating in Sweden.

The 2000 tons of bombs dropped by 600 R.A.F. bombers devastated the precious machinery and killed a large number of technicians, but they did not halt the course of events. The V-2 had already moved into the construction stage at the invulnerable underground factories of Mittelwerke at Nordhausen in Saxony, at Bleicherode, Konstein, Sonderhausen, Sallfeld, and in still other parts of south-central Germany, as well as in Ebensee and at the Rax Werke in Wiener Neustadt in Austria.

The air attacks on Peenemünde, which was so furiously defended by fighters and flak that the British lost over forty bombers there, did, however, delay the final perfecting of the V-1 by eight months, thereby saving the Normandy invasion troops what might have been a frightful decimation. This device too was conceived and grew in a propitious atmosphere of unbroken mystery until several radio-controlled prototypes accidentally veered off the experimental path and instead of plunging into the western Baltic crashed on Swedish soil and on some Danish islands.

On May 15, 1942, returning from a photographic reconnaissance flight over Kiel—a flight which from the start gave little promise of yielding anything of interest—Lieutenant D. W. Steventon swung his Spitfire toward the Baltic. Flying at a very high altitude, he looked down on the island of Usedom, in the estuary of the Oder River, some sixty miles northeast of Stettin. The island had never attracted the attention of the R.A.F., since it held only some small villages occupied for the most part by simple fishermen. Nevertheless, something caught the pilot's eye. Undoubtedly that carefully smoothed out terrain was a recently constructed airfield. And what about those narrow concrete runways? And those unusual-looking buildings, unusual even on a military airfield? Keeping below the clouds, the pilot shot his last few feet of film and then returned to his base with his throttle wide open, believing he had done a good day's work. And he had. With those photographs as a clue, the agents operating in Sweden and Norway managed to poke their noses into what was going on at Usedom by pretending to be herring fishermen. And in December a voluminous bundle of papers (the *Secret Weapon Trials Report*) was on its way to London, where it now rests in the files of the Intelligence Service.[4]

While the Anglo-Swedish work on the reconstruction of a V-2 rocket that had crashed near Baeckedo went on feverishly, additional "confidential" news came from Stockholm in the spring of 1943 alerting the Allied authorities to the fact that the remains of two German secret devices that had been experimentally launched had been found on the coast of Skania. Two British agents immediately made contact with the people who had the wreckage in their possession. Although the violent shock of the crash had rendered them almost unrecognizable, fragments of glass and aluminum and pieces of wing surfaces permitted the agents to make a hasty reconstruction that differed radically from that of the torpedo rocket that exploded in the sky over Baeckedo.

The belief that the islands of Ruegen and Usedom were hiding war secrets of the greatest importance was confirmed. In May a British reconnaissance plane flew over the region and in the center of some camouflaged buildings spotted and photographed a strange device placed on inclined rails, ready for launching. From photographic enlargements the R.A.F. experts learned that it was a small pilotless aircraft and that the dark marks on the ground—caused by the very hot exhaust gases—meant that a jet-propulsion system was being used. It was the final experimental model of the V-1 flying bomb, and its being caught on the launching ramp was truly fatal for Germany, even though a total of 26,000 flying bombs did leave —too late, however—the production lines set up first at the Volkswagen factory in Fallersleben and then—after it received the ruinous attention of the R.A.F.—in the vast subterranean factories in Nordhausen.[5]

In the spring of 1943 the great Zeppelin factory at Friedrichshafen, which suffered from its proximity to the Swiss frontier, met a similar fate. The secret agents who swarmed in every neutral country had their eyes on it. They discovered that in 1937-1938 its subsonic wind tunnel had measured the aerodynamic characteristics of the tail assemblies to apply to the A-3 and A-5 rockets (the precursors to the V-2), and that among the various things in gestation under the veil of military secrecy were highly advanced antiaircraft radio finder apparatuses. On June 20 sixty Lancaster bombers devastated a great part of the plant, but they were unable to stop the production lines of the various subsidiaries that had meantime been relocated in underground or camouflaged quarters in the Black Forest.

This whole series of unfavorable events would certainly not have occurred if these vital secrets had been hidden, as they are today, in the middle of some vast steppe, on the edges of a desert or in a large mountainous and wooded land, instead of being on a plainly visible islet in the Baltic or along a heavily trafficked central European border.

But let us continue our criticism of Bandini's requirements.

THE POSSIBILITIES AND LIMITS
OF SECRET MANUFACTURE

More than once the flight characteristics of the UFOs have been described by experts in aeronautical matters as "far beyond anything our technology can achieve."

But since 1947, and on up to today, the speeds and altitudes of the UFOs have been approached even by conventional air technology (progress never stops, not even to please the ufologists). Are the aforementioned experts—almost always members of civilian research institutes—aware that a private body cannot even remotely compete with a military institute or with one subject to military control, which is favored by an almost unlimited wealth of experimental and financial means?

For example, the German rockets financed by the Nazi government were reaching altitudes of sixty miles when their Anglo-American counterparts developed by private initiative were barely able to get up to twelve miles or so, and with ridiculously small payloads. In the postwar period the V-2 rockets and their derivatives wiped out all the second-rate efforts produced by American, Russian, and British designers.

An appropriate and typical case is that of the turbine-powered planes that were secretly flown in prototype at German research centers during 1939–1940, just when the most authoritative and highly quoted technical journals in the field were expressing doubts about the practical solution of the problem of the rotary internal combustion engine for the near future. And that wasn't all. The secret was so well kept even from friendly powers that the first news about German turbine-engined planes came to the ears of Italian military authorities only in 1942. The general public did not learn about them until two years later, during the winter of 1944, at the time of the first official German communiqués.

The first real turbojet plane (the Heinkel HE-178), in fact, first flew on August 27, 1939, powered by a Heinkel-Hirt HE-HI-S-3 giving 1,100 pounds of static thrust. In following years came different, greatly improved and more powerful types, but it was only when the first models were delivered to the airfields that the secrecy was in large part relaxed.[6]

The appearance of the German jet planes was a bitter surprise for the Allied fighting men, particularly for the bomber crews of the American Eighth Air Army, which on August 14, 1944, encountered the first ME-163 rocket fighters over Leipzig, with heavy losses for the bombers.

The existence of this daring new plane was known to the British General Staff only through photographs. On June 23, 1943, the British airman E. P. H. Peek had photographed an experimental model of the fighter ready to take off on the Peenemünde airfield. The Allied authorities, faithful to an old and tested system, said nothing about it until the war was over. There was no reason to do so before. It would only have demoralized their own crews and let the enemy know that one of their war secrets had become known and so force him to plan further measures.

When questions that involve the destiny of a whole country are concerned, a single day can change the whole course of events (as the Arab-Israeli Six-Day War demonstrates). The UFOs constitute too important a trump card not to wait until the proper time to make them felt upon the course of history. History, therefore, goes on . . .

FURTHER REFLECTIONS
ON WHAT CONSTITUTES "PROOF"

Mr. Bandini said that if he were to be convinced that the flying saucers were of terrestrial origin, he would have to be shown somehow that there existed:

1) an experimental center that could handle the job;

2) production lines actually in operation at certain companies, which logically could not long hide their highly specialized type of construction.

He summed up his ideas with the following: "What nation can be interested in conducting its experiments publicly, and in air space that is not its own? Can we possibly grant that for a number of years a group of specialized mechanics and equally specialized pilots and strange installations—in short a rather conspicuous and costly organization—could have existed without anyone's having found any traces of it even in the budgets of individual countries? In addition, since these discs have been sighted all over the world, we must suppose either that their radius of action is virtually 'world wide' or that a chain of bases must be scattered about here and there. The first supposition encounters almost insurmountable obstacles: it is impossible today to conceive of any rocket plane capable of flying nonstop around the world. The second likewise seems impossible. A single base can be so well situated and hidden as to make it virtually disappear from the face of the earth. Not so a chain of bases. Among other things, it is necessary to build the bases, equip them, bring in the rockets, the fuel and the personnel to operate them. Too many things are involved to be able to hide them all."

The list of the "proofs" he demanded thus included the following:

3) select personnel of three types: navigators, specialists, and flyers;

4) one or more specialized and visible airport installations from which the mysterious devices would take off;

5) a series of financial allocations that could be observed in the military budgets of the nations building them;

6) the presence of auxiliary bases in different parts of the world.

The sixth point is immediately eliminated because of the special operating cycle of the UFOs, which do not require the auxiliary bases that are absolutely indispensable to aircraft of the conventional type. But to go into this matter at the moment would be premature.

The remaining objections can all be easily demolished. Let us, then, take up each of these points in order.

Today there is no plane that is wholly built by the firm whose name it bears. The system of subcontracting is the rule. Electrical and radio equipment, hydraulic circuits, certain parts of the landing gear, the tires, sometimes even the engine and propeller or the jet engine, all the ball bearings, cables, nuts and bolts, semi-finished parts, paint, instruments, Plexiglas for the cabin, parts in rubber or plastic, certain types of pumps and auxiliary electric motors, oxygen masks, various sorts of pressure tanks, a large part of the gears and gear boxes, fire-control systems, weapons, and so on, all flow to the contracting company from a myriad of small companies. The central firm is responsible first of all for the planning and design of the new airplane, then for the preparation of the most important elements in the construction (wings, fuselage, tail, etc.), and finally for the assembly of the whole machine, which leaves the plane ready to fly.

Within limits, the central firm can also order the elements that it would normally build from subcontractors, who would construct them within certain tolerances. In such a case the central firm would then do nothing more than assemble the parts (in sheds or on secret sites)—or not, as in the case of planes built on licensing agreements.

If the planes are to be built secretly—that is, outside the plant of the contracting firm—the flow of materials follows a broken itinerary on trucks or trains operated by or under the supervision of the personnel of the subcontracting firms. Not knowing the design of the whole, they cannot logically guess what sort of aircraft these components are destined for. They have merely supplied certain girders bent in a certain way, certain sheets cut or curved in some special shape, anonymous tubing in light alloy shaped according to detailed designs that gives no hint about itself other than its shape and dimensions, and accessories common to many well-known types of aircraft.

When the material is brought into military warehouses, all civilian interference automatically ceases. Halfway to the secret bases, the highly trusted representatives from the bases themselves come into the picture. This representative joins the personnel of the warehouses and is responsible for making sure that the various parts of the aircraft get where they are going by the most suitable and most appropriately camouflaged means available. When they reach the base, they are assembled by crews of trusted specialists.

Not tons of thousands but a few hundred, or fewer, highly

selected men can thus gradually get ready whole fleets of new, supersecret flying machines.

The same procedure works even more easily in supplying the food, fuel, barracks, and everything that makes life tolerable for a relatively small human nucleus secreted in a remote or deserted area.

CAMOUFLAGING MILITARY SECRETS

Special, deliberately misleading buildings with conventional signs provide a tested method of masking secrets of this type.

Organized by the Gestapo—which, as everyone knows, did not take matters of secrecy lightly—the Volkswagen factory was concerned in 1938 with the publicity campaign for the "one-thousand-mark utility car." Described as the *ne plus ultra* of this type of automobile (four seats, four forward speeds, fifty-five mph, twenty-eight miles per gallon), the car caused a sensation and an avalanche of orders came in. With the money that was collected, three huge factory buildings were constructed in a few months for mass production of the car under the supervision of the Labor Front, headed by Dr. Ley.

The first models of the people's car were a big hit at the Berlin automobile show in February 1939. Then came the summer, the ideal time for taking a vacation in the little car. But nothing was coming off the production lines. Indeed, no cars could come off the production lines because all three factories were really producing parts for the Panzers that three months later were swarming off toward the Polish plains. The individual parts were secretly shipped to military warehouses, where crews of trusted mechanics took care of the final assembly. Q.E.D.

And now let us come down to more recent times.

In August 1941 the British used the generic name of "compressor" to refer to the plans for the first De Havilland "Goblin" turbojet engine in order to mislead enemy spies. And when the jet engine began its bench tests on April 13, 1942, at the experimental center of Hatfield, the military authorities spread the rumor that a new type of electric-power station was being tested, in order to explain the characteristic whine of the new engine. As expected, the populace accepted the odd explanation; so did even the technicians at the center who had nothing to do with the project.[7]

Again in 1941, this time in occupied France, the SO.CE.M.A. firm secretly began its project for a turbine aircraft engine of 3000 horsepower called the T.G.A., the initials of which were officially interpreted as *Turbo-Groupe d'Autorail* (railway turbine). To add verisimilitude, the contract was placed under the aegis of the Ministry of French Railways. Naturally, this interpretation sought to mislead the German occupying forces, who, though they had excellent informers, never suspected the true nature of the project.

Agreed, these projects were somewhat limited in scope. But the Manhattan Project, which was responsible for the research that made the atomic bomb possible, was certainly not. The population of the state of Tennessee truly believed that the imposing complex of concrete walls in Oak Ridge was a hydro-electric power station under construction, temporarily being used as a military depot for unspecified war materials—until the historic day that the bomb was dropped on Hiroshima. Indeed, a strange news story from the papers of the time confirms the almost incredible state of ignorance of a great part of the people who actually took part in the enterprise:

"The seventeen thousand people who worked in the huge government establishment on the production of the bombs never knew exactly what they were doing. Working in shifts, shielded by thick walls of reinforced concrete, they put together the various pieces of the mechanism without knowing the final result, until President Truman announced that a new bomb of unheard-of power had been dropped on Japan."

Examples of this sort, taken from the events of the last war, could be multiplied by the hundreds. But it is well known that the British and Americans have a special predilection for this kind of camouflage, which they also adopt in peacetime for their confidential plans. These misleading labels serve not only to keep the public ignorant of this or that stage of research or production (generally the public doesn't even know about the existence of the project itself), but to keep the parts of the military not concerned with the project in the dark about what is going on and thus minimize the danger of involuntary leaks of information.

It is clear, then, that secret activities *never* come to the attention of the profane (especially if the project centers are set up in areas difficult to get to), and experts are deliberately kept at a distance by clever subterfuges of various kinds.

A word or two on the matter of transatlantic shipments during the period 1945–1946. A state of war provides a favorable atmosphere for keeping "confidential" materials concealed, since people are accustomed to seeing continuous shipments going off to distant or unknown destinations. It was precisely in this sort of propitious atmosphere that the plan for the UFOs ripened. It should not be forgotten that their first public appearance goes back to June 1947. Estimating at least a year for the preparation of the airfields and the machines as well as for the first small local flights (the real experimental flights), one comes to the spring of 1946. Hostilities against Japan had ended only a short time before, in August of the preceding year. During all of 1946 the traffic of men and materials from the pacified sectors of Europe and Asia toward the American continent was exceedingly heavy. Could there have been a better moment to complete the delicate and extensive shipments that were necessary to the whole plan of the new machines, without their being obvious both to lay observers and to the agents of other countries? In the vast general confusion brought about by the ending of the war, who would have noticed?

In any case, these limited and furtive movements of men and materials were, after all, merely a problem in logistics, which in the military sphere are always set and solved privately by specially trained personnel.

There is certainly nothing new in the formation of small specialized groups, carefully chosen from units already composed of selected men with a high degree of competence in their own fields, strong, healthy, bright, able to get along with one another, possessing a strong *esprit de corps*, sober, reasonably abstemious (*in vino veritas!* heavy drinkers talk too much), possessing no moral skeletons in their closets, having an excellent military, technical, and cultural background and a high sense of duty, and preferably without any emotional, or at any rate forbidden ties—all these qualities bound together by strict discipline and a high sense of duty combine to form these nuclei of uniformed supermen.

In this way and this way alone the British formed their commandos and T-Men, who took part in exceedingly daring and successful enterprises, and the Italians their frogmen of the X Flotilla M.A.S. The legendary group of special troops organized by Colonel Skorzeny, the German torpedo men, the British submarine men who went into the Norwegian fjords to blow up the *Tirpitz*, the American frogmen who preceded the invasion troops on D-Day and removed the mines along the parts of the French coast where the debarkations would take place, the Japanese kamikazi and human torpedoes—to cite a few famous examples of special units—were all formed in the same way.

The world at large knew nothing of the complex job of selecting these groups, of their long and careful training and their technical and moral problems. Only when the enemy acknowledged the heavy damage that had been done—and this is how the veil of secrecy was lifted—did the existence of these groups become known to everyone. Had those special units been formed overnight? They had involved bringing special tools and weapons, food, fuel, barracks equipment, and so on together at one central point . . . just as with the UFO bases!

"PACKAGED" PORTS
AND INVISIBLE AIRFIELDS

Even before the war it was thought that the various methods for disguising airfields would not guarantee them against enemy attack.

In England three different types of artificial underground arrangements for fixed airfield installations were investigated. The British study, which was supposed to be "classified" but which was fully divulged in the *Deutsche Bauzeitung* of September 12, 1938, contemplated the following arrangements:

1) the excavation of a long tunnel, with several lateral branches, in the side of a dune along the coast or in the side of a hill, followed by a large flattened and smoothed area to serve as the runway;

2) the excavation of a tunnel directly beneath an already existing runway that would be served by a ramp and winches for hauling the planes to the surface for take-off;

3) the excavation of a deep tunnel, without a runway and with a launching catapult located adjacent to an elevator shaft which would bring the planes up. A group of apparently innocent buildings would mask the opening and the catapult. This system, which had been suggested by aircraft carrier practice, seemed particularly well adapted for the protection of frontier areas.

Events moved along so rapidly that there was no time to experiment with any of these systems. In any case, it is doubtful that there was any intention to do anything about it for some time. Toward the end of the war, Germany was the only country that tried to put military airfields underground (the already mentioned U fields in Bavaria). Indeed, it put at least 300 factories producing missiles, planes, engines, accessories, and liquefied gas underground to protect them from the devastation of the air bombings.[8] Although this expedient came too late to save Germany from defeat, we know that it proved to be extraordinarily effective.

For example, the Heinkel firm mass-produced the HE-162 *Volksjäger* jet fighter in an underground factory hidden in a large salt mine near the Elbe. It was protected against any kind of aerial attack, for it was 1300 feet underground. It reportedly prepared 700 to 750 fighters a month and employed over 2000 workers. Only the fuselages, complete with accessories, were built in the salt mine; these finished products were then taken by night to Bernberg, where there was a camouflaged assembly hangar. Here the wings and jet engines were mounted, and the finished planes were then distributed to the various airfields in the vicinity.

The existence of the factory was kept top secret, and in order to distract attention from it, the normal mining of salt was carried on at 600 feet. Hundreds of electric trucks were used to carry manufactured parts through huge tunnels carved in the rock salt from one department to another, and at night enormous hoists carried them up to the surface.[9]

During the last winter of the war hundreds of ME-262 jet fighters came out of the huge network of tunnels dug in the hills of Kahla (Jena), but lack of fuel kept them from taking off and they were destroyed on the airfields in Thuringia.

In the autumn of 1944, in a large well-equipped natural cavern near Haigerloch, in Rhenish Prussia, the Germans prepared a large uranium pile that, when it was almost completed, fell into the hands of the Americans.

A small portion of the synthetic gasoline industry was also put underground.

The only aim of putting the plants underground then was to protect them from aerial attack. *Nevertheless, after Germany was occupied the Allies had a hard job locating the whereabouts and the entrances to several underground factories, despite the fact that their presence in the zone had already been indicated with sufficient accuracy by secret agents.*

This type of protective camouflage, then, worked very well even after the bombs stopped falling!

Since the old methods of camouflage by means of nets and branches have definitely seen their day (for modern aerial reconnaissance permits one to distinguish between live and cut vegetation by spectrographic photography), the only truly valid protective camouflage, aside from underground installation, is natural camouflage, which combines marvelously well with prefabricated buildings.[10]

At this point conventional people will, as usual, rise up and proclaim that in any event a large-scale movement of parts of prefabricated buildings and unusual equipment could not have escaped the attention at least of the technicians charged with transporting them, even if their destinations lay overseas, beyond the reach of the merely curious. And there would be all the more reason, they will say, for this complicated activity to have alarmed the inhabitants in the areas where the buildings were to be erected, particularly when the destination, even if sparsely populated, was Europe or North America.

Now if one were to talk to these conventional people not

about airfields but about secret, prefabricated seaports, the least that could happen would be that they would be struck dumb, for if it is difficult for them to imagine hiding a certain number of hangars (which in point of fact can be set up anywhere, even in the depths of the remotest regions, by transporting them by air and dropping them by parachute), it would seem absolutely impossible that a port could be hidden. After all, by its very nature it must be located along some well-defined stretch of coast. And yet even this extraordinary "miracle" of military technology has already been accomplished a number of times.

In order to avoid any misunderstanding, we transcribe here the main points of a British news item of 1954 that treats of the construction of several stand-by prefabricated ports:

"Great Britain has quietly prepared a good number of 'standby ports' as replacements for her major ports in case they become damaged or destroyed by atomic attacks. These are prefabricated ports, made up principally of pieces in reinforced concrete similar to the huge floating caissons of the famous Mulberry artificial ports that were towed to the Normandy beaches in June 1944 and made it possible for the Allies to supply the forces on the beachheads quickly. The various parts making up the moles and warehouses—as well as the necessary ancillary material (cranes, elevators, railway tracks, mooring bitts, etc.)—have been concentrated at chosen strategic points in the vicinity of the ports where they would be installed in case of necessity. The necessary preparatory work of widening and dredging the channels has already been completed in the ports themselves, and new fuel tanks have also been constructed. The whereabouts of the warehouses containing the stand-by ports as well as the coastal areas that have been chosen to take the place of the great harbor areas that might be destroyed are kept secret. Those who have taken part in the various aspects of the undertaking still do not know what they are to be used for. Only a few trusted civil servants in the Admiralty know anything about the details of this vast plan worked out immediately after the war as soon as the government leaders became aware of the offensive possibilities of atomic weapons. In the last few years the work has been speeded up and tens of millions of pounds have been spent on it. It is estimated that Great Britain today has at least six large artificial stand-by ports ready to go into operation in case of emergency."[11]

While we are dealing with British secrets, it would not be a bad idea to remember that in February 1954 the Air Ministry revealed for the first and only time that Great Britain had a protective shield of radar installations throughout the Kingdom, with the key parts of the extensive organization in underground quarters and protected by massive concrete shields.

As with the artificial ports, the radar network was set up without the press's getting wind of it or the workers on the job knowing exactly what the underground installation was for. Rumor has it that the workers of one of the contractors involved in the construction were led to believe that they were working on the foundations for a new hot springs pavilion.

Whatever may be one's deep personal convictions about "unknown flying objects," one must certainly agree that these Cyclopean undertakings are even more astonishing than the UFO bases, because they were not secretly carried out in the fastnesses of some large forest on the coast of Africa or in the desolate reaches of the Arctic, but along the heavily populated coasts of England—which more than any other European country insists on freedom of the press.

After all this evidence, is it not perhaps legitimate to argue that only "a few trusted civil servants" in the Ministry of Supply, the R.A.F., and the Hawker Siddeley Group know anything about the impressive project to hide the bases of the so-called UFOs in the dense Canadian forests?[12]

NOTES

1. That the authorities charged with keeping the secret tolerate, approve, and even, through more or less unknown dummies, encourage the wild theorizings of the ufologists can doubtless be understood, for so long as they succeed in making people believe that the UFOs come from somewhere in cosmic space, they can continue their work undisturbed.

2. It has sometimes been pointed out that there is an inherent danger in the UFOs, inasmuch as they are liable to "hostile action" *vis-à-vis* some great power, with international reactions and consequences that are difficult to foresee but would certainly be very serious. In fact, a power possessing an air weapon without another power's being able to identify either its ownership or the point from which it was launched could carry out sneak bombings over a period of time until the enemy country was annihilated, without having to fear any reprisal from the country that was bombed—and that, indeed, might possess even more powerful weapons—and without experiencing any moral condemnation for the treacherous aggression. If one really succeeded in making world public opinion accept the idea that a mysterious air weapon was of extraterrestrial origin, any attack would in fact pass for an act completely independent of the human will! Fortunately, the possessors of the portentous secret of the UFOs have not been and will not let themselves be tempted into some ruinous adventure which would not accord either with the mentality or the interests of the British ruling class; and besides, who can guarantee that the UFOs are really still not identified in the secret files of the Russian, American, and Chinese general staffs? Perhaps the statements prepared for the press and thus for the public at large—forever ignorant of everything—by the various scientific commissions of inquiry are as ambitious in their intentions as they are mediocre in their futile conclusions? . . .

3. Nevertheless, atomic secrets had already been violated several times, although the public at large did not know it, by both disputing parties. In February 1943 Anglo-Norwegian commandoes flying from England seriously damaged the Hydro-Norsk factory at Vermork in Telemark, which produced "heavy water" for the Germans. The latter were, in turn, generally aware that the United States was diligently working in the atomic field, but a surprise roundup of Nazi agents in 1942 cut off any possibility of trouble before it got under way.

4. See Constance Babington-Smith, *Evidence in Camera* (London, Chatto & Windus, 1958), pp. 199–232.

5. See General Walter Dornberger, *V-2, the Nazi Rocket Weapon* (New York, The Viking Press, 1954), pp. 152–160.

6. On September 28, 1942, the aeronautical attaché of the Italian Embassy in Berlin had communicated to the Technical Direction of the Italian Ministry of Aeronautics the first vague confidential information concerning the twin-jet Heinkel HE-280 and a Messerschmitt jet fighter of analogous design (probably the famous ME-262). This information led Italian technicians to sit on and finally shelve Italian plans in the field of jet propulsion (Caproni-Campini jet engines). At about the same time, the Allied secret services also came into possession of some data regarding the new German products, which were expected to be "excellent from every point of view."

7. And since we have mentioned the De Havilland Company, it will not be amiss to quote from the Italian press what the aeronautical authority Charles Gardner wrote in the autumn of 1949 about a well-kept British secret of the period immediately after the war concerning the famous civil air transport four-jet DH-106 Comet, with a speed of 500 miles per hour: ". . . The story of the Comet is quite interesting. The first design goes back to 1944–45, but was not until 1946 that the chief designer of the De Havilland firm, R. E. Bishop, drew up the guidelines for its construction. . . . Until March 30, 1949, the particulars about the construction of the craft constituted one of the most impenetrable secrets of the entire field of international civil aviation. At Hatfield rumors circulated at one time about a stratospheric craft with swept-back wings and a cruising speed of 453 mph, but the company maintained absolute silence in this regard, refusing to contradict or confirm the rumors. There was a good reason for the policy of secrecy: England was then and still is the only nation that constructs commercial turbojet or propjet planes, and these machines—which include the DH-106 and the Vickers 'Viscount'—were to restore its old prestige to British civil aviation and make up for the years lost during the war. British supremacy in the field of jet engines is beyond question, but until the new craft had been finished and flown, it would have been possible, at least theoretically, for our rivals [the Americans]

to introduce something similar. . . ." Since the performances of the UFOs decidedly surpass all conventional limits, it seems logical to deduce that the secret concerning them has rightly lasted and will last much longer.

8. In addition, with the enormous work force available in the huge numbers of prisoners of war, who were used for the hardest labor, they put a number of special experimental facilities underground in man-made caverns. One good example is the wind tunnel for measuring the ballistic behavior of aircraft weapons. This wind tunnel, built completely underground at the L.F.A. center in Volkenrode, was a good 1300 feet long and could be brought down by means of powerful pumps to 1/30 atmosphere so as to simulate air pressure at 32,000 feet altitude. But this tunnel was particularly distinguished by the fact that the two ends (which housed, respectively, the weapon being tested—mounted, if necessary, on the complete airplane—and the target) were camouflaged as "model farm" buildings, with many stables, hay lofts, barns, etc., so that we can easily understand how even the most skillful air reconnaissance pilots finally had to give up trying to locate the L.F.A.

9. The factory functioned, however, for only a brief period because of the worsening military situation and the difficulty of supplying raw materials. When it was occupied the Allies learned that only four fuselages a day were coming out of the mine. From the technical point of view, however, it functioned perfectly.

10. The American U-2 reconnaissance planes uncovered secrets from the air on the basis of previous briefings by agents operating directly on Soviet territory or on its borders. The routes of the U-2s were carefully studied and worked out in advance. If the pilots had flown over the vast reaches of Siberia at random, one could be mathematically certain that they would not have photographed anything really interesting or that at the most they would have discovered only one important

bjective for every ten or so completely fruitless but dangerous
ights.

1. See *News Chronicle* and *Messaggero Marittimo* No. 61,
964. One must also add, to be perfectly candid, that the
British were not novices at this sort of enterprise. Two "secret
orts" of somewhat smaller size were in fact readied at Gare-
och-on-Clyde and at Carnyarn in Scotland between the autumn
f 1940 and June 1942, to spread out coastal ship traffic en-
angered by German submarines and bombers. (*Cf. "Porti
egreti in Scozia," Rivista Marittima,* Ministry of the Navy,
Rome, August–September, 1945, p. 54.)

2. The thick forests of British Columbia are well known.
The region is favored by regular rainfall and a rather temperate
limate, as well as by the characteristic mountain and river
ystem of the region (tortuous mountain chains alternating
with wide valleys). Here centuries-old trees thrive—pines,
edars, spruce—which easily grow as high as 150 feet and,
n some particularly long-lived species, even 300 feet. (They
were saplings when the Lombard invasion was breaking up
what was left of the Roman Empire after it collapsed in Italy.)
Thus, considering that the UFOs can take off and land verti-
ally—as proved by their ability to hover motionless in the
air—it follows that a UFO airport does not need the long
ement or asphalt runways that characterize our airfields and
make them visible. Simple round open spaces cleared in the
midst of forest glades or on the shores of peaceful mountain
akes, properly camouflaged and marked by hidden radio
eacons, could easily take care of the take-off and landing of
a number of flying machines without too many operative
complications. These installations would easily be overlooked
by aerial reconnaissance, even if a plane's route happened to
coincide with the location of the secret airfield. For what,
n fact, is a total of a square mile or two covered, for example,
by possibly a hundred open spaces and prefabricated circular
angars compared with the nearly four million square miles of
Canada?

CHAPTER 10

In Which,
for the Present, We Conclude . . .

In order to demolish completely the grotesque edifice of idio
cies and mental blocks fabricated by the ufologists, it remain:
to clear up the fifth question: How was the undertaking
financed?

In aeronautical jargon—which is appropriate to the subjec
matter—we now have to make another long power dive into
the past and focus our light on the misunderstanding abou
the so-called R.A.F. scandal, which had a profound impac
on British public opinion some dozen years ago.[1]

At the beginning of 1955—while British aeronautical au
thorities were preparing to mount a propaganda campaign sup
porting the R.A.F.'s claims to the category of Senior Service
traditionally held by the Navy—the opposition press unleashed

bitter attack on the air force, illustrating "with an abundance of facts what experts term the disastrous situation of our air defense."

On January 15 the principal exponent of this dissatisfaction, the *London Daily Herald,* under the headline, "Britain Has the Men—But Not the Planes; Britain Is Unprepared for a Full-scale Modern War," wrote, "Britain is rapidly losing her claim to be among the countries with effective air-power. . . . During the last 3 years the Government aimed to spend nearly £1000 million on aircraft and equipment for the RAF and on research. Much of this money has been spent but the goods have not been delivered. . . . The failure in the electronic field is an ominous pointer to the development of British guided missiles. Several have been launched and engaged targets successfully. But these were only test vehicles. *It might be better for us to build American missiles under license—missiles which are proved successes.*"

Naturally, these depressing statements made a great impression on the ignorant public, alarmed by the huge headlines, and the members of the opposition got up in the House of Commons and demanded explanations. To hear them, it seemed that England was about to go under from one minute to the next: the Air Force was without airplanes, the Army was short on men and arms, the Navy was in decline.

The situation in England was not, in fact, rosy, for military life no longer appealed to the younger generations as it once had, and in the Commons Churchill himself had evidenced some concern about this state of affairs, which was still, however, far from being or even seeming catastrophic.

As far as the Air Force was concerned, the opposition pointed out that the number of extremely modern prototypes was constantly being exaggerated, yet they remained unproduced for far too long a time. The opposition even spoke of a "great R.A.F. scandal" and of chaos in high military circles, indicating that the guilt lay with the Ministry of Supply, which was accused of perpetual shilly-shallying, inability to coordinate, obtuseness, and still more.

Directly involved, the government defended itself by publishing a White Book. A picture of the fluid situation that had resulted from the transitional epoch introduced by nuclear

arms emerged from the White Book, despite all obvious un
communicativeness and the lacunae dictated by the necessitie
of military secrecy. It also said, in no uncertain terms, that the
R.A.F. *was the central pillar of defense of the British Isles and
the Commonwealth and that it would be developed to the
maximum.*

Instead of stopping, the criticisms mounted in intensity; and
severe punishment of those responsible and a detailed account
ing for aeronautical expenses were demanded—unsuccessfully
The British government not only took refuge in stubborn
silence but also, in the annual allocation of the military
budget, increased the R.A.F.'s share by £22 million, sizably
decreasing the amounts destined for the Army and Navy.

In sum, during the fiscal year 1955–1956, British aviation
—scandal or no—had a budget of £513,900,000, which, like
the previous billions, were largely spent without anyone's
knowing how or where.

The opposition would not give up, however, and finally
succeeded in getting a special parliamentary commission set up
to investigate aeronautical contracts. On January 21, 1957
it concluded its work and in its subsequent report recom-
mended to the government that the entire contract system be
reviewed. In particular, it hit at the costly financing of several
types of airplanes that were never constructed. *Ghost planes*
the critics called them. "The 8 jet Boeing 52 [the American
strategic superbomber] is years ahead—five years ahead, at
least—of anything we have got."[2]

"We have spent too much time and money in relation to
what has been achieved," concluded Sir Roy Fedden, former
chief engineer of the Bristol Airplane Company and a member
of the investigating committee. "In five years, from the budget
of 1950–51 to that of 1955–56, more than seven billion pounds
have been spent and we have had seven ministers of defense, all
of which, however, has done little to improve the military efficiency of the United Kingdom."

In the allocation of monies, the lion's share always went to
the Ministry of Supply, and rightly so, in view of its functions.
In 1946 alone its budget for "aeronautical research" ran to £28
million. Previous to that it had received other money for various
reasons, and it received much more in successive budgets.[3]

In the area of military expenditure, to ask for greater clarification would be grotesque, to say the least, but even if the British authorities prefer to remain silent concerning the destination of that stream of money and its fruits, the figures speak loudly enough.

THE TUG OF WAR BETWEEN
THE U.S. AIR FORCE AND THE UFOS

While the storm generated by the opposition in England was about to reach its peak, in the United States the press was again exerting pressure on Air Force authorities to express an opinion on the wave of UFO sightings of the previous autumn, which, although mainly observed in Western Europe, had also appeared sporadically in various parts of the United States, causing the usual conflicts between public, press, and authorities.

As usual, there was a flood of reassuring if inconclusive statements. Summing up seven years of investigation and study (*ad usum Delphini*), the most authoritative figure in the country, President Eisenhower, declared parenthetically to the press that he was personally in a position to exclude the possibility that the UFOs had an extraterrestrial origin!

For their part, the experts of the Air Technical Intelligence Center in their nth final report repeated their previous assertions, protesting that they did not possess "any authentic physical evidence . . . establishing the existence of space ships from other planets or secret experimental weapons launched by the United States or by any other nation on earth, again for experimental purposes. The flying saucers, we repeat, exist only in the imagination of the so-called witnesses." It was the intention of the Air Force that the UFOs were and were to remain nothing more than a modern myth.[4]

Although the intervention of the highest political power in the country did not dissipate the suspicions of those who believed in the existence of the mysterious machines, as had been hoped, it did succeed in eliminating once and for all the suspicion that the UFOs were American-made airplanes

Catching the ball on the bounce, the specialists in extra terrestrial flying saucers and similar mysteries aggravate matters by maintaining that if the craft were not extraterres trial something would surely have leaked out after eight full years of continuous sightings, because "no secret weapon in a democratic regime could remain secret for such a long period of time!"[5]

From that moment the activities of Project Blue Book— which had been reestablished without fanfare and on a com pletely different basis—were quietly continued in order to keep the principal source of "official" information for the public under strict control.

Periodically—but sometimes at long intervals—the Depart ment of Defense, in agreement with the U.S. Air Force, sen out a new series of news releases for the press that were de signed to wear out even the most indefatigable petitioners.[6]

The news release of October 25, 1955, carried Secretary Quarles's statement verbatim, with its reference to the Avro Car. A lengthy release followed on November 5, 1957. I repeated the usual identifications, thereby reducing the propor tion of flying objects that remained "unidentified" to less than 2 percent. The third release, on November 15, 1957, disposed of certain inexplicable electrical phenomena that had ac companied the appearance of the UFOs over the south-central states.

The fourth release, which came nearly a year later (October 6, 1958), demolished at one fell swoop all the incidents that had taken place up to July 31, reasserted that such apparitions were in no way dangerous, and praised the work of Dr. J. Allen Hynek, now "Chief Scientific Consultant" to the Air Force on matters concerning UFOs.

The brief release of January 22, 1959, again summed up the 269 American sightings of the preceding year in statistical form, rejoicing in the obvious drop (.67 percent) in the annual per centage of sightings that could not be explained by reference to ordinary phenomena. On July 15 a very short release—tabu lating the cases that had occurred during the first part of the year—declared with ill-concealed disappointment that there

ad been a 2.09 percent rise in the notorious rate of popular
lusions, notwithstanding that the number of sightings had
early dropped by half.

The two complementary releases of January 29 and July 21,
960—after concisely summing up all the data gathered since
947, which brought the total U.S. sightings to 6,312 cases
of which 1,501 pertained to the well-known 1952 flights over
he capital)—went off into a wordy explanation that was taken
vhole cloth—without changing even a comma!—from the re-
ease of November 5, 1957. Evidently Project Blue Book
vanted to perform a kind of brainwashing on the ufologists,
vho appeared disinclined to accept the repeated, passionate
leclarations of ignorance and innocence made by the new
eaders of the project. A special scolding was then administered
o the various private associations that accused the Air Force
·f concealing the most significant information or that boasted
·f officially exchanging information with the Air Force con-
erning the activities of the extraterrestrial airships.

The tug of war between the U.S. Air Force and the UFOs,
·r, better, between the Air Force and the ufologists, then
·egan to decrease rapidly in intensity and pungency with the
·eginning of the astronautical program, which divided the
·ttention of the public—which is inclined to focus its immediate
nterest on what is visible, tangible, and explicable—until . . .

Until August 1965, when, after years of sporadic sightings
hat were of little interest for the ufologists, a new wave of
inknown flying objects appeared in the skies over New Mexico,
Texas, Kansas, and Oklahoma, catching the attention of, among
·thers, numerous qualified observers, such as police officers,
weather bureau experts and radar specialists of the U.S. Air
Force.

Strangely enough, however, for the first time the American
press—perhaps influenced by the enormous amount of military
counterpropaganda—was not inclined to build up a new
"case," and this was a mistake because the phenomenon had
been verified on a large scale over Mexican territory as well,
and new appearances of UFOs were about to complicate
matters, as at the time of the tumultuous "celestial invasions" of
1948 and 1952.

THE "UFO SUMMER"

The first UFO apeared over Wynnewood, Oklahoma, a littl
before dawn on July 31 and remained visible to the eye fo
about forty minutes. Its presence was also detected by th
radar screens at the Tinker and Carswell air bases (even thoug
Air Force authorities subsequently decided to deny the fact).

The next night, triangular and diamond formations of UFO
and scattered, individual UFOs flew by at an altitude esti
mated at slightly more than 10,000 feet, going north and show
ing "frequent changes of color, from reddish to blinding whit
and from white to greenish blue, sometimes shifting from on
side of the formation to the other."

Project Blue Book's immediate denial was as punctual as i
was futile: A spokesman said that no radar sighting of un
known flying objects had been confirmed. It was suggested tha
"the objects observed may have been the planet Jupiter or th
stars Rigel, Capella, Betelgeuse, or Aldebaran, which wer
visible. At the time of the reported sightings, the azimuth
and elevation of the reported sightings supports this pre
liminary conclusion." A planet that frequently and rapidly
changes color and whose radar image splits and resemble
objects propelling themselves through the sky? That is indeed
a novel occurrence and should not fail to interest astronomers
even in these times of telescopes and extragalactic mysteries

Three days later, as the result of a "very bad occurrence,"
the gray eminences of Project Blue Book were flatly contra-
dicted by the personnel of the U.S. Air Force bases at Kewee-
naw Field in Houghton, Michigan. (Perhaps someone, out of
regard for truth, compromised his career.) A "solid radar contact" had been established with about ten UFOs flying at
hypersonic speed (9300 mph?) at a high altitude over Lake
Superior and going in the direction of Canada. The incident
was also reported to the U.P.I. press service, which immediately sent it out over its teletypes.

The official explanation, "a flight of weather balloons," took
advantage of the simultaneous appearance of other objects
that had been seen while "they hovered motionless or moved

slowly, frequently changing direction, over several outlying sections of Minneapolis." This city is, in fact, the site of one of the largest American centers for the production and launching of the gigantic stratospheric weather balloons. But when seven of these phantom "weather balloons" were pursued by a jet in the sky over Duluth, they rapidly left the jet behind while it was flying at a speed exceeding a thousand miles an hour. Since when do the winds of the stratosphere blow with such terrible violence?

The curve of these appearances reached its peak during the night between August 2 and 3, and were concentrated over New England in particular. In fact, although not neglecting more distant states, such as Texas and California, the UFOs seemed to show a decided preference for the southern regions of New Hampshire, where, according to numerous inhabitants, they had flown over the local high-tension wires several times, perhaps in order to get recharged. This strange suspicion— strange but not impossible—subsequently led ufologists to launch a new case, called the "incident at Exeter" in honor of the small town where the greatest number of sightings took place, the last of which, on September 3, seemed to bring the display of luminous bodies and their mysterious operations to a close.[8]

After three months of intensive observations, which occurred with an almost regular daily rhythm, the number of sightings rapidly and progressively decreased as before. Project Blue Book's news release of October 27, 1965, which was got up with the public relations offices of the Pentagon, brilliantly solved the affair by referring to high-altitude exercises which had been carried out at that very time by the bombers of the Strategic Air Command (S.A.C.), and on a widespread "thermal inversion" produced by a thick layer of cold Canadian air which had crept between two warmer layers over the New England states. According to the Air Force experts, this natural phenomenon had the miraculous power of making the stars and planets seem to tremble in such a way as to give the impression that they were flying in the sky.

"They can stop kidding us now about there being no such things as 'flying saucers,'" the Fort Worth, Texas, *Star Telegram* rightfully protested. "And it's going to take more than a statistical report on how many reported 'saucers' have turned out to be jets and weather balloons to convince us otherwise."

Taking the lead from the insubordinate behavior of the Houghton radar operators, the Alameda, California, *Times Star* in turn commented in an indignant editorial: ". . . the Air Force spokesmen, whose job it is to explain away the seemingly improbable in terms of the commonplace, have been getting such a workout lately that either they are starting to break down or their superiors are finally coming to the conclusion that they are making the Air Force appear ridiculous."

Notwithstanding a spate of such acid comments in the press, the Air Force did not budge an inch from the line to which it had always adhered. It was sure that its previous experience of mass psychology would be repeated. Experience had taught it that even the most incredible statements are forgotten by most people with the passing of time, together with the facts that prompted them, and those who are really skeptical can, in any case, think what they please.

AFTERTHOUGHTS AND NEW INVESTIGATIONS

The news release of February 1, 1966, taking advantage of the winter disappearance of the objects in order to implant the anti-UFO dogma decreed in high places ever more firmly in the minds of the American public, with almost saintly patience reiterated the old explanations (birds, balloons, airplanes, sputniks, meteorites, and so on) with consummate ability and the sober language of the hidden persuaders. But it was fated that all this art and craftiness would in the final analysis prove self-defeating.

With the coming of spring—specifically between March 20 and 23—renewed activity on the part of the UFOs again posed the same old dilemmas for the Americans. For the most part, the characteristics of the new sightings did not differ from those of the past summer and of the preceding years. The area, however, was restricted to the states of Michigan and Ohio, and one brash UFO went so far as to fly right over the Wright-

Patterson base, the permanent home of Project Blue Book, giving rise to no little hilarity among those who already harbored little esteem for the illustrious group.[9]

Without even waiting for the last UFO to disappear, the scientific consultant for the Air Force, Dr. Hynek, held a press conference in Detroit to "debunk" the events of the month.

Having conducted a personal investigation, he said, he felt it was certain that the wandering lights observed by more than fifty witnesses in the environs of Ann Arbor were nothing more than natural gases produced in the swampy ground; spring gases that burst into flame on contact with the oxygen of the air, causing will-o'-the-wisps of varying sizes. According to the investigator, proved hoaxes and false reports had also influenced a number of witnesses.

This hypothesis was not much more far-fetched than some of the others, and it too might have achieved its aim, but this time the decisive entry into the controversy of ufological associations—headed by the powerful N.I.C.A.P.—did not give the U.S. Air Force authorities the chance to shelve the affair so quickly.

The Republican congressman Gerald Ford proposed that a special congressional committee of investigation be set up, and the proposal added fuel to the already heated dispute between the press and the military, causing even Secretary of Defense McNamara and Chief of Staff General Wheeler to intervene and deny, with the full weight of their authority, the physical existence of the UFOs and quash the possibility of adding a civilian office to the one that had long been operating so efficiently within the Air Force.

However, perhaps Dr. Hynek had tired of blindly supporting the Air Force's strictly negative policy. Leaving aside the possibility of a wildly Machiavellian scheme to achieve exactly the opposite of what he claimed, the following August the magazine *Science* published an excerpt from an open letter from Dr. Hynek in which, reversing opinions that he had held for twenty years with regard to the UFOs, the scientist proposed that the problem be faced squarely once and for all.

Published in its entirety by the *Saturday Evening Post* of December 17, 1966, the contrite confession of the greatest

American ufophobe set forth the following four possible explanations:

1) are they hallucinations or hoaxes? If so, it must be proved, and given the present state of our understanding, it would be even more difficult to prove this than it would to prove the opposite;

2) are they military devices that someone is experimenting with? The affair has gone on for too long and has involved too many countries in every part of the world for this to be acceptable;

3) do they come from outer, even interstellar, space? This cannot be totally excluded, even if conclusive proof is lacking. "Some skeptics who scoff at reported UFO sightings often ask why the 'flying saucers' don't try to communicate with us. One answer might be: Why should they? We wouldn't try to communicate with a new species of kangaroo we might find in Australia; we would just observe the animals."

4) are we faced with a natural phenomenon that as yet defies our scientific knowledge? "Think how our knowledge of the universe has changed in 100 years. In 1866 we not only knew nothing about nuclear energy, we didn't even know that the atom had a nucleus. . . . Who can say what startling facts we will learn about our world in the next 100 years?"

Concluding this belated self-criticism, the scientist declared: "Although the Air Force has probably spent less on UFO's so far than it has on wastebaskets, I realize that it is impractical to expect the service to set up a costly 'flying-saucer' surveillance system across the country. . . . [But] all of the valuable data that we have accumulated—good reports from all over the world—must be computerized so that we can rapidly compare new sightings with old and trace patterns of UFO behavior. . . . I recommend that every police chief in the country make sure that at least one of his squad cars carries in its glove compartment a camera loaded with color film."

Dr. Hynek emphasized his views on a "controversial subject": "During all of my years of association with the Air Force, I have never seen any evidence for the charge about UFO's most often leveled against the service: that there is deliberate cover-up of knowledge of space visitors to prevent the public from panicking. The entire history of the Air Force and the UFO's can be understood only if we realize that the Pentagon has never believed that UFO's could be anything novel, and it still doesn't. The working hypothesis of the Air Force has been that the stimulus behind every UFO report ... is a mis-identification of a conventional object or a natural phenomenon. It is just as simple as that.

"Now, after a delay of 18 years, the Air Force and American science are about to try for the first time, really, to discover what, if anything, we can believe about 'flying saucers.'"

THE UNIVERSITY OF COLORADO
INVESTIGATION

Would the $313,000 rushed through to the University of Colorado as a special fund for a new series of investigations furnish an answer that would satisfy both the demands of the Pentagon and the curiosity of American taxpayers?

Such was the sum that the Air Force allocated to the University to finance a new program of scientific research on the UFO question along the lines suggested by Dr. Hynek, to study future sightings, to reexamine the 10,147 reports accumulated by Project Blue Book, and to clear up—if possible—the 646 cases that remained unexplained.[10]

News release No. 847–66 of October 7, 1966 (Title: *Air Force Selects University of Colorado to Investigate Unidentified Objects Reports*) faithfully reflects the orders of the then Air Force Secretary, Harold Brown, but it does not clear up in any convincing way the real reasons for the liquidation of the Air Force's Project Blue Book. For better or worse, Project Blue Book had been functioning for almost twenty years, had been under attack several times in the past (when people were ingenuous enough to demand the truth), and had never been seriously strengthened even after the attacks. Why had it been ditched for a new organism that was completely unprepared simply because it was new?[11]

Nor was the reason the Air Force gave for choosing the University of Colorado at Boulder in the least convincing: it is

". . . an institution of sufficient prestige to enjoy the faith of the public"—and, obviously, escape the absurdity of what was considered an unimportant matter.

The length of the contract between the Air Force and the University of Colorado was fixed at fifteen months, extendable if warranted, and at its expiration a detailed report was to be written and presented—at the specific request of the Department of Defense—for final critical evaluation by a group of eminent specialists designated by the National Academy of Sciences to attest to the "validity of the methods and means used in the investigations." Was this a ready-made alibi in order to camouflage possible—and not unlikely—failure? High-level censorship? Or was it an attempt to set up a highly authoritative and final liquidation of the UFOs?

Some biographical data on the leaders of the new investigation, which some ufologists proposed calling—rather prematurely—"Operation Clearance," sheds some light on this cloudy affair.

The organizer of the enterprise seems to have been Dr. J. Allen Hynek, director of the Lindheimer Astronomical Research Center and chairman of the Astronomy Department at Northwestern University at Evanston, Illinois, "Scientific Consultant to the U.S. Air Force," and "Special Investigator of UFOs," again for the Air Force. It was he who, as we said, suffered a sort of scientific *"crise de conscience"* over the attitude that the Air Force had always maintained and still maintains on the thorny problem of UFOs (an attitude which is, in brief, frivolous and which Dr. Hynek himself had energetically supported for some twenty years).

The sixty-four-year-old Dr. Edward U. Condon was appointed director of the new project. Dr. Condon had formerly been a member of the staff of the nuclear center at Los Alamos for the development of the first atomic bombs.[12] Professor of physics and astrophysics at the University of Colorado, Condon immediately put all his cards on the table when he was appointed to investigate the UFOs, stating that he would not be able to dedicate all his time to the project; hence he should be considered only as its "scientific director." In fact, he continued to exercise his old and new functions in an office in the Joint

Institute Laboratory for Astrophysics, of which he had been an influential member for some time.

The job of principal assistant and actual coordinator of the entire program—the project coordinator—was, therefore, assigned to Dr. Robert G. Low, formerly Assistant Dean of the University of Colorado Graduate School. Some hundred scientists chosen from the University of Colorado, other American universities, and various governmental and civil agencies scattered throughout the country would be working under him, though with complete freedom of action. When the "UFO Probe Committee" was installed in the old Woodbury Hall building it included the following members:

—three psychologists (Drs. Stuart W. Cook, David Saunders, and Michael Wertheimer), all from the University of Colorado;

—one astrophysicist (Dr. Franklin Roach) of the Environmental Science Services);

—one astrogeophysicist (Dr. William Blumen, a Fellow of the University of Colorado);

—one physicist (Dr. Joseph H. Rush of the National Center for Atmospheric Research High Altitude Observatory);

—two University of Colorado graduate students in psychology and one in liberal arts;

—two secretaries and one typist.

The total full-time membership of the staff, including leaders, amounted to fourteen actual members, not one of whom was skilled in the fundamental technical disciplines that concern aviation, such as aerodynamics, aircraft construction, electronic engineering, chemistry, and applied physics.[13]

Failure to enlist the aid of such experts certainly signified that the promoters of "Clearance" still believed that the UFOs were—or should be, for the public—unknown natural phenomena or flights of the imagination.

Aside from the fact that after years of tedious repetition the strings used in manipulating some of the tricks were becoming visible, it was clear that—despite the enthusiastic endorsement of the new committee by the American and world press—we should not have expected great things or sensational revelations from it. The hope early went glimmering that the Colorado project might finally acquaint everyone with everything—or at least part of it—that only a very few have known for some time.[14]

Now that the contract has expired, nothing will be easier than for the Air Force—after simply denying for more than twenty years that the phenomenon exists—to stop deriding the easy (because undemonstrable) explanation of a putative extraterrestrial origin for the UFOs, and even to accept the existence of some new or at least unexplained type of atmospheric phenomenon, in order to supply the required though meaningless sop for the millions of American taxpayers who are disturbed by the fantasies and foolishness of ufologists, and so to protect the sacred principle of "freedom of the press."

A WAITING GAME?

When we examine the whole of the many years' work that has gone on backstage, we see that the behavior of the various American authorities—especially at the time the first investigations covering the period from 1947 to 1955 were carried out—has frequently been contradictory and sometimes, but only in appearance, even incoherent.

For a short time, in 1954, the alternation of hasty explanations with subsequent reversals was even taken to be an astute plan to cover up indefinitely the secret that the UFOs were American-built, or as a clever way of gradually informing the world that they were indeed standing on the runways of secret national airfields. The ridiculous references to the inhabitants of Mars or Venus, to the Uranians, or to star people made by third parties, or certain scattered allusions to the possibility that the UFOs might have come from behind the Iron Curtain (the impossibility of which was obviously discounted to begin with)—these things were taken to be part of a game by a complex bureau whose aim was to encourage friends and warn enemies by frightening the public. The protestations of technical people, or their refusal to make statements, was, moreover, interpreted to mean that the invention was in the process of being perfected.

Otherwise, it was said, how could one explain the inexplicable calmness which the leaders of the country had on several occasions exhibited in the face of an extraordinary phenomenon that was upsetting the whole nation?

For example, when reporters asked an official at the control tower of a civil airport in Washington in July 1952 why he had not alerted the antiaircraft defense center when the machines first approached, he answered drily: "We were too busy with more important matters, and besides those 'things' don't harm anybody"!

A high Air Force official, commenting on the formation of Project Blue Book, declared in effect: We do not know the causes of the observed phenomena, but we are convinced that they represent absolutely no threat to our country. They have been around for five years and they have never struck. If they are man-made, the men who make them are aeronautically superior to us. If it turns out that they are enemy aircraft, we will capture them.[15]

Aircraft of huge size, with no recognizable system of operation, perhaps (or not even "perhaps") with men on board, from some admittedly unknown country or world (friend? neutral? enemy?), capable of rising vertically with dizzying speed and flying horizontally at speeds unmatched by even the fastest known types of jets—*was none of this even a potential threat?* On the face of it this view, if taken literally, is an absurdity.

In fact, these unknown machines roamed far and wide, undisturbed, over the entire United States, and not infrequently remained for lengthy periods over or in the neighborhood of military bases, governmental scientific laboratories, and centers for nuclear research. Yet anyone who is at all familiar with air routes and who travels by air knows quite well how much governmental red tape and regulations—certainly partly justified on the grounds of everyone's safety—must be put up with by anyone who wants to go, not to the Antipodes, but merely from one local airport to another.

Thus one cannot *a priori* exclude the possibility that, while unimportant military offices were stumbling around in the dark, Air Force top brass was far better informed than it would have had people believe, at least from 1952 on. Nor can one exclude the possibility that it might finally have got wind of something through secret service channels (though it could not copy the craft for lack of detailed information or of specific technologies). Nor the possibility that, through diplomatic channels (a report made to a confidential Blue Book?), the builders of the UFOs (for no other reason than the need to make a rendezvous in the sky over the capital, as in the summer of 1952) had secretly notified some high-ranking person— let us say the President of the United States or someone in his immediate circle—to avoid precipitating some dangerous anti-aircraft activity, which, in fact, never occurred either in Washington or at the more heavily armed missile bases which the UFOs overflew a number of times.[16]

PROJECT BEACON

And this is not all. Beginning in June 1952, Air Force investigating authorities seemed particularly interested in the intense, changing lights that usually accompanied the moving objects, rather than in the saucers themselves—which leads some of the most highly qualified experts to suspect that the United States was already aware of where the saucers came from and that it especially wanted to glean some useful data on the type and chemical composition of the formidable fuel used by the UFOs.[17]

During this period, while the Project Blue Book investigations were getting under way, the Air Force Chief of Staff, Hoyt S. Vandenberg, did, in fact, have the Laboratory of Applied Physics at the University of Los Angeles construct a spectroscopic motion-picture camera which could photograph the flight of an unknown object and provide an instant analysis of its light energy.

This project, which went under the name of "Beacon," envisaged setting up two hundred such cameras at an equal number of observation posts established along the routes that the machines most frequently traveled, principally in the south-western area of the United States. Seventy-five American military bases abroad were also supposed to receive these UFO-detectors.

The final report on this highly specialized investigation, which was slated to come out in December of 1953, was never published. Was it perhaps, as American ufologists maintained, because no solid information was obtained (1953 was, in fact, a year that was almost totally devoid of American sightings)? Or was it, as the French ufologist A. Michel wrote, because it was judged opportune to draw the curtain of military secrecy over the results that had been obtained?

Neither hypothesis corresponds to the truth. Captain Ruppelt himself reported that the apparatus, which was completed after a year of study, "wouldn't satisfactorily photograph a million-candle-power flare at 450 yards. The cameras themselves were all right, but in combination with the gratings, they were no good." Which leads one to suspect that the project never really got under way, at least to the extent publicized by the press.

That secret information reached the Pentagon, on the other hand, seems to be indicated by the following enigmatic episode, also revealed by Captain Ruppelt after he had taken the bitter step of handing in his resignation:

"In some aspects the Washington National [Airport] sightings [of July–August 1952] could be classed as a surprise . . . but in other ways they weren't. A few days prior to the incident a scientist, from an agency that I can't name, and I were talking about the build-up of reports along the east coast of the United States.[18] We talked for about two hours, and I was ready to leave when he said that he had one last comment to make—a prediction. From his study of the UFO reports that he was getting from Air Force Headquarters, and from discussions with his colleagues, he said that he thought that we were sitting right on top of a big keg full of loaded flying saucers. 'Within the next few days,' he told me, and I remember that he punctuated his slow, deliberate remarks by hitting the desk with his fist, 'they're going to blow up and you're going to have the granddaddy of all UFO sightings. The sighting will occur in Washington or New York,' he predicted—'probably Washington.'"

And they did, in fact, fly over Washington, passing back and forth a number of times.

Finally, it is certain that if any one of the three American service branches—Air Force, Navy, or Army—really had had those flying machines in operation, no military office, bureau, or committee—every one of which is a direct extension of the Pentagon—would ever have set foot on the treacherous ground of speculation, and then of dispute. They would have cut short all speculation by the press at the start with a dry "No comment!" The United States would never have been subjected to the bitter, repeated humiliation of unsuccessful satellite launchings, because then it could have quietly shelved the little artificial moons altogether, or put them in orbit with different and less chancy methods. And, viewing the matter with the advantage of hindsight, we can say that what is astonishing is the rash attitude taken by the responsible agencies, which at the time of the first sightings perhaps actually did tremble at the idea that those phantom aircraft secretly bore the emblem of the Red Star.

Once it was clear that there was no threat and the true nature of the sightings became evident, there was no sensible alternative for these agencies but to issue something like the following communiqué—which, unfortunately they did not do: The authorities of the United States are cognizant of the origin and purpose of the so-called UFOs. They are perfectly harmless mechanical constructions, and it is absolutely forbidden to any pilot, military or civilian, to interfere in their activity. The authorities could then have curtly refused to answer further requests for clarification, promising to do so at "the proper time." Such are the demands of military secrecy, that incurable but unfortunately necessary disease which retards progress by preventing scientific exchange among nations, forces the inventive genius of man into the shadows, and tempts him to blackmail and treason.

NOTES

1. As long ago as 1952 the editors of the London aeronautical magazine *Flight* (see No. 2300) bemoaned the lack of high-speed rocket interceptors in Britain's air defense. They com-

plained principally of alleged operational deficiencies in the R.A.F. and deplored the shelving of the Miles supersonic plane, the failure to develop the Vickers and Fairey antiaircraft rockets, and the overemphasis on preparing the Class "V" superbombers ("Victor," "Vulcan," and "Valiant"). Nevertheless, these complaints of British experts were only a very modest skirmish in the huge storm that had been brewing for some time.

2. See ANSAER No. 96 in *ANSA: Notiziario Aeronautico* (Rome, January 21, 1957).

3. *Cf.* the statements of Undersecretary Strachey in the House of Commons (session of March 12, 1946). In addition, from the 1946 White Paper we learn that of the £411-million British budget, about £30 million were assigned to the Ministry of Supply and an additional £100 million were assigned to the Air Ministry for production and various services.

4. After welcoming the wildest explanations, the European press, which only a few months before had opened its columns to extensive coverage of the mysterious apparitions, did an abrupt about-face, printed the authoritative American denials, and seconded them warmly. Most curious of all the interpretations of the "myth" was that suggested by the French weekly *L'Illustration*. In the autumn of 1952 the magazine had unsuccessfully tried to get in touch with the first American eyewitness, and in 1954 it tried to at least get hold of "a copy of *The Coming of the Saucers* of which Kenneth Arnold is allegedly the author" but still without success. The French writer then came to these surprising conclusions: "These facts are somewhat suspicious and have led us to form three different hypotheses: 1) Arnold made a mistake in good faith, and his silence means that he wants both the mistake and himself forgotten; 2) he deliberately lied out of a mania for exhibitionism or a desire to create the biggest hoax of the century; 3) he does not in fact exist as a person of flesh and blood. The origin of a myth, he is himself a myth. Behind his name is concealed some military body or organization that has 'in-

vented' the whole story for mysterious reasons. There are, indeed, some who lean toward this last hypothesis—which injects a new mystery into the greater mystery of the flying saucers."

5. This is a foolish notion. Exceedingly well-founded rumors and evidence of some time ago make it certain that beginning in 1946 several models of electromagnetic cannons—captured in Schlosscranzbach, Germany—have since been developed at a secret experimental center belonging to the U.S. Army. See Combined Intelligence Objectives Sub-committee, *Geschäft für Gerätebau: Electric Guns* (Report No. XXXI-59, London, H.M.S.O., 1945), p. 19; "'Toothpaste' Shell May Beat Atom," *Union Jack* (Southern Italy Edition, June 19, 1946), p. 1; and Col. L. Simons, "Electromagnetic Artillery," *German Scientific Establishments* (Report PB 19849, Brooklyn, 1947). No clear details, however, have as yet leaked out. Here, then, is a "democratic" secret whose life also spans two decades—and it remains unfathomed. Nevertheless, it is probable that the mysterious "green suns of Arizona"—mistaken for a new type of flying saucer in 1951—are the sole visible manifestations of those experiments. See R. Vesco, "*I getti di metallo fuso antiaerei*," *Rivista Militare* (Rome, Ministry of Defense: Army, September 1954), pp. 910–921.

6. See Lt.-Col. L. J. Tacker, *Flying Saucers and the U.S. Air Force: The Official Air Force Story* (New York, Van Nostrand, 1960), pp. 136–161.

7. Isolated UFOs had, however, already previously appeared elsewhere. On July 3, 1965, the military and scientific personnel of several Argentine, Chilean, and British naval bases in the Antarctic saw and photographed a large, circular, shining body that passed over at a low altitude. Before disappearing over the horizon, it had changed speed and direction several times, circling several miles away from the tender *Punta Medanos,* whose compasses temporarily "went crazy," indicating intense electromagnetic interference which undoubtedly came from the

object. There was official confirmation from Argentine and Chilean sources. Photographs were not released. (*Cf.* Frank Edwards, *Flying Saucers—Serious Business* (New York, Bantam Books, 1967), pp. 160–183.

8. See John G. Fuller, *Incident at Exeter* (New York, Holt, Rinehart and Winston, 1966). It is doubtless possible, and even probable, that a substantial portion of the sightings reported can be explained as the spontaneous production of local electroatmospheric phenomena caused by high-tension transmissions which were present in the areas of the principal sightings, as suggested by several experts of the Westinghouse Research Laboratories. See Philip J. Klass, "Plasma Theory May Explain Many UFOs," *Aviation Week and Space Technology*, vol. 85, no. 8, New York (August 22, 1966), pp. 48–61, and "Letters: UFO Theory," *Aviation Week and Space Technology*, vol. 85, no. 15, New York (October 10, 1966), p. 130. But the production of corona effects and of discharges of the globular type caused by temporary overloading in the distributive network —due to damage or testing—does not eliminate the certainty of the fleeting presence over the region of flying machines that were unknown because radically dissimilar in design and in behavior to ordinary airplanes. There really seems to be no reason why the two phenomena could not coexist and sometimes appear simultaneously, without thereby mutually eliminating one another. Moreover, the cycle of summer sightings of 1965 was not limited to the territories of the United States. Flights of UFOs also took place over France, Portugal, Spain, Argentina, Chile, Peru, Brazil, and in the vicinity of the Australian airport of Canberra. The skies of northern Mexico —which had on several occasions been traversed by UFOs— were also crossed by a formation of "fiery balls," which at a certain point seemed to converge in an orderly fashion toward a large cigar-shaped craft at the head of the silent, lofty procession. This sighting and maneuver remain inexplicable, but they had previously appeared in the annals of ufology (*cf.*, for example, the French sightings of Oloron and Gaillac in 1952). The Air Force has several times stated that "skepticism is healthy" when dealing with UFO reports. True, but only if it is

not transformed into a convenient screen and the screen into an outrageous abuse.

9. On March 27, 1966, a highway patrolman, G. Landversicht, having observed a strange, shining object in the sky heading toward the air base, took several feet of motion-picture film and handed it over to his direct superiors. The frames were then examined by experts of the Air Technical Intelligence Center, which maintained the most absolute silence on them. If the UFOs do not exist, why not make these innocuous frames (preferably without biased mutilating or retouching) public property?

10. *Cf.* Luke Frost, "A Cloak of Respectability: $313,000," *Flying Saucers—UFO Reports,* No. 2 (New York, Dell Publishing Co., 1967), pp. 26–29. The director of Project Blue Book, Major Hector Quintanilla, was to fulfill only the functions of "special military consultant" to the new committee, since the whole matter had been handed over to civilians. In addition, he was instructed to place at the disposition of the investigators the whole body of reports gathered in 1966 (of which there were 1060, the highest figure after the 1501 sightings caused by the so-called "mass hysteria" of 1952), as well as whatever reports might be received by the military office in 1967.

11. The proposal to entrust the task to civilians was apparently advanced as early as 1965 by Major General E. B. Lebailly, the director of the U.S. Air Force Information Bureau, for two seemingly valid reasons: 1) to quash criticism from the public and press regarding the behavior of the Air Force, which according to him was wrongfully accused of keeping the most interesting news secret; 2) to dissipate growing suspicions that the Air Force was developing special, top-secret starships for the War in Space. His suggestion, which was examined and favorably received by the Air Force's Scientific Advisory Board, was promptly translated by the eager board into the "recommendation" that "an independent UFO investigation unit" be set up—independent (at least in theory) from the Air Force but coinciding in its "declared" aims, perhaps in

homage to the mechanical principle that the vectors of two equal but opposing forces (in this case, civilians and the military) cancel one another and their common origin (in this case, the UFOs) no longer has any direction. However, it was specified that the investigation—which was then entrusted to the University of Colorado—wouldn't kill off Project Blue Book. The reason given for this duplication of effort was: "The Air Force will continue to collect reports of UFO sightings, as in the past, unless persons are reluctant to work through USAF channels and prefer direct contact with the University of Colorado scientists. Under a regulation issued last month by Air Force Chief of Staff Gen. John P. McConnell, the USAF's Foreign Technology Div. at Wright-Patterson AFB, Ohio, is authorized to use other government agencies, private industrial companies and contractor personnel to assist in analyzing and evaluating UFO reports as necessary.'" See "Colorado to Study UFOs," *Aviation Week and Space Technology*, vol. 85, no. 16, New York (October 17, 1966). Everything was clear, everything was arranged with the greatest care and started off for a happy ending, but it would remain to be seen what hidden role would be played by competent bureaus of the Central Intelligence Agency, given the precedent of the "Robertson Report." In 1953 the Air Force called a top-level scientific meeting on the UFO problem, which had become particularly acute after the incidents of the summer of 1952. The meeting was presided over by Dr. H. P. Robertson of the California Institute of Technology, and gave rise to many animated debates conducted on a "very concrete level," but—according to the subsequent testimony of one of the participants, the physicist James E. McDonald of the University of Arizona, and there is no sound reason to doubt him— the minutes of the gathering and even the final report were "classified" at the specific request of the C.I.A. *Cf.* "Dr. Condon Diagnoses the UFOs—Will He Unravel the Baffling Riddle?" *UFOs '67*, No. 1, 1967 (New York, K.M.R. Publications), pp. 36–39.

12. In 1948 he was investigated by the House Un-American Activities Committee. Then, cleared of all charges against him, he resigned from the post of Director of the National Bureau

of Standards and joined the Corning Glass Works as a civilian scientist, where he was part of a team that developed cones for atomic missiles and heat-refracting screens for space capsules.

13. This omission is rather significant because it forces to mind a sort of aphorism that has always been dear to high-ranking officers of the Air Force. The aphorism makes plain the tacit connivance between those officers and the world of a certain self-satisfied branch of science. It goes as follows: Astronomers, astrophysicists, and their assistants are the only people really qualified to express an opinion on the subject of UFOs. (*Cf.* Lt. Col. Lawrence J. Tacker, *Flying Saucers and the U.S. Air Force.*) Now the privilege of taking part in this "monologue" is apparently also extended to experts in psychology.

14. Once again, in order to quell the doubt, curiosity, or fear of the "man in the street," would nearly a third of a million dollars be spent just in order to go through the motions of an investigation? So it would appear, according to certain authoritative program specifications. Did not Dr. Condon himself perhaps candidly declare just before taking on the job that when the contract expired the mystery of the UFOs might still not be completely solved despite the best efforts? And hadn't the Secretary of the Air Force perhaps imprudently revealed his hidden intentions when he made clear that the choice of the University of Colorado was suggested above all by its "proximity to the famous National Center for Atmospheric Research (N.C.A.R.) and to the Research Headquarters of the Environmental Science Services Administration, organizations specializing in research on the properties of the natural environment in which man lives, including in particular the physical characteristics of the atmosphere and of outlying Space"? According to Mr. Brown, these organizations could thus furnish "tremendous help" to the Boulder investigators. . . .

15. An opinion and a confidence that is much more widespread among the upper ranks of the Air Force than ufologists think or say they think. When asked to express his confidential opinion on the UFOs, Chief of Staff General Twining gave a half-

brusque, half-facetious reply to the pilots of the Amarillo Air Force Base in Texas on May 15, 1954: "Even if they did come from Mars we would not be afraid of them!" Then he made clear that he did not seriously believe either in explorers from Mars or in the existence of the "so-called UFOs."

16. This fact is all the more disconcerting since, according to Captain Ruppelt, any attempt to intercept—or better, to approach—a UFO by means of jet fighters entailed an average expenditure of about $2000 per air hour, with absolutely negative results because of the manifestly inferior maneuvering ability of the pursuers. A volley of radio-guided earth-to-air missiles or seek-destroy air-to-air rockets would have cost much less than the countless futile efforts to learn something about the discs by sending up interceptors and much less than the money that would probably be wasted on the civilian program now under way. In any case it would surely have downed the UFO, and experts could then have examined it on the ground with all the care that circumstances demanded. In 1944 the English "reconstructed" the V-2 torpedo-rocket found in the vicinity of Baeckedo by patiently reassembling the more than ten thousand fragments. The Swedish air force experts who found it had previously succeeded in reconstructing the gigantic rocket on paper. In regard to the U-2 spy plane piloted by the American flyer Powers, even though it was flying at an altitude of more than 54,000 feet, the Soviets reacted in a rather harsh but extremely profitable manner: one well-aimed shot. And by piecing together the various bits of wreckage, they also "reconstructed" the evidence. People in aeronautical circles uncontaminated by the ufological craze are asking why on earth the Americans have not taken a similarly resolute and drastic but definitive step with regard to the UFOs? *Politesse* toward our Brothers from Space? Apparently not, for the military authorities have never evidenced the slightest belief in their existence. Fear of diplomatic complications which would follow the shooting down of a craft that might turn out to be Russian? Even this should not have stopped them from intervening against the invaders of their air space, especially in view of the fact that they so decisively met the much more

serious problem of Cuban-Soviet missile bases. And then, since the Russians did not stand on ceremony in the U-2 case, there is no reason why the Americans should not do likewise. Ignorance of the real nature of the UFOs? Given their potential danger, this should have been all the more reason to take any steps that would clarify matters. Whoever feels himself threatened by an obscure danger attacks first, if he is able. And then? . . . And then one does not shoot at "strangers" who are friends through ancient racial ties, even if the political, economic, and military bonds between Americans and British are getting looser and looser. It has long been the custom to develop one's military secrets—or potential secrets—jealously and in private, revealing them to a friendly nation only when war changes friend into ally. These are almost metaphysical subtleties, but no other motive stands up to the most elementary criticism. Besides, the only report of an armed attack against the UFOs was never confirmed, even semiofficially, by the appropriate Air Force offices. We refer to the alleged communiqué issued by the head of the U.S. Air Force Defense Headquarters-D in Tokyo on May 9, 1953, quoted by an English ufologist, in which he says that "in recent weeks our ships and planes have observed numerous unidentified flying objects. In pursuing them we got a line on their course, which permitted us to draw some conclusions regarding their take-off and landing bases. One of these craft [without crew and radio-controlled?] was hit by one of our planes armed with special equipment, and went down in the ocean off Tinian Island in the archipelago of the Mariannas." Even if authentic, and there are grave doubts on the matter, this operation apparently was transformed into a chase without any prey!

17. Without neglecting, of course, the aerodynamic and mechanical aspects of the flight of UFOs. We do not know what actual means the U.S. Air Force uses to conduct its secret investigations but one presumes that everything the press suggests today (with the exception of the firing of antiaircraft rockets) has already long since been put in motion without the public or ufologists ever having been informed of the fact or of the results obtained. As Captain G. H. Oldenburg—an official

of the Information Service of the Air Force base at Langley, Va.—declared in no uncertain terms on February 13, 1958: "to make public the data gathered on UFOs is contrary to Air Force interests and regulations." *Cf* L. Jerome Stanton, "Science vs. Saucers," *Flying Saucers, UFO Reports*, no. 2 (New York, 1967), pp. 40–44.

18. The institution that could not then be named was, in all probability, the RAND Corporation (*i.e.*, Research and Development Corporation), a civilian organization of a very high scientific level that does every kind of research and consulting work for the U.S. Air Force (from reports on technical progress in the U.S.S.R. to analysis of the "productivity" of national industries, from the selective control of projects to "confidential" investigations of the UFO problem), and that is cited in passing in the book by Lt. Col. L. J. Tacker (*The Flying Saucers and the Air Force*, p. 16). Tacker says, in fact, that the RAND Corporation was also involved in 1948—together with the Scientific Advisory Board, the Weather Bureau and the Federal Bureau of Investigation—in the first attempt to work out a preliminary scheme for an initial standardized approach to the problem. Moreover, Ruppelt himself recently indirectly confirmed this identification by also mentioning the RAND Corporation—"a group of high-level researchers that have nothing to do with the industrial company of the same name"—in a detailed review of saucer history (see Capt. Edward J. Ruppelt, "Why Don't the Damn Things Swim So We Can Turn Them Over to the Navy?" *The True Report on Flying Saucers* (Greenwich, Conn., Fawcett Publications no. 1, 1967), pp. 36–39 and 57–74. The conclusions that the RAND experts reached in 1949—on the basis of the examination of 375 sightings selected by Dr. Hynek—did not differ from those which prevailed in Air Force circles: We have found nothing that seriously contradicts the simple, rational explanation of the various phenomena observed by the appearance of weather balloons, conventional airplanes, planets, meteorites, pieces of paper, optical illusions, hoaxes, psychopathic hallucinations, and so on. (One assumes, however, that these were the conclusions for the public and the press.) It seems that the RAND

Corporation had also cooperated with Air Force Intelligence in the elaboration of the famous (and infamous, for the ufologists) internal regulation, Air Force Regulation 200-2, compiled at the order of the then Secretary of the Air Force H. Talbot, issued for the first time on August 26, 1953, and continuously brought up to date. A true masterpiece of precision, prudence, and foresight, which sometimes even verges on the superfluous. The reading of this regulation—which every ufologist should know by heart—is particularly interesting because it offers clear proof of the fact that the Air Force really does *take the question very seriously, seeks to obtain detailed technical information on the behavior of the UFOs, and does not at all neglect sightings over foreign territories!* The last version of the Regulation (AFR. 80-17 of September 19, 1966) was drawn up by the Air Force Research and Development Department rather than by Air Force Intelligence as in the past, and Paragraph Two (Objectives of the Program), Section A (General Provisions), states that the Air Force is interested in the UFOs in order to establish whether they constitute a possible threat for the United States *and in order to take advantage of the technical and scientific data gained from the study of the related reports.* The Regulation says *it is possible that foreign countries may succeed in building aircraft with revolutionary shapes and means of propulsion.* Consequently one must know what these means of propulsion are and, if possible, copy them and perhaps even improve on them, especially if it is established that they are of Soviet origin and hence particularly to be feared. Here then is one more irrefutable proof that the Air Force is engaged in a deliberate game of duplicity, one, it goes without saying, that was forced on it by the demands of national security but was conducted with means and methods that seem to us to be self-defeating or disproportionate to the case.

THE WORLD'S MOST SPECTACULAR NEW
COMET HAS ARRIVED! IS IT A MESSEN-
GER OF DOOM FROM OUTER SPACE? OR
A SCIENTIFIC CLUE TO THE BIRTH OF
OUR UNIVERSE?

THE COMET KOHOUTEK

GREATEST FIERY CHARIOT OF ALL TIME

BY JOSEPH F. GOODAVAGE

Popular and bestselling
SCIENCE FICTION
FUTURISTIC · HORROR